How the Banana Goes to Heaven

And Other Secrets of Health from the Indian Kitchen

ratna rajaiah

westland

westland ltd
Venkat Towers, 165, P.H. Road, Opp. Maduravoyal Municipal office, Chennai 600 095
No.38/10 (New No.5), Raghava Nagar, New Timber Yard Layout, Bangalore 560 026
Survey No. A-9, II Floor, Moula Ali Industrial Area, Moula Ali, Hyderabad 500 040
23/181, Anand Nagar, Nehru Road, Santacruz East, Mumbai 400 055
47, Brij Mohan Road, Daryaganj, New Delhi 110 002

First published by westland ltd, 2010

ISBN: 978-93-80658-60-5

Typeset by Art Works, Chennai

Printed at Manipal Press Limited

ACKNOWLEDGEMENTS

It's an interesting theory – and perhaps a comforting alternative for those of us who have difficulty acknowledging a chimpanzee as a great-great-great-grandpappy. That our true ancestors were millions of zillions of droplets floating around millions of zillions of years ago in what Charles Darwin described as 'a warm little pond, with all sorts of ammonia and phosphoric salts, lights, heat, electricity…' Some scientists propose that the droplets were primarily a collection of different kinds of fat molecules, others suggest that they could have been amino acids, the building blocks of life.

What I mean to say is that it is almost impossible to pinpoint the real origin or the true creators of anything. All the same, I do know some of the people without whom this book would definitely not have seen the light of day. So I would like to acknowledge them with the deepest gratitude.

Shekhar Gupta, Editor-in-Chief of the *Indian Express,* and TJS George, well-known author, journalist, founder-editor of *Asiaweek* and long-time associate of the *New Indian Express,* for believing that I could conceive of and write a weekly column in the *New Indian Express.*

Mr and Mrs Padmanabhan of Westland Limited who saw the possibility of a book in that column and made that possibility become a reality.

Veena Seshadri who set me off on the path of hammering out that book and Aruna Nambiar, whose invaluable editorial skills guided me in putting together a book that I am proud of.

My late beloved father, SBJ Rajaiah, whose presence I still sorely miss, even ten years after his passing.

And finally, my mother, Sunanda Rajaiah. Best friend, mentor, guru, guide and unfortunately sometimes also punching bag. She not only inspired much of this book but also stoically bore the brunt of having a daughter who took her mother's participation in its long and difficult gestation for granted.

So, I dedicate this book to my dearest Mumsie.

CONTENTS

PREFACE
A Return to Joy

'Eat food. Not too much. Mostly plants.'
The Omnivore's Dilemma: The Natural History of Four Meals by Michael Pollen

Have you noticed how, of late, many of us have begun to battle with our food, viewing it as Enemy No. 1, the Devil Incarnate that lures us to obesity and disease? Our relationship with food is increasingly an unhappy one. We eat too much – or then, too little. To add to our woes, there is the additional pressure of not only having to be healthy but also to be thin. And almost every piece of new research or expert-speak on the subject of healthy eating – popping up with the irritating regularity of zits on a teenager's skin – contradicts the previous one.

So coffee was bad for you, now it's good. Chocolates were almost a mortal sin. Now they may actually help in lowering cholesterol. (But don't bet on it because we're still researching.) Talking of cholesterol, we hope you're seriously cutting down on all that fat – butter, *ghee*, cream etcetera, etcetera – you get our drift. Except vegetable oils – a bit of those are alright. As long as they don't include saturated fats.

Er, hold on a minute. About those saturated fats – we've just found out that some of them may not be the deadly villains that we thought they were. (We hope you didn't chuck out that bottle of coconut oil as yet.) It's actually the trans fats that are the problem.

Trans fats? You mean like transatlantic – is that what they cook airline meals with?

Oh never mind – let's keep this for some other time. (Perhaps some other book?)

Meanwhile, we hope you are also counting those calories. No, no, it's much better to calculate your BMI and then figure out your calorie quota. But remember to factor in your age, bones, sex (and we didn't mean frequency), lifestyle, your family history, your dog's family history…

Actually, forget counting. Just eat from a smaller plate.

No, no. Make that smaller meals – but at least six times a day.

Rubbish. Just three large meals and nothing in between…

And just in case you are not traumatized enough, stirred into this bubbling cauldron of toil and trouble – as urban middle-class India gets more prosperous and as globalization invades your kitchens and your dining tables – are fast foods, instant foods, heat 'n' eat foods, ready-to-eat foods, two-minute wonder foods. Culinary modcons but nutritional paupers. And as India gets fatter and more unhealthy (it is among the world's ten most obese countries and one of the epicentres of both heart disease and diabetes), everyone is running around in stressed-out, feverish, confused circles, trying to figure out what and how much to eat.

I stood twitching and hyperventilating at this very same crossroad a few years ago. And I remember thinking that it wasn't always like this.

Food was a happy thing. It was a celebration. Food was a *sadhana*, both the cooking and eating of it. We were connected to it in a thousand ways. It was the *prasadam* with which we propitiated our gods, it was the harvest that we gratefully and joyously received as blessings of bounty from Mother Earth. (And that is the reason why so many of our festivals, like Pongal and Sankranti, celebrate harvest time!) Food was our public relations manager with which we conveyed to our guests exactly how welcome they were. Food was our almanac, marking the seasons. It was our biographer, participating in each rite of passage from birth to death. And perhaps most important of all, especially in today's context, food was also medicine. Or rather, medicine was food, depending on how you looked at it.

When did it all change? When did we become such guilt-ridden, unhappy eaters? And more importantly, was there a road that would take us back to that joyful, nourishing, healing avatar of food that is India's heritage?

As I asked myself these questions, I got an opportunity to write a weekly column in the Sunday edition of the *New Indian Express*. And it was in the writing of these columns that I decided to find the answers because I felt that there were hundreds like me, anxiously looking for the road that would take us back to happier, healthier mealtimes.

I started by revisiting foods that were old buddies. (My first food column was about curd!) Foods that I had grown up eating, that were knitted into some of the most beautiful and indelible memories of my childhood; fabulous tapestries of tastes and aromas, many of them forgotten and rolled up in some dusty, dark corner of my mind. These foods instantly transported me into my mother's kitchen and conjured up her cooking; simple, no-nonsense, no-fuss fare, rustled up in a trice and always with the freshest of ingredients, filling both belly and soul with the deepest contentment. (My mother has the deepest aversion for leftover food, so you will never find any in her refrigerator!) They were foods that had been served up to me with the sagacity of two of the wisest women I have ever known – my mother and my maternal grandmother.

That's all very well, but why would anyone be interested in my private collection of favourite foods? After all, I am no size-zero celebrity, flaunting my fashionably tiny shanks whittled down by iceberg lettuce and feta cheese.

Ah, but there was one more reason why I revisited these foods – because I vaguely remembered that they were also very healthy.

But were they?

What I discovered was astonishing – that the nutritional and medicinal wealth that these foods contained was far beyond anything I could have ever imagined. And in the course of discovering this, I also peeped into the medicine chests of ancient civilizations all the way from Mesopotamia to Magadha. I met their great medicine men: Sushruta and Charaka, the renowned Indian sages of Ayurveda; Hippocrates of Greece and Galen of ancient Rome, whose works and theories would ultimately shape modern Western medicine; the Chinese Emperor Shen Nung considered to be the father of Chinese medicine; the Persian Avicenna, or Ibn Sina, astronomer, mathematician, philosopher, physician and founder of the Unani system of medicine, who studied not just the mortal human body but also pondered on immortality. I made acquaintance with medical texts thousands of years old, many written by these men and some – like the *Egyptian Ebers* and *Edwin Papyrus* – by authors who remain unknown. I was astounded by the vast expanse and sophistication of the knowledge that was inside.

And the question that popped up again and again in my astounded head was – how did these people know?

With nothing that even remotely resembled the laboratories and research technology that we have access to today, these men knew about the medicinal and therapeutic properties of hundreds of foods. For example, in Ayurveda, curry leaves have long been used to treat diabetes. Several thousands of years later, we now know that this is because they slow down the breakdown of carbohydrates to glucose. This in turn regulates the release of glucose into the bloodstream. Similarly ginger's therapeutic powers were used in almost every ancient system of medicine to cure disorders ranging from dyspepsia to rheumatism. Today, we know that ginger is a powerful anti-inflammatory and a potent antioxidant.

For me, these men were some of the greatest explorers of the world because they dared to chart unknown worlds inside the human body. They delved inside the tiniest spice, the most delicate herb, looking for weapons to fight beasts and monsters that they couldn't see but were no less fierce and dangerous than the mighty oceans.

I journeyed back in time to visit the fabulous pharaohs of Egypt, the magnificent empires of the Mayas, the Aztecs and the Incas. (I even sipped a cup of hot chocolate with Montezuma – laced with chillies!) I was privileged to peek into sumptuous feasts in the glittering courts of the great royal dynasties of China and India and be privy to what the gods favoured – all the way from ancient Greece to the magnificent temples of South India. I went inside caves where humans lived and painted tens of thousands of years before they could speak or write, and to an era when time was measured in *yugas* and the great wisdom of the *Vedas* was handed to us. And to a time even before that – when we humans must have been just a dream, an idea, a notion, afloat on plankton in some primordial sea.

It was an incredible journey. (And somewhere during that journey, the newspaper column grew up and became a book.)

But often, it was also a difficult one. All these foods are ancient nutritionists and healers, many of them native to India, growing in our land for centuries. Yet sadly enough, information was only available about the foods that had been lately 'discovered' and 'adopted' by the West, and had become the darlings of its high-profile New Ages gurus. And most of this information came from Western studies. There is little initiative in India to research local foods and the studies that have been done languish in obscure, inaccessible places.

So, for example, there was no dearth of research available on turmeric, currently a superstar among anti-carcinogenic foods in the West. But, there was almost nothing on *ghee,* considered by Ayurveda to be of great therapeutic and nutritional importance, promoting everything from intelligence to sexual vitality. Data was equally hard to come by about *urad dal* (black gram). Or jaggery. Or local greens.

But that made me even more determined to write about these foods. Even though I knew that if I were to write about even half of them, I'd need at least another lifetime and the contents would probably fit into two *Encyclopaedia Britannicas* – just about. So I chose a select few that would serve as a tantalizing appetizer to India's agricultural biodiversity. (After all, we are home to at least twenty thousand species of rice and over five hundred species of mango!) That, I decided, would be my show window for foods eaten for thousands of years all over India in millions of delicious repasts and bursting with health and nutrition, but many of them now either forgotten or misunderstood, maligned and relegated to that purgatory called 'unhealthy food'. Foods that made me a humble and proud witness to my country's true wealth.

They also made me remember who I am, because the food of our ancestors is as much a part of our identity as our genes. They made me understand that it's not just an apple a day that keeps the doctor away. It's also a handful of sprouted *mung* or roasted *channa* or peanuts. A bowl of rice *kanji*. A curry of *methi* and *alu*. A *katori* of curd. A simple *dal*, seasoned with a devil-chilli or two, a smidgen of mustard and a few pinches of turmeric. Washed down with a glass of cool, creamy buttermilk spiked with a few fragrant slivers of ginger and a handful of curry leaves. Signed off with a banana or a few portions of mango or jackfruit.

All of which grow in great abundance in our country, many of them in our backyards. Yet, malnutrition and nutrition-related diseases are rife and we see the most painful evidence of it in our children. We may well be a nation where one in every two Indians has a mobile phone but we will also have to realize that true development is when nutrition and good health is available to all of us.

I also wrote for one other reason – to reconnect with the joy of eating. As children, all of us have at some time or another been admonished not to talk while eating and to chew our food well before swallowing it. There is a very good reason for those rules – chewing each mouthful forty-two times not only improves your digestion, but you also get to experience the little symphony of all five senses that plays so joyously with every mouthful.

So, my point is this. Nutrition, like food, should be a celebration. As our cells are nourished and replenished and rejuvenated, as the nasty invaders bearing disease and distress are summarily dismissed, our noses should exult in the embrace of a hundred aromas, our taste buds should laugh joyously at being tickled by all six tastes. (Yes, six – because Ayurveda says so!) Our tongues and fingers should be seduced by the soft and the crunchy, the cool and the hot and our eyes should feast on colours stolen from the sun and the rainbow. And at the end of every meal, a gentle, happy little burp should escape our lips, just loud enough for the gods to hear our paean of gratitude.

I'd like to leave you with the Kannada phrase with which we traditionally exhort our guests each time we sit them down for a celebratory feast.

'*Nidhanavagi oota maadi!*'

The literal meaning is 'Please eat slowly!' But it means so much more. It's an invitation to cruise on the river that gently and ever so slowly takes you upstream to the land of happy, healthy meals.

A Word about the Recipes

'*Recipe: A series of step-by-step instructions for preparing ingredients you forgot to buy, in utensils you don't own, to make a dish the dog wouldn't eat.*'
Author Unknown

Over the years, I have watched many good cooks in action. (I fancy myself to be a fairly decent one.) And I have observed that using a recipe is a bit like interpreting a *raga* in Indian classical music. You known all the necessary notes (or ingredients); you have a good idea as to how to go about putting those notes or ingredients together. But in the end, the result has to be your own rendering of the *raga*... or the dish. So, when using the recipes in this book, I urge you to try them out for size a couple of times, adjusting the ingredients – especially the quantities of salt and sweeteners – to your individual preference. And when you are sure you like what you taste, debut it on your dining table!

A Word about Nutritional Information

The amount of nutrients in a natural food (vegetables, fruits, grains, etcetera) varies depending on factors like the particular strain/variety of that food, the soil, climatic conditions where it is grown and so on. So the nutritional content for the foods in this book is an approximation; a summary of information available through research studies, books and other sources. Nevertheless, it gives a good idea of the type of nutrients available in various foods and how good a source each food is of different types of nutrients.

...and Finally, A Word of Caution

Please consult your doctor before using any of the remedies in this book, especially if you are already under treatment and medication.

PROLOGUE
Setting the Table

*'Let him always worship his food, and eat it without contempt; when he sees it,
let him rejoice, show a pleased face, and pray that he may always obtain it.'*

From the *Manusmriti* (*Laws of Manu*)

Many famous playwrights are of the view that if the drama soon to unfold is to captivate and enthral, it is important to present the context, perhaps introduce the main characters, even hint at how it will all end. And just as many renowned chefs will tell you that if the meal soon to be served is to gratify and please, then it is essential to create an ambience that will whet the appetite and gently get the juices flowing.

In other words, it is important to set the stage... or the table.

So, I set this table with a brief note about nutrients.

How strange, you think. Isn't that a bit like putting the protein before the *dal*? (Or for that matter, the vitamin before the *methi-aloo*?) Actually, no. Because the point that I want to make is simply this…

Everything is interconnected – we all know that. But look how this works in nutrition. We mostly see nutrients as separate entities that work independent of each other with mutually exclusive functions and areas of operation. When, in fact, they are all linked to each other to form an exquisitely complex circuit board that functions as one integrated whole to nourish, protect and maintain every cell of the body. So, if even one wire is disconnected, we could be short-circuiting the entire process of nutrition.

For example, it is fairly common knowledge that the mineral calcium is vital for bone health. But that's only part of the story. Firstly, for good strong bones, you need not just calcium but a combination of calcium, phosphorus and magnesium. Secondly, for the body to be able to absorb calcium, the presence of Vitamin D – which we get primarily from sunlight – is absolutely imperative and without it, any amount of calcium ingested is useless. Similarly, the synthesis of dietary protein needs energy, which the body produces from carbohydrates. So, without enough carbohydrates in the diet, the body cannot digest proteins efficiently. But perhaps the best example of the interconnected functioning of nutrients is the B family of vitamins. The functioning of each of these eight vitamins is so interdependent on the presence of the other family members that they are often collectively referred to as the 'Vitamin B complex'!

The understanding of how nutrients work is a recent thing. The first glimpses into the chemical make-up of carbohydrates, proteins and fats were provided by the nineteenth-century German

Get Fresh!

The nutritional value and the therapeutic powers of a food are dependent on two things. One, the freshness of the food, and that is because nutrients are delicate darlings that deplete easily, affected by temperature, exposure to light and time. For example, spinach stored at room temperature loses between 50 and 90 per cent of its Vitamin C content within twenty-four hours of being picked.

Two – how free the food is of contamination, which could be in the form of pesticides or food microbes. But the ground reality is that we live in a world where pesticide-free foods are hard to come by (or a luxury that only the rich can afford) and where, more often than not, fresh produce must travel hundreds of miles before they reach us.

Even so, following these few simple rules will ensure that you are eating the freshest possible food.

Eat seasonally

Apart from the fact that foods that are in season simply taste better, they are also at their freshest, since they have probably not been stored for long and have not spent too much time travelling from the fields or the orchards to your dining table. That means that they are loaded with nutrients.

Eat freshly cooked food

Ideally, the best way to eat much of our food would be the way the rest of the animal kingdom does – raw and fresh. That is because cooking or even simply freezing or cutting a vegetable or fruit can reduce its nutrient content, especially the delicate vitamins and antioxidants. But that would be both impractical and dangerous, given the large-scale use of pesticides and chemicals in agriculture.

So, eat freshly cooked food and minimize leftovers. Even if it means more time spent in the kitchen, it will have a long-term impact on your health. That is because the older the food, the less nutrition it has. And since heat destroys nutrients, when food is reheated, whatever little nutrients remain are further diminished.

Eat locally

Locally grown foods come from nearby farms and therefore are both in season and the freshest. Besides, when we eat what is grown locally, we help the small farmer – about 70 per cent of India's population is still dependent on agriculture for its livelihood and most of our farmers are small or marginal farmers.

chemist, Justus von Liebig. More than 150 years later, in spite of the huge strides that we have taken in that direction, we are only beginning to grasp a small percentage of the connections on that circuit board. So, as is the case in any work-in-progress, what was considered gospel truth just a while ago becomes as nutritionally relevant as junk food.

But this much is now clear. Nutrition should not come out of a bottle, mainly because Nature didn't intend it that way. That is because each natural food – be that a curry leaf or a potato – is an intricately interconnected, interdependent complex of nutrients that interacts with the body in equally intricate, interconnected ways. So, for example, Vitamin E is a very powerful antioxidant, offering protection against cancer and lowering the risk of Alzheimer's by as much as 67 per cent. But recent research has shown that this happens only when this vitamin is consumed in the form of natural foods and not as man-made supplements! Similarly, one of the best sources of protein is *mung* (green gram) – not only because about one-third of its weight is protein, but also because it is loaded with two other nutrients which the body needs to synthesize proteins – potassium and niacin (Vitamin B3).

Natural foods also complement each other nutritionally. So, when you eat whole grain – like rice or wheat – with a pulse, you are getting the complete set of proteins that your body requires. The presence of natural fats like *ghee* and vegetable oils makes sure that fat-soluble vitamins become accessible to the body. Spices and herbs act as digestives. Probiotic foods like curd, aided and abetted by dietary fibre, create an intestinal environment that promotes the proliferation of friendly bacteria (gut flora), which in turn aid digestion, unlock nutrients and mop up nasty toxins and unwanted cholesterol.

In other words, nutrition basically boils down to a simple rule. Eat natural, eat whole and eat everything. Our ancestors knew this and traditional diets are often the healthiest. According to Ayurveda, *prana* – the life energy that sustains all living things including us humans – is all around us. In the air we breathe, in the water we drink and in the food that we eat. And the fresher the food and the closer it is to its natural form, the more *prana* it contains and therefore, the more nourishing it is. That's just a three-thousand-year-old way of saying what is currently on 'The Nutrition Source', the website on healthy eating maintained by the Harvard School of Public Health: 'Eat a plant-based diet rich in fruits, vegetables, and whole grains…'

Ayurveda says one other thing. Eat consciously and joyously; seeing, feeling, smelling and tasting every mouthful. When you do so, all systems in your body including your digestive system are on 'go' – ready to absorb and synthesize the nutrients that are coming their way. In the words of MFK Fisher, that great writer of all things that nourish and nurture (including food!), '…man's need for food is not a grim obsession, repulsive, disturbing, but a dignified and even enjoyable function.'

Rice: First among Foods

'Rice is a beautiful food. It is beautiful when it grows, precision rows of sparkling green stalks shooting up to reach the hot summer sun. It is beautiful when harvested, autumn gold sheaves piled on diked, patchwork paddies. It is beautiful when, once threshed, it enters granary bins like a (flood) of tiny seed pearls.'

Shizuo Tsuji, celebrated Japanese chef

Rice. Ancient, sacred, benevolent, nourishing rice. It has fed us humans for far longer than any other food in the world and today, it provides more than one-fifth of the calories that the world consumes, making it the second most eaten cereal grain in the world. (Maize is the most consumed grain, but if we take into account that much of this consumption is by animals, rice becomes the most eaten cereal.)

In many Asian cultures, rice is a synonym for food itself. For example, in Sanskrit and in Kannada, the generic word for food is also the word for cooked rice – *anna*. In Japanese, the word for a meal is *gohan* which also means 'cooked rice'. In Mandarin, the word for rice is *fan* which, once again, is also the word for food. Perhaps the reason for this is that Asia is where, thousands of years ago, we humans first 'tamed' a grass and turned it into a staple food that would ultimately feed over half the world's population. However, what is a matter of ongoing debate is where exactly in Asia …

Gondwana's Grass

The ancestor of the rice we eat today was a wild grass that most probably grew in the super-continent of Gondwana at least 130 million years ago. From this ancient grass, two mother species evolved and they parented the approximately 120,000 varieties of rice that grow all over the world today, staple for more than half the world's population. (An astonishing 20,000 of those varieties come from India. In fact, the *Shunyapurana*, written by the thirteenth-century Bengali poet, Ramai Pandit, mentions more than 50 varieties of rice growing in Bengal!)

The cultivation of rice by man is said have begun at least 15,000 years ago in a region that stretches from north-east India through

Burma, Thailand, Laos, Vietnam and into southern China. Evidence of this is scattered in several archaeological sites all across this vast area. But the question that has been the centre of a long feud is – who cultivated it first, the Indians or the Chinese? Those who think it was the Indians cite the fact that remains of cultivated rice have been found at the archaeological site at Koldihwa near Allahabad in Uttar Pradesh, dating back to anywhere between the fourth and the seventh millennium BC. That would make rice cultivation in India at least 6,000 to 9,000 years old. Or even older if one is to take into account the terraced fields of Kashmir. These fields are typical of rice cultivation and they date back to 10000 BC. So perhaps rice was grown here?

More recent archaeological finds seemed to tilt things in favour of the Chinese camp. Rice remains dating to 8000 BC were found at the Jiahu archaeological site in the Henan Province of eastern China and even earlier evidence going back to at least 12,000 years was discovered at the Yuchanyan archaeological site in the Hunan Province of southern China. Then, in 2003, archaeologists found 59 burnt rice grains in the village of Sorori in the Chungbuk province in South Korea, which they dated as being about 15,000 years old!

But whether it originated in India or not, for Indians, rice is inextricably intertwined with every aspect of life. For Hindus, rice – *anna* when it is cooked and *akshata* when the raw grain is used – is one of the most sacred of foods and no *puja* or ritual is complete without its presence and offering. As laid down in the *Grihya Sutra*, during *anna prasanna*, the ceremony of feeding an infant its first solid food, the child is fed a sweet preparation of rice and milk. During the *namakarna*, or christening ceremony, the child's name is announced by writing it in rice grains that have been spread out on a *thali*. And it is considered auspicious to begin a child's first lesson by making it trace an alphabet in rice.

So, for many Indians, rice is like a parent – we know it from infancy and its presence in our lives is so all-pervading that to devote just one chapter to it is like trying to fit the *Bhagavad Gita* on… well, on a grain of rice! But then, a book on Indian food without a section on rice would be like *pulao or biryani* without rice in it! So, I would like to present one of the simplest yet most delicious and nutritious avatars of this beloved grain…

Thief Catcher!

The *Sukraniti*, a medieval treatise on public policy comprising of 2,575 Sanskrit *slokas*, prescribed rice as a means of determining guilt. During this *divya sadhana* (divine test), the suspect was given a handful of raw rice and asked to chew it. The reasoning was that because fear and apprehension would make the mouth dry, the guilty person would not be able to masticate the rice.

Globetrotting Gruel

It is called *jook* or *zhou* or *geng* in China, *juk* in Korea, *chao bo* in Vietnam, *lugaw* in the Philippines, *okayu* in Japan, *khao tom gung* in Thailand. But its most popular name is of Indian origin – 'congee', which comes from the Tamil word *kanji*. I speak of course, of that wondrous, marvellous broth, the gruel made by cooking rice in four to six times its volume of water till it takes on a thick, porridge-like consistency. (Incidentally, *kanji* also refers to the starchy water that is drained off after rice is cooked.)

It can be served piping hot or cold, freshly cooked or fermented overnight. It can be eaten with almost anything – eggs, fish, chicken or shrimp, mushrooms, bamboo shoots or any vegetable from bitter beans to brinjal. And sometimes, even with milk – cow's or the milk from a coconut! It can be flavoured with myriad ingredients – sesame seeds, roasted peanuts, dates, ginger, chilli paste, garlic, black pepper, cumin, roasted red chillies. Or then, it can be gobbled up just by itself, with nothing to accompany it other than a spoonful of *ghee* and a few pinches of salt.

Savoury, sweet or sometimes even sour. Eaten for breakfast, lunch or dinner. Or in between, as a delicious, nourishing snack. When the body is sick or cold or hungry or tired – or all of that. When the spirit sags and droops. For digestions as delicate as a baby's or as frail as its grandma's. Medicine, tonic, even aphrodisiac. And today, as global as the United Nations, because *kanji* has been embraced by the Western nutritionist and gourmet alike. In fact, you will find *kanji* on the menu of some of the most posh restaurants from New York to Sydney!

Marchioness' Treasure

For thousands of years, *kanji* has occupied pride of place in two of the world's most ancient cultures – India and China.

Now, almost all scholars and experts say that there is no reference to rice anywhere in the *Rig Veda*, considered to be the oldest-known Indian text. Yet in the eighth book of the *Rig Veda*, in the myth of the boar Emusa (a reference to Lord Vishnu's third avatar, Varaha), there is a mention of *odana*. Some scholars translate this to mean 'rice gruel' and if that is the case, then the very first mention of rice in ancient Indian texts is as *kanji*!

In India, *kanji* has been both poor man's staple and royal fare for centuries. According to the *Manasollasa*, the monumental encyclopaedic work written by the twelfth-century Chaluyan king Somesvara III, *kanjika*, or fermented rice gruel, was eaten as a relish! *Kankija* was also a term used for the water in which rice had been cooked and allowed to ferment and according to the *Manasollasa*, the ancestor of the modern *dahi vada* was made by first soaking the *vadas (vatakas)* in *kanjika* and then in curd. *Kanjika* was also used as a medicine, as a marinade for meats, as well as a preservative to pickle fruits and vegetables!

In China, congee was the staple of nobility during the reign of the Han Dynasty that ruled China from 206 BC to AD 220. When archaeologists unearthed the fabulous two-thousand-year-old tomb of the Marchioness of Dai, a Han noblewoman, amongst the bamboo baskets and fifty-one ceramic containers that they found inside (most of them full of food), they also found *dings* – the special vessels in which congee was both cooked and served!

Grain of Tranquillity

'Rice is vitality, rice is vigour too, and rice indeed is the means of fulfilment of all ends in life. All gods, demons and human beings subsist on rice.'
Krishi Parashara (400 BC), book on agriculture written in Sanskrit

Naturally, *kanji* derives all its nourishing and therapeutic values from rice. In Ayurveda, rice is considered one of the earth's first foods. Both the *Charaka Samhita* and the *Sushruta Samhita* have detailed references to rice, describing at least twenty types of rice by colour, fragrance and shape, including one resembling a bullock's face (*nandimukha)* and another resembling a grasshopper or locust (*patanga)*! They also classify rice by seasons, duration of crop, water requirements, nutritional value, medicinal properties and so on. For example, transplanted rice is referred to as *sali* (grown from July to November-December), broadcasted rice as *vrihi* and summer rice as *sashtika*. All varieties of *sali* rice were considered sweet to taste, cooling by nature, easy to digest and capable of imparting strength, but the *red sali (raktasali)* was the most valued for its therapeutic properties and was used as a diuretic and tonic and to treat – among other things – fevers and ulcers.

And because of this, in Ayurveda, rice is considered the perfect healing food – tranquil, soothing, nourishing and full of healing.

Buddha's Gruel

Every year, the Chinese celebrate the eighth day of the twelfth lunar month of the Chinese calendar by making a special hot *kanji*, called *laba zhou* (meaning 'twelfth-month congee'). Many do this mainly to kick off the celebrations for the approaching Chinese New Year. But the original reason – a tradition dating back to more than a thousand years ago to the Song Dynasty – was to commemorate the day when the Buddha, after six years of living an ascetic's life and surviving on only one bowl of rice gruel a day, had his first revelation.

Brown or White?

The debate rages. Which is healthier? Unpolished, 'brown' rice or 'white', polished rice?

First, let us get the definitions right. Unpolished or brown rice is rice with only the outer husk removed but with the outer bran and germ layers intact. It is one of the healthiest foods you can eat, rich in the B vitamins and many minerals like selenium, magnesium and manganese. Polished or white rice on the other hand has been milled and processed to have its husk, bran and germ removed, making the rice grains look white and 'polished'. But this rice has also been stripped of more than 60 per cent of nutrients, especially the B vitamins and minerals like iron. So, nutritionally speaking, like white bread, white or polished rice has far less nutrients.

However, because of the presence of rice bran, which contains oil and has a tendency to go rancid, brown rice does not store well, spoiling quickly. White rice, because it has been stripped of all the bran, stores well for long periods of time.

But is all 'white' rice polished?

Most probably, the answer is no. And that is because of what is called 'parboiled rice'. The best way to describe it is that it is the amazingly ingenious middle path that allows the rice to retain most of its nutrition while doing away with the parts that spoil.

Like polished rice, parboiled rice is also milled. But traditionally, before milling, the paddy is first soaked in water for one or two days until the kernels are saturated. Then it is boiled for about an hour, and the boiled paddy is thoroughly and completely dried. It is only then that the rice is milled.

Now, what this three-step process does is astonishing. It drives almost all of the nutrients, especially Vitamin B1 (or thiamine), from the outer rice bran into the grain, making parboiled rice almost as nutritionally potent as brown rice.

Even more amazing is the fact that it is a process that has been in existence for thousands of years in India and many other parts of Asia where rice is the staple food. (Probably, the original reason for parboiling rice was to make it possible to remove the husk without breaking the grain.) An estimated 25 per cent of the rice produced annually is converted into parboiled rice.

Needless to say, parboiled rice is also one of the best kinds of rice for making *kanji*. In fact, in Dakshina Kannada, only a special variety of parboiled rice (called *oorpel ari* in the local language, Tulu) – a reddish-pink grain, which fades to pale pink when cooked – is used to make *kanji*.

Modern-day nutritionists agree with our ancients but they put it a little differently. Firstly, according to them, rice is one of the easiest foods to digest and completely free of allergens. (Perhaps that is what the ancients saw as rice's affable, soothing nature!) Secondly, though rice contains less protein than wheat – by weight, 7 per cent versus 10 per cent in wheat – the protein in rice is superior to that in both wheat and corn. And this is because of higher amounts of lysine – an essential amino acid that is one of the body's vital building blocks and necessary for calcium absorption. Thirdly, rice has no cholesterol, is low in fat and sodium and, in its unpolished or parboiled form (see box 'Brown or White?', page 19), it is a slow-digesting complex carbohydrate, rich in most of the B vitamins and in many of the minerals like iron, magnesium, potassium and zinc. If that is not the résumé of a perfect healing food, then what is?

And when this grain, as nurturing as Mother Nature herself, is cooked to become *kanji*, all its nutritional benefits become available in an even more easy-to-assimilate and digestible form.

Medicinal Gruel

No wonder then that in many ancient systems of medicine, *kanji* is everything from comfort food for the sick to nourishment for nursing mothers, even baby food. In Ayurveda, healing diets are considered absolutely vital during and after *panchakarma* treatments. And the list of sixty-four fortifying foods used in these diets includes different kinds of rice gruel. Described in great detail, they are classified both by the main ingredients used and by consistency. For example, a thin gruel made from rice and water is called *mantha*, whereas a thick gruel made from any grain including rice is called *krushara*.

Rice gruel is also used to treat many ailments, especially digestive disorders. For example, probably the oldest oral rehydration treatment for diarrhoea is in the *Sushruta Samhita* – *kanji* water mixed with a little salt. Many of the other major Ayurvedic texts including the *Madanapala Nighantu* and the *Kashyapa Samhita* also mention the therapeutic properties of rice gruel.

Congee occupies no less a place of importance in the traditional Chinese medicine chest. By itself, it is used as a tonic to nourish and strengthen various organs, especially those of the digestive system. It is also recommended for lactating mothers to improve the production of breast milk. Medicinally, it is used as a diuretic and as a laxative.

But when combined with various other foods, congee really comes into it own and is used to treat a whole host of ailments like diabetes, high cholesterol, rheumatism, digestive ailments like diarrhoea and vomiting, fevers and also as a tonic to bolster weak constitutions. For example, spinach-stalk congee is used to treat the thirst that is a common problem for diabetics and carrot congee for intestinal cramps and flatulence. I guess this is why many Chinese claim that congee has the ability to bring back a person from the brink of death! And it is still a practice among many Chinese families to eat congee once a week because it is believed to stave off disharmony.

How to Fall in Love with Rice

Cook some plain steamed rice. The best way to do this is by the 'absorption' method – which is to boil the rice in water that is just enough to cook it, leaving no liquid left over when the rice is done. (Most varieties of rice require water between two to two-and-a-half times the volume of rice.) Then cover the pot with a tightly fitting lid and let the rice sit for about fifteen minutes. The steam inside the pot will gently nudge the rice to 'bloom' into beautiful, fluffy grains. Also, whatever extra moisture there may be will get absorbed by the rice.

Now open the pot. Let the delicate aroma of the cooked rice float up into your nostrils. Enjoy for a few seconds. Serve a few spoonfuls of the steaming hot rice into a bowl. Dribble into it a little *ghee*. Mix gently and then eat the rice while it is still hot.

Life will never be the same again…

A Bellyful of Joy

Some of the happiest parts of my childhood were the summer holidays spent in what to me is the *kanji* heartland of India – south coastal Karnataka. Every morning, come breakfast time in my maternal grandmother's home, a huge, burnished, red-gold copper vessel reminiscent of a massive and rather bad-tempered onion would sit seething in one corner of the kitchen, spitting out impatient wisps of steam from under its thick, tightly fitting wooden lid. Every now and then, the lid would be opened and, as fragrant clouds of steam spewed out, large dollops of hot *kanji* would be served onto a *thali*.

It was one of the most beautiful sights in the world.

Big, fat rice grains of the palest pink flecked with tiny specks of deep maroon – so soft that they were barely keeping their shape – swimming in thick, pearly *kanji* liquid. The trick was to down the *kanji* as hot as your fingers and mouth could bear to, even in the peak of summer. In fact, the copious sweating that followed was an essential part of the whole *kanji* experience! Accompaniments varied – sometimes just a spoonful of *ghee* or mango pickle, sometimes a serving of dry, spicy vegetable, but always the tiniest quantity, because the star of the show was the *kanji*!

And with a bellyful of that *kanji*, you were deemed ready to face anything that the day had in store. (Incidentally, when we came back home in the evening, the angry copper pot would be waiting, with more hot *kanji* to welcome us.)

For those initiated to the joys of *kanji*, there is nothing else like it. My mother's eyes still glaze over rapturously at the thought of it. And like so many of the best things in life, *kanji* is the simplest of foods. All you need is a large pot, a few cups of rice and lots of water. You can make it anywhere, eat it anytime and with anything. And for just a few rupees, you have one of the most delicious, satisfying, nourishing meals.

What's in a Name?

Like the debate about its birthplace, there are two opposing schools of thought about the etymology of the botanical name of rice, *Oryza sativa*. Though most experts agree that *Oryza* is from the Greek word *oruza* meaning 'of oriental origin', many trace the origin of *oruza* to *arisi*, the Tamil word for rice. Others disagree saying this is not possible because the ancient Greeks exported rice that was grown in Orissa, transporting it from the ancient port of Barygaza, or present-day Bharuch in Gujarat, and so they would have had no contact with the Tamil-speaking rice-growing regions.

The etymology of the word 'rice' is equally contentious. Some trace it to one of the Sanskrit words for rice – *vrihi*, which in turn is said to originate from *ari*, the name for rice in Proto Dravidian, the ancient ancestor of all Dravidian languages. Others maintain that the words 'rice' and *vrihi* have no connection at all to Tamil and that they are derived from *vrizhi*, a primitive Aryan word for rice.

Language	Name (Raw Rice)	Name (Cooked Rice)
English	Raw rice	Cooked rice
Botanical	Oryza sativa	Not applicable
Sanskrit	Vrihi, tandula, dhanya	Anna
Hindi	Chawal	Bhaat
Gujarati	Choka	Bhaat
Bengali	Chaul	Bhaat
Marathi	Tandul	Bhat
Tamil	Arisi	Sadam
Telugu	Biyyamu	Annam
Kannada	Akki	Anna
Malayalam	Ari	Choru

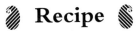 Recipe

Roasted Rice Dumplings

(Serves 3-4)

The roasted rice gives a delicious, unusual flavour to these dumplings. They are normally served with chutney but they taste just as good with a dab of ghee or homemade butter. And if you are feeling particularly indulgent, you may even want to try it with my dad's favourite accompaniment – a little sugar mixed with ghee!

INGREDIENTS

¼ kg rice
1 tbsp oil
¾ tsp mustard seeds
½ dried red chilli, broken into pieces
7-9 curry leaves
A pinch of asafoetida
1 tsp salt (adjust to taste)
2 tbsp grated fresh coconut
2 glasses of water (about 1 litre)

METHOD

Wash the rice thoroughly and drain out the water completely. Next, spread an absorbent cotton cloth over a large *thali* or tray. Spread the drained rice thinly on the cloth-covered tray and leave for about 3-4 hours or till the rice grains are completely dry.

Now, in a heavy pan or *kadai*, dry-roast the rice over very low heat till the grains turn golden-brown and give off a roasted aroma. (Stir constantly, so that the grains roast evenly and do not char.) Allow to cool and then grind to a coarse powder the consistency of semolina (*rava*).

Heat the oil, add mustard seeds and dried red chilli. When the mustard seeds stop spluttering, add the asafoetida and curry leaves. After a few seconds, add the roasted rice powder, grated coconut and salt and fry for about a minute or so till all the ingredients are well mixed. Boil the water and add to the roasted rice-powder mixture. (Add the water very carefully and slowly because the rice-powder mixture will splutter and spit when it comes in contact with the hot water.) Over very low heat, cook the mixture, stirring constantly till all the water has been absorbed and you have a thick *upma*-like mixture.

Allow to cool. Now take about two tablespoons of the mixture and shape into a slightly flattened ball. Repeat till all the mixture has been used up. Steam the balls for about 10 minutes in a pressure cooker without using the weight, or 15-20 minutes in a rice cooker.

Serve hot with *ghee* and coconut chutney.

Ragi: Raghuvamshi!

After Lord Rama's triumphant return from exile, as an ecstatic Ayodhya was still joyously celebrating, Lord Hanuman expressed a desire to return home to Kishkinda. He also asked for a few things that he wanted to take along with him. One of them was a grain called *ragi*. Rice, greatly incensed by this, angrily demanded to know why *ragi* was being given so much importance when it should have been obvious to everyone that it was rice that was the superior grain, so superior that it was even offered to the gods.

Soon a hot debate raged between *ragi* and rice. When Lord Rama heard about this, he decided that Lord Indra, who was soon to arrive in Ayodhya for a visit, should settle the matter. But that visit was delayed for a very long time, perhaps because the Lord of Devas was held back by more pressing heavenly matters. When Lord Indra did arrive in Ayodhya finally, Lord Rama presented the problem to him. In the splendour of Lord Rama's assembled court, *ragi* and rice were asked to appear. Lord Indra took one look at both the grains and declared, 'The verdict is very clear. Just by looking at them, you can tell which is the superior grain. It is obviously *ragi*!' And that was because, in the long wait for Lord Indra, the rice had been ruined, infested with all kinds of pests, while *ragi* had remained fresh and pest-free – as if it had just been harvested…

I was told this story by Dr AS Seetharam, former National Co-ordinator, Small Millets Project, Indian Council of Agricultural Research (ICAR). It is a story that he often used when he talked to farmers about the importance of growing *ragi*. You see, the reason why the *ragi* remained pest-free was because it is a naturally pest-resistant crop that can be stored – and *is* stored – not just for years but for decades. In fact, this is also the reason why *ragi* is called the eco-friendly crop because it is perhaps the only widely available grain today that is grown without the use of pesticides!

So what is this *ragi*? Known as finger millet in English, it is a cereal and consists of tiny, round grains that look like lighter, orange-red versions of mustard seeds. When ground, it becomes a beautiful, pale, pinkish-brown flour, scattered with tiny maroon speckles. This flour is made into a wide variety of foods like *rotis, dosas, idlis, laddus* and even porridge.

Ragi has traditionally been one of the major cereal crops in several parts of eastern and southern Africa and parts of tropical Asia, especially India. And it is in India where, for centuries, this most nourishing of cereals was treated with the respect that it deserved, so much so that it was even considered safe and nutritious enough to be given to infants as weaning food. (See box: 'Baby Food').

But in recent years, its popularity waned and it began to be dismissed as a 'coarse' food and an 'inferior crop', fit for consumption only by the poor and by cattle. Not for long though, because now, things have come full circle and this poor man's food is making a comeback to rescue the rich man from the side effects of his wealth!

Queen Sheba's Grain?

Lord Hanuman's patronage notwithstanding, *ragi* did not originate in India. Its birthplace is said to be in the regions of Eastern Africa that stretch across Ethiopia, Sudan and Uganda. Remains of *ragi* grains have been found in Neolithic sites in Kadero in Sudan which date back to the second half of the fourth millennium BC. They have also been found in Axum in Ethiopia, once the capital of the Axumite Empire (which was at its zenith as a naval and trading power from the first century AD to the seventh century AD) and possibly the birthplace of the Queen of Sheba.

Ragi came to India as a result of the ancient trade links between India and Africa, most probably travelling on the Sabaean Lane, the sea route connecting the north-eastern coast of Africa to the western coast of India. (We imported ivory, gold and emeralds from the Axumite Empire and exported silk and spices to it.) So, though a foreigner, *ragi* took up residence in India thousands of years ago. Remains of *ragi* have been found in the Harappan archaeological site (1600 BC) at Surkotda in Kutch, Gujarat and in archaeological sites in South India like the Hallur site on the Tungabadra river in Karnataka which dates back to 1800 BC and in Paiyampalli (third to first century BC) in Andhra Pradesh.

Poor Man's Boon, Rich Man's Saviour

Of all the places in India where it is grown, Karnataka is *ragi* heartland. The millet traditionally occupied a very special pride of place in many parts of the state, so special that a day without a bellyful of *ragi mudde* was – and still is – unthinkable. (*Ragi mudde*

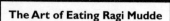

The Art of Eating Ragi Mudde
There is a special technique to eating *ragi mudde*. You break off a bit, dip it in your preferred *ragi mudde* accompaniment – usually *soppina saaru* (a curry made with greens) – then put it in your mouth and just swallow!

means 'lumps of *ragi*' and is made by moulding dough made out of cooked *ragi* flour into large lumps and steaming them.) Now, those lumpy (what else!) pinkish-brown *mudde* may not score very high in terms of culinary sophistication, but for Karnataka's rural folk who toil hard and long in the fields, those unprepossessing lumps are manna that they wouldn't swap for anything else in the world.

Why? Well, because *ragi* contains a nutrient that has become something of a celebrity in this Age of the Fitness-Obsessed. Devoured by health freaks, prominently displayed on the labels of fashionable, upmarket health foods, it is what nutritionists have decreed that your daily bread should never be without.

Dietary fibre.

Those indigestible carbohydrates present in fruits, vegetables and whole grain that are vital for keeping the food moving along in your digestive system, but at a nice, slow and easy pace. Something that is important for those who do hard physical labour because it means that a meal will be digested slowly, lasting the long, strenuous hours till the next one. But it is even more important for a sedentary business executive because it helps to keep many born-at-the-desktop diseases at bay.

Like diabetes.

Dietary fibre plays a key role in controlling and regulating the release of blood sugar. This means that *ragi* is invaluable in both helping to prevent and manage diabetes. And that is especially good news for India because, as of 2009, Indians accounted for over 17 per cent of the global population of diabetics; that is, there were over 50 million Indian diabetics! Or to put it a little more frighteningly – it is estimated that by 2030, India's share of the estimated global population of 370 million diabetics will go up to about 21 per cent, translating to 80 million Indian diabetics!

Dietary fibre also plays a key role in helping to prevent heart disease. This is because it serves as food for the friendly bacteria (called gut flora) in the large intestine which convert it into certain fatty acids that – among other things – lower levels of 'bad' cholesterol (LDL) and increase levels of 'good' cholesterol (HDL), thus reducing the risk of heart disease. The implications of this may be judged by the forecast that by the year 2020, India will have 100 million people

suffering from heart disease – nearly 60 per cent of the global population of heart patients!

One of the fallouts of a diet poor in dietary fibre is constipation, a condition that is aggravated by a sedentary lifestyle and lack of exercise. And if you remain chronically dietary-fibre-deprived, it could lead to more serious rectal and intestinal diseases like piles (haemorrhoids) and irritable bowel syndrome. And possibly even cancers of the colon and rectum. (The link between low consumption of dietary fibre and cancer of the colon and rectum is currently the subject of both debate and investigation in the West.)

Desi Milk of Magnesia?

According to Ayurveda, *ragi* is a 'cooling food' because its essential nature is alkaline. And so, it is the perfect food for irate digestive conditions like acidity, heartburn, even ulcers.

Dietary fibre is also the dietician's darling because the fibre acts like a sponge, absorbing water and thus increasing the 'bulk' of the food. The result is obvious – you eat less and as a consequence you lose weight.

After *bajra* (pearl millet, a close relative of *ragi*) and Bengal gram, *ragi* has more dietary fibre than any other grain, pulse, vegetable or fruit. The required amount of daily dietary fibre for an adult is generally pegged at around 40 grams. With every 100 grams of *ragi* that you eat, you get almost 50 per cent of that requirement!

So, think about it. By eating just a couple of *ragi rotis* or a bowl of *ragi* porridge (or even a *ragi mudde* or two!) every day, you are fuelled with enough energy to slave on a farm. Your digestion is tickety-boo, your heart and arteries are coaxed to stay fit and your blood sugar behaves itself. And you get that waistline under control! Can a food offer any more healthfulness?

Actually, yes…

And India's Too…

Vitamins B1 (thiamine), B2 (riboflavin) and B3 (niacin) – three important members of the illustrious B family of vitamins. All three are needed for conversion of carbohydrates into energy, but each of them also plays very important roles separately. Thiamine is critical for the proper functioning of the nervous system. Riboflavin is vital for healthy eyes and skin and for the other B vitamins to function, as is niacin, also indispensable for healthy heart and skin.

And all these three vitamins are present in substantial amounts in *ragi*.

27

But one could argue that all cereals are rich in the B vitamins, so what's so special about *ragi*? Well, like rice, *ragi* is a fairly good source of protein, but one Indian variety has almost twice as much protein as rice! More importantly, *ragi* protein contains an amino acid that is missing in most cereals – methionine. Methionine is one of the nine essential amino acids, critical for healthy skin and nails and most importantly for a healthy liver. It is normally present in dairy products, eggs, meat and fish. And that is why *ragi* is such an important food crop for India, where often dairy products are an out-of-reach luxury and many people are vegetarians, either by choice or because they cannot afford to eat non-vegetarian food.

Last but not the least, *ragi* is also rich in many minerals. It has good amounts of iron and phosphorus, but also very high amounts of calcium. This is of particular importance for thousands of Indian mothers and their children who require extra calcium but cannot afford many of the calcium-rich foods like milk.

If I were the Prime Minister of India, I would make *ragi* the national food! (One erstwhile Prime Minister, Deve Gowda, although he didn't make it the national dish, had grandly declared that even after taking office he continued to eat his beloved *ragi mudde*!)

And so it is time to return to the story of the war between rice and *ragi* at the beginning of this chapter. There is a slightly different and more popular version of the story and it is one of the best-known works of Kanakadasa, one of Karnataka's great philosopher-poets. (He is considered to be one of the three great saints of the Haridasa movement, the other two being Purandaradasa and Sripadaraya.) In his narrative poem called 'Ramadhanya Charithre', the dispute between rice and *ragi* is settled by Lord Rama himself who imprisons both the grains for six months – perhaps to give them time to cool off, calm down and introspect. At the end of the imprisonment period, when the grains are released, Lord Rama sees that rice has been totally ruined by pests and disease while *ragi* has remained beautifully preserved. Lord Rama is so impressed by the 'poor man's food' that he christens it *ragi*, derived from one of his own names, Raghava, which in turn is derived from the name of his royal dynasty – Raghuvamsha.

A befitting knighting of a truly noble grain.

Ragi Reckoner

- The *ragi* plant is basically a grass, as are all the other cereals like wheat, rice, *bajra* and *jowar*.
- There are around 6,000 varieties of millet in the world.
- *Ragi* is a hardy crop that can grow with little water and little help from fertilizers.
- The Defence Food Research Laboratory of India (under the aegis of the Defence Research and Development Organization) has developed *ragi*-based convenience foods that can be eaten by Indian *jawans* when they are posted in remote areas.

What's in a Name?

Ragi's English name – finger millet – is said to be inspired by the flowers of the *ragi* plant that grow in a formation that resembles a human hand with the fingers sometimes curved inwards to resemble a fist.

The word *ragi* is said to trace its roots to the Proto South Dravidian *iraki* or *eraki*, which was also the generic name for grain or fodder, giving a good indication of the importance of *ragi* as a staple food in ancient India.

Language	Name
English	Finger millet, African millet
Botanical	Eleusine coracana
Sanskrit	Rajika, krishna
Bengali	Madua
Gujarati	Bhav
Hindi	Nachni, ragi
Marathi	Nachni
Tamil	Kelavaragu
Telugu	Ragulu, taidalu
Kannada	Ragi
Malayalam	Kooravu

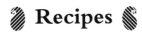

Recipes

Breakfast Ragi

(Serves 3-4)

Called huri hittu *(meaning 'roasted flour') in Kannada, this is a great breakfast food – hearty and nutritious, the roasted grain lending a delicious nutty flavour to it.*

INGREDIENTS

For the huri hittu
¼ kg whole ragi *grain*

For one serving of breakfast ragi
1-2 tbsp grated jaggery (adjust to taste)
1 tbsp fresh grated coconut (optional)
1 cup hot milk

METHOD

To make the *huri hittu*, roast the *ragi* in a thick pan over a slow fire till the grains change colour and become darker. Allow to cool, then grind to a fine powder. This can be stored in a dry container and used as needed.

To make one serving of breakfast *ragi*, serve 2-3 tablespoons of *huri hittu* into a bowl; add grated jaggery and grated coconut. Now slowly pour in the hot milk, stirring till you have a porridge-like consistency.

Variation: For a really hearty breakfast, you can add half a chopped banana, raisins, nuts, etcetera. And if you have the time and inclination and want a really nutritious meal, sprout the *ragi* grains before you roast them!

Spicy Ragi Rotis   (Serves 4)

Ideal for breakfast, tiffin or even a quick main meal, these rotis *also keep for a couple of days, especially if stored in the fridge.*

INGREDIENTS

¼ kg ragi *flour (You can substitute a quarter of this flour with wheat flour to make thinner* rotis *and to make them easier to roll out.)*
1 small onion, finely chopped
2 tsp fresh grated coconut (optional)
2-3 green chillies, finely chopped
2 tsp fresh coriander, finely chopped
½ tsp cumin (jeera)
A pinch of asafoetida
½ tsp salt (adjust to taste)
Vegetable oil for cooking the rotis

METHOD

Mix together all the ingredients with a little water to make into *roti* dough. Roll out into thick *rotis*. (You will not be able to roll out thin ones because of the chopped onions and other ingredients. Also *ragi* does not have any gluten and therefore the flour does not have the 'stickiness' needed to roll thin *rotis*.) Cook on a *tava*, applying a little oil to each side of the *roti*. Serve hot with homemade white butter, *ghee* or plain curd.

Sea of Tranquillity – White and Brown Rice

What a Dal – Green and Dried Pigeon Pea

Carbohydrates
A Simple Take on a Complex Issue

'Carbs are not monsters.'
From *Healthy Carb Cookbook for Dummies* by Jan McCracken

Every year, plants produce more than 100 billion tons of carbohydrates through the process of photosynthesis. Carbohydrates (or 'carbs' as they have been nicknamed) are the fuel that keeps the engine of life chugging on our planet. Yet, in recent times, if there is a word that has evoked almost as much love-hate as the word 'fat', it is 'carbohydrate'. It instantly conjures up foods irresistibly forbidden, that tremble so deliciously for those fleeting seconds on our lips, only to overstay their welcome and spend a lifetime on our hips – not to mention stomachs, thighs, bottoms etcetera, etcetera! And for whose 'illicit' pleasures we pay with ill health, all the way from hypertension to heart disease.

Or so we have been made to believe.

The truth is that not all carbs are monsters. There are the good carbs and there are the not-so-good ones. And the good carbs are so essential for good health that according to most leading nutritionists, 50-55 per cent of our daily diet should consist of these once-vilified nutrients. This is because carbohydrates are the primary source of fuel for our body. So, neglecting your carbs is like trying to run your car on an empty fuel tank.

Anatomy of a Carb – A Simple Complexity
Bio-chemically (and simply) speaking, carbohydrates are molecules comprising of carbon, hydrogen and oxygen. There are essentially two kinds of carbs: the simple sugars and the complex carbo-hydrates.

The Simple Sugars
The basic units of carbohydrates are called sugars, not to be confused with the sugar that we add to our food and drink. And the most abundant and important example of this kind of carb is glucose because it is the fuel that is generated and used as a source of energy by almost all living organisms on this planet, from bacteria to humans. Glucose is also one of the end products of photosynthesis in plants. And in the human body, glucose – also known as blood sugar – is the end result of the body's synthesis of dietary carbohydrates.

Simple sugars also sweeten natural foods. For example, glucose is found in certain fruits, many vegetables, in grains like corn and in honey. Fructose, as the name indicates, is what makes most fruits so deliciously sweet. Lactose is found in milk and sucrose is found in sugarcane.

The Fibre of Our Being

Our Stone Age ancestors ate about 100 grams of it every day. To be healthy, we need to eat at least about 40 grams. And till recently, the Indian diet was well stocked up on it, the average daily consumption being between 60-70 grams. But the rate at which we are embracing fast food and white bread, we may soon be competing with the West, where, according to most estimates, the average consumption is about one-third the daily requirement – or even less than that. (The average American eats only around 10-15 grams!)

I speak of course of dietary fibre. This is a kind of complex carbohydrate abundantly found in fruits, vegetables, whole grain, legumes and other plant-based foods that the body can't digest – so it is also referred to as 'unavailable carbohydrates'. But its presence in food is so critical for human health that Captain TL Cleave, one of the pioneers in propagating the benefits of dietary fibre, said that its deficiency is the root cause of most diseases of modern civilized society.

There are two kinds of dietary fibre – insoluble and soluble. And it is the partnership of these two kinds of fibre that determines good health.

Soluble dietary fibre slows down the movement of food in the small intestine, where a major part of the digestive process takes place. This ensures that food is digested thoroughly and the resulting end-product, glucose, is released into the blood at a controlled, slow, steady rate. Actually, the word 'soluble' is a bit misleading because soluble fibre does not actually dissolve. Rather, the gut flora, or the friendly bacteria in the large intestine, feed on it to convert it into short-chain fatty acids (SCFA). These fatty acids keep the large intestine healthy, help reduce 'bad' cholesterol (LDL) and promote the production of HDL or 'good' cholesterol.

Insoluble dietary fibre speeds up the movement of undigested food in the large intestines. This is where the last stage of the digestive process takes place – mainly the production of faecal matter. So food has to move faster here, staying only long enough for the proper formation of faeces. Insoluble dietary fibre thus aids regular and more frequent bowel movement, preventing constipation and more serious rectal and intestinal diseases like piles (haemorrhoids), irritable bowel syndrome and ulcerative colitis. Insoluble dietary fibre is also a detoxifying agent, removing food toxins and bad cholesterol. Last but not the least, it increases the 'bulk' of the food by sucking up water – the result is that you eat less…and lose weight!

The Complex Carbs

When several (ranging from several dozens to several thousand) of these simple sugars are joined together, they form complex carbohydrates.

Why are they called 'complex'? Well, primarily because their molecular make-up is far more complex than that of the simple sugars. But it is also because these kinds of carbohydrates take much longer for the body to digest and synthesize and that is why they are the good carbs.

But only if you eat them in their natural or least processed state – which means whole and natural foods like fruits, vegetables, nuts, seeds and whole grains. These foods contain two kinds of complex carbohydrates – starches and non-starches. Starches are broken down by the body's digestive process to ultimately become glucose, which the body tissues then use as energy. Dietary fibre (or the non-starches), on the other hand, remains largely undigested but its presence in food is so critical that it determines how healthy a carbohydrate is. (See box, 'The Fibre of our Being', for more details.)

Moreover, in the largely unprocessed and natural form, these foods also provide us with generous helpings of many other nutrients like proteins, vitamins, minerals and antioxidants.

That still leaves a few questions…

Are all 'simple sugars' bad carbs?

No, not if they come from fruits and other natural foods. Fruits, for example, are rich in simple sugars (fructose) but they are also excellent sources of dietary fibre as well as vitamins, minerals and antioxidants. Also, since many fruits are very high in water content, the quantum of sugar that you consume in each helping of fruit is relatively small.

If I'm eating good carbs, can I eat as much of them as I want and still not become overweight?

No. If you eat more carbohydrates than what your body needs to combust for its energy needs, then the body will store the excess carbohydrate by converting it into adipose tissue – or body fat.

Can a low-carbohydrate diet be harmful for health?

Yes, if the amount of carbohydrates in your diet is so low that the body has to look for other sources of energy to burn – like the protein in body tissue. Therefore, the right amount of carbohydrates in the diet makes sure that your body's proteins are spared for the critical functions that they are needed for – this is called 'protein sparing'.

Do carbs have any other function apart from being the energy source for the body?

Yes and very important ones. For example, their presence in cells acts as markers, helping cells to recognize and communicate with each other. So blood cells recognize other blood cells of the same blood group because of certain sugars (simple carbs) found on their surface that help to determine our blood type. This is particularly important during blood transfusion.

Similarly, some carbohydrates are exclusively involved in helping to bolster the immune function. Called fructo-oligosaccharides, they help the body's immune cells to communicate with each other better, thereby improving the body's protective response to invasions. They also function as food for the friendly bacteria in the intestines.

So now you know. That carbohydrates are not Enemy No. 1 – at least not the ones that Mother Nature so generously and unflaggingly fills her gardens and fields and orchards with. And so, it's time to shrug off those fears and reinstate carbohydrates into their rightful place in our diet.

Pigeon Pea: Protein Power!

al-chawal. Two words so inextricably attached to each other that they could be just one; two words that in a twinkling conjure up the unrivalled pleasure of simple, home-cooked food for millions of Indians. It is perhaps astonishing that something as basic as plain, steamed rice (*chawal*), accompanied by an equally unpretentious stew of boiled pulses (*dal*) often tempered with nothing but red chillies, cumin and asafoetida fried in hot *ghee*, could be viewed as something approaching ambrosia. But then, you know what they say – that the greatest pleasures of life are the simple ones.

In South India, the *dal* is frequently spiced up to become preparations like *sambar* or *saaru*. But the basics are the same – rice accompanied by pulses (a kind of legume). And the English name of the little, round, red-gold legume that is most commonly used to make this *dal* (or *sambar*) is a curious one – pigeon pea. Apparently the English botanist Leonard Plukenet (1641-1706) named it thus when he observed that in Barbados it was grown primarily to feed pigeons, who are particularly partial to it. But nowhere as much as we Indians are, growing over 80 per cent of the world's annual pigeon pea crop and consuming even more than that! And we do so, it seems, for a very good reason because the pigeon pea (more commonly known as red gram, *toor dal* or *tuvar dal* in India) is one of the most nutritious legumes.

Pharaoh's Food or Appeaser of Mars?

Now, it would be natural to assume that a food that is mentioned in the *Puranas* would have originated in India and indeed, the widely held opinion is that the pigeon pea's birthplace is the Eastern Ghats. (Archaeological remains have been found in many sites in Central India including Tuljapur in Maharashtra, and Peddamudiyam and Sanganakallu in Andhra Pradesh, dating back to the mid to late second millennium BC.) From India, it is believed to have travelled to Africa and the Far East through ancient trade routes, and from Africa to the Americas, aboard slave ships. However, a few botanists are of the opinion that the pigeon pea originated in East Africa – perhaps because it has been staple food in many parts of this region for thousands of years. A single carbonized seed, closely resembling the pigeon pea, was found in tombs of the Egyptian pharoahs of the XII dynasty (2200-2400 BC).

Whatever be the place of its origin, by the time the great sage Sushruta compiled the *Sushruta Samhita* around the sixth century BC, the pigeon pea had firmly established itself as an Indian. Not just as food but also as medicine and even as sacred offering. In Hinduism, the *navagraha puja*, or the worship of the *navagraha* (nine planets), is an important ritual. During this, each of the nine planets is propitiated by an offering of a grain that is associated with it – the pigeon pea is associated with and offered to Mangala, or the planet Mars.

But curiously enough, though references to the pigeon pea are found in ancient Buddhist and Jain texts dating from 300 BC to AD 300, there is no mention at all of this pulse in Tamil Sangam literature (first century BC). This, in spite of the fact that one of the pigeon pea's Sanskrit names, *tuvarika*, is said to be derived from its Tamil name, *thuvarai*. And despite the fact that the pigeon pea is one of the main ingredients not only in *sambar* but also in *sambar* powder. Nor is there any mention of the pigeon pea in the *Mahabharata*, in which there are several references to other pulses like green gram (*mung*) and black gram (*urad*). In fact, the first reference in ancient South Indian texts is in the *Manasollasa*, the massive twelfth-century encyclopaedia written by King Somesvara III, son of the Chalukyan emperor Vikramaditya. And the first mention of *sambar* is to be found only in Kannada literature dating to the seventeenth century.

But ever since, the pigeon pea has been a beloved, indispensable part of almost every Indian kitchen…

Made For Each Other

One of the most memorable and perhaps most romantic lines in cinema is from the film *Jerry Maguire*. At the end of the film, the central character, Jerry Maguire, goes to his sister-in-law's house hoping to reunite with his estranged wife Dorothy. Standing at the front door, he spots her across a room full of women. Their eyes meet and he simply says, 'You complete me.'

That one little line could just about sum up why the simple, inexpensive combination of *dal-chawal* is so nutritionally important. In many regions of the world – like India – the large majority of people can afford to get their daily requirement of protein only from plant sources like legumes, cereals, seeds and nuts. Now, plant proteins are often called 'incomplete proteins' because they do not

---

Crispy 'n' Golden

While soaking the rice and *urad dal* in water for making *dosa* batter, add a handful of split pigeon pea. It will make your *dosas* very crisp and give it a lovely 'extra-golden' tint!

have all the amino acids that are essential for the body. But when two different sources of plant protein are combined together, they make up for each other's deficiencies. For example, many cereals – like rice – are low in the essential amino acid lysine, but many legumes – like the pigeon pea – contain high amounts of lysine. On the other hand, legumes are low in the sulphur-containing amino acids like methionine and cysteine, while cereals like rice are well stocked with them. So, by eating pulses and cereals together – like *dal-chawal* – the body's entire protein requirement is taken care of, providing it with the highest protein quality that is comparable to the protein derived from milk and other animal protein like fish.

What is even more amazing is that our ancestors seemed to know this, because for thousands of years, *dal* combined with *chawal* has been the centrepiece of an Indian meal. (Incidentally, the combination of *dal* and *chapatti* or *roti* is equally nutritious.)

And the pigeon pea's nutritional wealth isn't limited to protein, even though protein makes up as much as 20 per cent or more of this legume. Like all members of its family, it is also a rich source of carbohydrates and many other key essential nutrients – minerals like calcium, phosphorus, magnesium, iron, sulphur and potassium, and many members of the B vitamin family, especially thiamine (Vitamin B1), riboflavin (Vitamin B2), niacin (Vitamin B3) and choline.

There's a Medicine in My Dal?

But who would think that your average *dal* or *sambar* could have such a wealth of healing in it?

The clue to the pigeon pea's medicinal properties is in one of its Sanskrit names – *tuvara*, which mean 'astringent'. Both Ayurveda as well as traditional Chinese medicine use the pigeon pea as an astringent, in order to arrest bleeding. Charaka, for example, recommended it for bleeding piles. He also used it as one of the ingredients in a formulation to treat epilepsy. Chinese medicine and Ayurveda also use it to heal wounds and sores and to expel intestinal worms. And in traditional folk medicine in South America, the Caribbean and China, almost every part of the plant, including the roots, is used to treat all manner of ailments from sexually transmitted diseases to jaundice, bronchitis and mouth ulcers.

Since pigeon pea is considered one of the most nutritious of foods, it is also used in post-palliative diets. According to Sushruta, '…the

What's in a Name?

One of the reasons why many botanists favour India as the pigeon pea's birthplace is because, in several languages, its etymology seems to point in this direction. For example, one of its botanical names, *Cajanus cajan* is said to originate from the Malay word *cachang*. This is a corruption of the Telugu word *kandi*, which in turn apparently traces its origin to the Sanskrit word *kaand*, meaning 'stem', and is supposedly a reference to the long stem of the pigeon pea plant. The other botanical name for the pigeon pea is *Cajanus indicus* – *indicus* is the nomenclature used for species that originate in India.

The names for the pigeon pea in all Indian languages originate from two Sanskrit names. The first one is *adhaki* (from which originates the Hindi *arhar*). This comes from the word *ardha*, meaning 'one-half' and is a reference to the fact that the pigeon pea is almost always consumed after it has been hulled and split into two. In most Indian languages, the words *dal* or *paruppu* is added to the name to distinguish the split version of a legume from its whole form. In Hindi, for example, whole pigeon pea is *arhar*, while the spilt version is *arhar dal*.

The second Sanskrit name is *tuvara* (or *tuvarika*), an allusion to the astringent flavour of the green pigeon pea, from which originates many of the names in almost all Indian languages – *toor, tuvar, thuvaram, togari* and so on.

Language	Name
English	Pigeon pea, Congo pea, red gram, yellow dal, dal, Gungo pea, Indian dal, Indian pea, no-eye pea etc
Botanical	Cajanus cajan, Cajanus indicus
Sanskrit	Adhaki, tuvara, tuvarika, shanapushpika
Hindi	Arhar, tuvar (tuvar dal), toor (toor dal)
Gujarati, Marathi	Tuvar (tuvar dal), toor (toor dal)
Bengali	Arhar
Tamil	Thuvaram paruppu
Telugu	Kandi pappu
Kannada	Togari, togari bele
Malayalam	Thuvara paruppu

pulses such as the *mudga* (green gram), the *adhaki* (pigeon pea) and the *masura* (lentil) should be regarded as the best and by far the most nutritious of the cereals which fall under the respective heads of the paddy group (*dhanyavarga*)'.

Modern medicine has also begun to acknowledge the pigeon pea's therapeutic powers. Recent studies have shown that pigeon pea can cause reversion of sickled red blood cells in patients suffering from sickle-cell anaemia. Even more significantly, its ability to control blood sugar, recognized by Ayurveda thousands of years ago, has now caught the attention of the West. So much so that in August 2004, the US Patent and Trademark Office (USPTO) granted three patent rights to the American bio-pharmaceutical company, Insmed Inc, for its 'novel invention of pigeon pea extracts' for treating diabetes, hypoglycaemia, obesity and artherosclerotic cardiovascular disease!

Move Over, Pigeons! The Silkworms are Coming!

It's a fairly well-known fact that all legumes are a farmer's best friend, doing the all-important task of 'fixing' nitrogen into the soil. Nitrogen is an important constituent of amino acids and nuclei acids like DNA and is therefore essential for life on this planet. But even though almost 80 per cent of the earth's atmosphere is nitrogen, it needs to be 'fixed' into the soil so that it can be used by plants. This job is done by nitrogen-fixing micro-organisms, many of which live in the root nodules of leguminous plants like the pigeon pea.

But the pigeon pea is also the farmer's ally in so many other ways. For example, the pigeon pea is a hardy, sturdy plant that is used as a cover crop to prevent soil erosion, as windbreaks and to provide both shade and support for delicate vanilla vines. And even after the pigeon pea has been harvested, the plants are still of use – they are ploughed back into the soil to become nitrogen-rich green manure.

It is not just humans who benefit from eating this legume. The pigeon pea, its plants and even its seed coat make excellent cattle and poultry feed. And while pigeons may devour it as their favourite repast, perhaps one of the little-known facts about the pigeon pea is that in Madagascar, the plant serves as a host for silkworms and for the insects that produce lac. And its tiny, golden, exquisite, orchid-like flowers act as a magnet for butterflies and hummingbirds and are a rich source of nectar for honeybees!

The presence of the pigeon pea is so all-pervading in Indian food that the words *dal* or *paruppu*, the generic terms to include all legumes, are often used to refer to this little red-gold legume. There is a popular Tamil saying that goes, '*Paruppu illaada kalyanama?*' A loose translation would be, 'A wedding without *dal*? Unthinkable!' Actually, without the pigeon pea, life itself would be unthinkable.

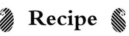 Recipe

Two-in-One Saaru   (Serves 4-5)

Saaru is the Kannada term for any stew-like dish made by boiling a legume – like pigeon pea – and then adding vegetables, spices and sambar *powder and seasoning it. This particular* saaru *is a traditional favourite in Karnataka, and an ingenious one because in one fell swoop, you have two dishes – a soup-like curry and a vegetable side dish. You can make this using a whole variety of vegetables like greens, green banana, green beans, bitter beans or ridge gourd.*

INGREDIENTS

¾ cup split pigeon pea, cleaned and washed
¼ kg of any of the vegetables mentioned above, washed cleaned and diced
(If you are using greens like spinach, two small-sized bunches will suffice)
1 ½ tsp sambar powder

Grind together

2-3 tbsp of grated fresh coconut
1 marble-sized ball of tamarind (adjust to taste)
1 tsp black sesame seeds
1 tsp roasted split Bengal gram (this is a thickening agent, so you can substitute with an equal quantity of Bengal gram flour)

Seasoning

(For the saaru)
1 ½ tsp salt (adjust to taste)
10-15 curry leaves
1 tsp lemon juice (optional)

METHOD

If you are using vegetables that take a little longer to cook – like green beans or bitter beans – pressure-cook the vegetables together with the *dal* and *sambar* powder (4 whistles). However, if you are using vegetables that cook in a jiffy – greens, green banana or ridge gourd – first cook the *dal* and *sambar* powder together (4 whistles). Then add a little hot water to the cooked *dal*, add the vegetables and simmer over low heat till the vegetables are cooked.

Now place a soup strainer over a large bowl and pour the cooked *dal*-vegetable mixture into the strainer. Allow it to remain in the strainer till all the liquid has drained out. Remove the *dal*-vegetable mixture from the strainer and gently press out any remaining liquid into the bowl. Keep aside.

Simmer the strained liquid over low heat till it comes to a boil. Now add about a cup of water (for a thinner, more 'soupy' *saaru*, add more water), the ground coconut *masala,* salt and 10-15 curry leaves and simmer for another few minutes, then remove from heat. This is the *saaru.* (If you want to increase the tartness, add some lemon juice, adjusting to taste.)

(For the side dish)
1 ½ tsp salt (adjust to taste)
1 tbsp finely chopped fresh coriander leaves

Tempering
1½ tbsp oil
1 tsp mustard seeds
1 dried red chilli, broken into pieces
7-8 curry leaves
A pinch of asafoetida
2-3 green chillies, chopped (adjust to taste)

Now heat the oil, add mustard seeds and red chilli. When the mustard stops spluttering, add the curry leaves and asafoetida. When the curry leaves begin to brown, carefully add about half a tablespoon of this tempering to the *saaru*.

To the remaining tempering, add the strained *dal*-vegetable mixture, green chillies and salt, and cook for a minute or so, stirring gently but well so that the seasoning and salt is well mixed into the *dal*-vegetable mixture. Add the chopped coriander, stir, cook for another few seconds and remove from heat.

Serve hot with plain steamed rice and a bowl of chopped onions!

Bengal Gram: Pulse of Health

It is a steep, punishing climb that only the bravest and the most sure-footed pilgrims would dare attempt: 4,450 feet to the top of Mount Parasnath in Jharkhand on which twenty of the twenty-four Jain *tirthankaras* attained *moksha*. Others less intrepid, like my parents, made it to the top sitting in what is known as a *doli*, or palanquin, carried by two *doliwalas*, who were local tribals from the area. These *doliwalas* carry loads that average between sixty and seventy kilograms nine miles up a pathway, which at times is just about a few feet wide, then another nine miles around the twenty holy spots and then back down again.

Naturally, halfway through, everyone needed a break. The *doliwalas* to tank up on some much-needed sustenance, and the ones sitting in the *doli* to put their hearts back into their chests after several terrifying glimpses of the breathtaking drop down which they would plummet if the *doliwala*'s mountain-goat-like sure-footedness faltered even the tiniest bit.

As they rested, my mother watched the *doliwalas* take out a yellow flour, which they mixed with water and proceeded to eat with a few green chillies. Intrigued, she asked them what they were eating. They told her that it was *sattu*, a flour made from roasted Bengal gram.

The Venerable One

It was called Bengal gram by the British because they first made its acquaintance in Bengal. But this pulse is of far greater antiquity. It has been found in several archaeological sites, two of the oldest being Çayonu, a Neolithic settlement in southern Turkey which existed from 7200 to 6600 BC, and Hacilar in south-western Turkey, dating back to 7040 BC. In India, it has been found in excavations at the Harappan site of Kalibangan in Rajasthan (3500 BC).

The *Markandeya* and *Vishnu Puranas* mention it, and references to it are found in several Indian texts on food down the centuries. There is also a mention of *sattu* in a sixteenth-century text, as one of the common foods eaten in the Gangetic plains. It served as fodder for animals as well – according to that great fourteenth-century traveller to India, Ibn Battuta, *channa gram* was soaked in water to

---

Kabuli or Bengali?

There are two varieties of Bengal gram. The one developed in the Indian subcontinent is smaller in size with wrinkled black skin. The other, larger with pale brown skin, is developed in the Mediterranean and known as chickpea or garbanzo bean. In India, this variety is popularly called *kabuli channa*.

which green–gram leaves had been added, then pounded with three to four pounds of *ghee* and fed to animals daily!

So you could say that this is no ordinary pulse, not only because it is at least seven thousand years old but also because it has remarkable nutritional and therapeutic qualities.

The Complete Food

Like the rest of the family of pulses to which it belongs, the Bengal gram is an excellent source of both carbohydrate and protein, which are respectively the fuel and building blocks of the human body. But it is also packed with so many other healthful goodies that it can almost be a complete meal by itself. Moreover, the Bengal gram is the highest source of dietary fibre amongst all the commonly eaten foods in India, including cereals, pulses, fruits and vegetables, with one cup of boiled Bengal gram providing as much as 60 per cent of the daily requirement.

Now dietary fibre is a vital part of any healthy diet because, among other things, it keeps our bowels functioning properly. But it is particularly important for people who do hard physical labour – like the *doliwalas* of Jharkhand – and for diabetics. And that is because dietary fibre slows down the digestive process. This is important for the *doliwalas* because it means that the meal will last the long, strenuous hours of hard labour. And for diabetics, it means that blood sugar is released into the system in a slow, controlled and regulated manner, something their bodies are not able to do naturally. This is why, along with many other traditional Indian foods like *ragi*, the Bengal gram, till recently scoffed at as 'inferior' or 'poor man's' food, is now making a comeback. Not just as a nutritious power snack but also as part of the recommended diet for Indian diabetics.

Bengal gram is also a very good source of Vitamin B1 (thiamine), Vitamin B6 (pyridoxine) and folic acid (folate/Vitamin B9) and of minerals like calcium, iron, manganese and magnesium. These nutrients, in a synchrony of nourishment, keep the blood healthy and the heart, muscles, bones and nervous system in excellent working condition.

The Healer

Both the Unani and Ayurvedic systems of medicine hold the Bengal gram in high esteem. An excellent energizing food, it is also considered effective in lowering cholesterol, expelling intestinal worms, in the treatment of bronchitis, several skin diseases, blood disorders, diseases of the liver and spleen, and even as an aphrodisiac! And it is not just the gram that has medicinal properties. The leaves of the Bengal gram plant give out acidic dew in the night, which is collected and used in the treatment of indigestion, diarrhoea and dysentery. And a bath prepared by putting the entire plant in hot water is considered an excellent treatment for painful periods.

The 'Fixer'

What do the farmers of India have in common with the mighty emperor Charlemagne? Wise agricultural practices. Charlemagne, a great monarch, whose empire included half of Europe, was also an astute ruler and administrator. At the end of his famous *Capitulare de Villis*, an administrative act which lays down a large number of rules, particularly agricultural rules, is a list of plants that should be grown in every imperial garden. The Bengal gram is one of them. And since ancient times, Indian farmers have traditionally used legumes and pulses – of which the Bengal gram is one of the most popular – for intercropping and crop rotation, where more than one crop is cultivated in the same space, at the same time or sequentially.

And for a very good reason. Pulses and legumes do the vital job of making nitrogen, one of the most important nutrients for all living organisms, available to plants. They do this with the help of certain bacteria (*rhizobia*) that live in the root nodules of plants. These bacteria convert nitrogen from its inert form in the atmosphere into nitrogen compounds that are useful for the plants. This process is called nitrogen fixation. And when these plants die and are made to decay by being ploughed back into the soil – another traditional agricultural practice in India – more nitrogen is put back into it.

Cook's Delight

Nutrition apart, the other amazing thing about the Bengal gram is that it is a culinary chameleon, transforming into anything from soup to sandwich spread to even a substitute for coffee! In its split form and without its skin (split Bengal gram/*channa dal*), it is cooked into *dals* and curries, made into all kinds of delicious *vadas, kababs* and *koftas*, used as stuffing for *puranpolis* (sweet, stuffed *chapattis*) and *kachoris* (deep-fried savoury snacks), even as a tempering ingredient along with cumin, mustard seeds and asafoetida. As flour (*besan*) it becomes a thickening agent, a batter

One of the Sacred Nine

The Hindus consider the Bengal gram one of the nine sacred seeds (*navadhaanya*) that are traditionally used in the *navagraha puja* to appease the *navagrahas* (nine planets). Bengal gram is associated with Brihaspati (the planet Jupiter). The association is an apt one because Brihaspati is considered the most auspicious and benevolent of planets, the guru of the *devas,* the patron deity of eloquence and wisdom.

What's in a Name?

Philosopher Cicero (106-43 BC) got his family name from the Latin name for Bengal gram, *Cicer arietinum,* because an ancestor had a facial characteristic that resembled a Bengal gram. The characteristic? A wart, or – according to other versions – a dent, on his nose. When Cicero entered politics, he was urged to change his name – after all it cannot do much for your image as a public figure if you are named after a pulse! But he refused, saying that he would bring great glory to it. The rest is history…

Language	Name
English	Bengal gram, chickpea, garbanzo bean
Botanical	Cicer arietinum
Sanskrit	Chanaka
Hindi	Channa, channa dal, kabuli channa
Gujarati	Channa, channa ni dal
Bengali	Chholar, chholar dal
Marathi	Harbara, channa
Tamil	Kadalai, kadalai parippu
Telugu	Senagalu, senaga pappu
Kannada	Kadale, kadale bele
Malayalam	Kadala, kadala parippu

for fritters and *pakoras,* dough for a whole host of traditional breads like *theplas* (savoury Gujarati *chapattis*) and the main ingredient in crisp fried snacks like *sev* and sweets like *Mysore pak* and *besan ke laddoo.* Whole and with its skin (chickpeas/*channa*), it is sprouted and used in *usals* and *poriyals* (stir-fried vegetable dishes accompanying the main course). Then, when roasted, *channa* becomes a delicious, nutritious snack, munched by itself or with a piece of jaggery and even doubles up as breakfast in many parts of rural India.

All over Bihar and Rajasthan, it turns into the poor man's powerhouse of nutrition and energy – as the ubiquitous *sattu*! In Karnataka, *soppina kadale* (literal translation – 'Bengal gram with leaves') is a traditional snack. It is so called because the green and maturing gram is plucked along with the entire plant. It was my father's favourite and I remember that as a child, part of the fun was riffling through the plant to find the little green pods, popping them open and then eating the slightly sweet, crunchy gram… raw!

One of India's greatest treasures is its cornucopia of highly nutritious natural foods. And among them is the Bengal gram not only because it is nutritious but also because it is inexpensive. So, for the poor *doliwalas* of Jharkhand and millions of others like them all over India who rely on long hours of hard, punishing manual labour to earn their living but cannot afford expensive foods like milk, fresh fruits and vegetables, the Bengal gram is a veritable blessing of health.

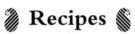 Recipes

Sweet-'n'-Saaru Channa Dal   (Serves 4–5)

*Two dishes at one go! Boil a pot of split Bengal gram (*channa dal*) and end up with a delicious sweet-and-sour* rasam *and an* usal. *Add a salad, serve with plain steamed rice, and you have a complete low-calorie, nutritious, delicious meal!*

INGREDIENTS	METHOD
¼ kg split Bengal gram, cleaned and washed 3 cups water	Boil the *channa dal* in three cups of water for about 15–20 minutes or till each grain of *dal* is soft when pressed between the fingers. Completely drain out the water in which the *dal* has been cooked and keep aside – this will be used to make the *rasam*.

For the Rasam

INGREDIENTS	METHOD
A ball of tamarind, the size of a small lemon, soaked in half a cup of hot water for about 15 minutes 125 gm jaggery 2 tbsp sambar powder 1 ½ to 2 tsp salt (adjust to taste) 25-30 curry leaves A pinch of asafoetida A few drops of ghee	Squeeze the soaked tamarind till you get a thick pulp, and discard the residue. Boil 3 cups of water, add the tamarind pulp, jaggery and *sambar* powder and cook till the jaggery melts. Add the water strained from the boiled *channa dal*, salt, curry leaves and asafoetida and simmer for another 10-15 minutes. Serve laced with a few drops of *ghee*.

For the Usal

INGREDIENTS

1 tbsp oil
1 dried red chilli, broken
1 tsp mustard
2-3 pinches of asafoetida
2-3 green chillies, finely chopped
3-4 small garlic cloves (optional)
1-1 ½ tsp salt (adjust to taste)
1 tbsp grated fresh coconut (optional)
2 tbsp finely chopped fresh coriander

METHOD

Heat the oil, add the red chilli and mustard. When the mustard stops spluttering, add the asafoetida, then the boiled *channa dal*, green chillies, garlic and salt. Stir carefully for a few minutes, then add the coconut and coriander, stir for another minute. Serve with plain steamed rice and the *rasam*. It can also be eaten by itself as a snack.

Channa Dal and Spinach Steamed Dumplings (Serves 6-7)

Very nutritious and low in calories, this simple recipe makes a diet snack, a hors d'oeuvre for parties or can even be included in school tiffin boxes as a side dish.

INGREDIENTS

¼ kg split Bengal gram, cleaned, washed and soaked for about 2-3 hours
1 large cup spinach, cleaned, washed, dried and chopped fine
2-3 green chillies (adjust according to taste)
½ tsp lemon juice
¼-inch piece of ginger
A pinch of asafoetida
1 heaped tbsp finely chopped fresh coriander
1½-2 tsp salt (adjust to taste)
Ghee *(optional)*

METHOD

Grind the *channa dal,* green chillies and ginger to a coarse paste, thick enough to be rolled into balls. Add spinach, lemon juice, asafoetida, fresh coriander and salt and mix well. Shape into lemon-sized balls. Steam in an *idli* steamer or pressure cooker (without the weight) for about 5-7 minutes. Serve hot with mint chutney or tomato sauce.

This recipe works just as well without spinach. If you are feeling particularly indulgent or serving the dumplings to children, some warm *ghee* makes a delicious dip.

Besanwaali Bhaji (Serves 3-4)

The simple addition of a few tablespoons of Bengal gram flour transforms a side dish of vegetable (bhaji) into something more substantial and deliciously different so that you can still serve it as a side dish or eat it by itself as a snack. I do both! The recipe below uses radish, but it works as well with spinach, brinjal or any other vegetable that cooks quickly.

INGREDIENTS

¼ kg radish, washed, cleaned and diced
2 tbsp oil

METHOD

Heat the oil in a pan, add the red chilli and mustard. When the mustard stops spluttering, add the asafoetida

½ dried red chilli, broken into bits
½ tsp mustard seeds
A pinch of asafoetida
½ tsp cumin seeds
2-3 green chillies, chopped
1 tsp salt (adjust to taste)
3-4 slivers of fresh ginger
2 tbsp Bengal gram flour (besan)
¾ tsp sambar powder (optional)
1 tbsp fresh coriander leaves, finely chopped

and the cumin. When the cumin swells and turns dark brown, add the chopped radish and green chillies. Sauté for a few minutes on low heat. When the radish pieces start to turn transparent, add the salt and the ginger, cover the pan and keep over low heat till the radish is cooked. Now, add the *sambar* powder and sprinkle the *besan* all over the radish. Cook for a few minutes, stirring continuously to prevent the *besan* from sticking to the bottom of the pan. When the flour is cooked, add the fresh coriander leaves, cook for another few seconds, stirring well. Then cover the pan and turn off the heat.

Beautiful Bengal Gram

The flour made from Bengal gram was a beauty aid of considerable and long-standing repute long before shampoos and soaps existed and much before 'facial scrub' was a phrase in the beautician's vocabulary!

One of the best natural skin cleansers, Bengal gram flour (*besan*) has been traditionally used both to bathe with and for washing hair. In fact, it is used even to bathe babies. The flour is also an excellent exfoliant, scouring away dead skin cells, grime and grease gently but thoroughly. This makes the skin appear lighter in colour, so the popular belief is that the regular use of *besan* makes the skin fairer. It is also considered particularly effective for treating problems associated with oily skin, such as pimples and dandruff.

So, Bengal gram flour is a multitasking beautician. And here are a few ways to use it. The basic paste is a very good cleanser and skin rejuvenator. When it is mixed with different ingredients, it doubles up as a face mask.

Basic Paste: Mix *besan* with curd, using two portions of curd to a portion of the flour. For **oily skin**, use curd made from skimmed milk. If you have pimples, add a few pinches of turmeric. For **dry skin**, use curd made from full cream milk or add cream – half a tablespoon for every two tablespoons of *besan*. Add water if the paste is too thick – the consistency should be such that the paste is easy to apply but does not drip.

Facial/Body Scrub: Apply the paste, rub for a few minutes in a gentle circular motion and wash off with cool water. You can use this basic paste on your face, hands and feet, even the whole body, as a substitute for soap.

Face Mask: Apply the paste on your face, leaving out the delicate skin on the lips and around the eyes. Leave it on for about ten to fifteen minutes. If you have oily skin, first rub off the mask very gently and then wash your face with cool water. Apply a non-oily moisturizer. If you have normal or dry skin, just wash off the paste with cool water and apply a moisturizer.

Summer Special: Make the paste by substituting a quarter of the curd with rose water or add a few pinches of pure sandalwood powder.

Winter Special: Make the paste by substituting a quarter of the curd with honey.

Mung: Queen Bean

This is a story about a queen. Not any ordinary queen, mind you. Older than Cleopatra, older even than the Queen of Sheba by at least a few thousand years. And to my eyes, even more beautiful. Which is no mean achievement because this is not even a human queen, but the monarch of a vast empire of pulses.

Now, before I tell you more about her, let me first tell you about the botanical empire over which she reigns. Legumes. The shortened version of the name of a family of plants called *Leguminosae* (or *Fabaceae*), the third-largest family of flowering plants, with over 19,000 species. The dried seeds of some members of this clan are called pulses, which make up some of the world's most valuable food crops – like beans, peas, peanuts and *dals*, many of which we Indians consume in huge amounts.

So, naturally the question arises – is the ruler of this vast realm a bean, a pea or a lentil? Or to confuse you some more, maybe even a gram, as we Indians tend to call pulses?

Let's work this out step by step.

In India, where she was born at least five thousand years ago, her Sanskrit name was *mudga*. It's a pretty enough name but doesn't do much to settle the bean-or-pea-or-lentil question. As the centuries passed, she began to be variously called *mung*, *mung dal*, even green gram. In the West, where her riches were discovered only of late, she is called the mung bean. Does that mean that she is bean *and* lentil *and* gram? Actually, yes. When she is whole and looks like – and *is* in fact – a tiny bean, covered in a beautiful *mehendi*-green skin, she is mung bean or green gram or just *mung*. When she strips off her green skin and splits into two, showing off her gorgeous golden-coloured body underneath, she is *mung dal*.

Or then, she is just simply Her Most Healthful Highness, Mung, the Queen of Legumes!

Venerable Lineage

Need I say the obvious – that *mung* is an Indian *maharani* of an illustrious lineage that goes back thousands of years?

In the *Rig Veda*, the three 'm's of health that get repeated mention are *mudga, masha* and *masura* – or *mung, urad* (black gram) and *masoor* (lentil). In the *Mahabharata*, when Bhishma lies dying in his bed of arrows and imparts profound wisdom to Yuddhisthira, he says, 'that shameless insensate man who, through stupefaction, steals paddy, barley, sesame, *masha* (black gram/*urad*), *kulattha* (horse gram), oil seeds, oats, *kalaya* (peas), *mudga* (green gram/*mung*), wheat, *atasi* (flaxseed), and other kinds of corn, has to take birth as a mouse.' And mung also finds place in the *Vishnu, Brahma* and *Agni Puranas*, in the *Laws of Manu* and in the *Devi Bhagavatam*. In his *Arthashastra*, Kautilya refers to the colour of *mung dal* to describe an alloy of gold and silver and also says that the best quality touchstone should be 'the colour of the *mudga bean*'.

Archaeologically speaking, there is evidence that *mung* has been growing in India since 1800 BC at least and remains of it have been found at archaeological sites all over South India (Adichanallur in Tamil Nadu, Utnur, Paiyampalli and Cuddapah in Andhra Pradesh, and Narsipur in Karnataka). Copper Age remains of *mung* have also been found in Navdatoli in Madhya Pradesh.

There is no definite information about how *mung* travelled from India to other parts of Asia but it probably arrived in China early, travelling on ancient trade routes between India and China. By the first or second century AD, the Chinese used *mung* as both medicine and food, eating it in hundreds of ways. So, for example, while the bean itself is boiled and made into a dessert, starch is extracted from it and converted into a kind of noodles, popularly called 'cellophane noodles' because when cooked, their transparent appearance resembles cellophane! And it is Chinese cuisine that is responsible for introducing the West to mung bean sprouts. Even so, the *mung's* reign remained restricted to the East for long despite her extraordinary nutritive and healing powers, and it is only in recent times that she has caught the fancy of Western nutritionists.

The Queen of Hearts

Our *mung rani* is literally the Queen of Hearts because like all legumes, she is an excellent source of the B vitamins, many of which play a very important role in preventing and managing heart disease. For example, one of the critical functions of Vitamin B1 (thiamine) is to produce neurotransmitters, the 'cables' that relay

messages between nerves and muscles. The heart is the largest and most powerful muscle in the body and thiamine helps the heart beat strong and steady. And just one cup of cooked *mung* has about 20 per cent of your daily requirement of this vitamin.

Mung is also loaded with many other B vitamins. Like Vitamin B6 (pyridoxine), often known as the 'happy vitamin' because it helps in the production of serotonin, the hormone that keeps you awake and in a good mood. (And we all know that if you are happy, your heart will be healthy and happy too.) And Vitamin B3 (niacin), which controls the levels of cholesterol and blood sugar in our bodies. And folate, vital for the production of red blood cells and therefore for healthy blood — one cup of cooked *mung* has over 60 per cent of your daily requirement! Mung also contains Vitamin B2, or riboflavin, which is vital for healthy eyes and skin.

In addition to this lovely cocktail of B vitamins, *mung* contains good amounts of dietary fibre. This, apart from playing a vital role in controlling cholesterol and blood sugar, also helps prevent those extra pounds from piling up because foods high in dietary fibre take longer to digest, keeping those hunger pangs at bay.

Queen Mung's Mines

Queen Mung is fabulously rich in minerals; precious nutrients that also help prevent and manage heart disease and diabetes.

It is abundant in potassium, which is vital to keep blood pressure down to healthy levels. In 1999, a study of six popular South Indian varieties of bananas found that eating two bananas a day for just one week caused an amazing 10 per cent fall in blood pressure. And one cup of cooked *mung* has more potassium than one banana!

Mung also has good amounts of iron (the key to haemoglobin production and healthy blood), copper, without which iron cannot produce haemoglobin, and zinc, in the absence of which the body's insulin response decreases, making blood sugar levels erratic. (Incidentally, without zinc, you also won't be able to smell or taste very well!) It also contains significant amounts of magnesium. One of the functions of this mineral is to act as a relaxant, calming the nerves and relaxing muscles. This means that it also prevents your heart from beating too fast or irregularly and so helps in preventing heart attacks; in fact, experts believe that magnesium deficiency is at the root of heart disease.

What's in a Name?

'It is unfortunate that green gram, which is widely known as mung bean, was not named Vigna mungo, thereby creating an avoidable confusion for which William Roxburgh, the botanist is responsible.'

Dr YL Nene, noted plant pathologist and founder of the Asian Agri-History Foundation (AAHF).

The confusion about *mung's* botanical name is primarily because botanists have interchanged the words *mungo* and *radiata* in the botanical names for *mung* and its close relative, black gram (*urad*). For example, the most commonly accepted name for *mung* is *Vigna radiata*. But previously, *mung* was classified under the genus *Phaseolus* (also part of the legume family) and so, many older texts – like Dr KM Nadkarni's *Indian Materia Medica* – state *mung's* botanical name as *Phaseolus mungo*. This is also one of the botanical names for black gram (*urad dal*).

Language	Name
English	Mung, mung bean, green gram
Botanical	Vigna radiata or Phaseolus aureus, previously known as Phaseolus mungo
Sanskrit	Mudga
Hindi	Mung, mung dal
Gujarati	Mag
Bengali	Moog
Marathi	Moog
Tamil	Pachhai payaru
Telugu	Pachhai pesalu
Kannada	Hesaru, hesaru bele
Malayalam	Cheru payaru

The Queen and the Sages

'I enjoin the taking of food made out of rice, barley, wheat, mudga, masha, masura and other grains…'

So said the Buddha in the *Lankavatara Sutra*.

Needless to say, the *rishis* and sages who were the founders of Ayurveda had twigged on to the medicinal and nutritional qualities of *mung* thousands of years ago. According to the sage Kashyapa, 'a soup' (the preparation of lentils that we Indians call *dal*) of *mung* is 'appetizing, beneficial for the heart'. The sage Sushrutha said that *mung* was better than the other pulses and recommended *mung* soup both as convalescing food and as part of the daily diet. And the sage Charaka said that *mung* should be a part of the regular supplies of a good hospital!

Which brings us to my theory as to why *mung* is considered so supreme among legumes. It is not only that it is so rich in nourishment; all pulses are excellent sources of many vital nutrients, especially protein. In fact, many nutritionists say that pulses contain more protein than eggs, fish or meat. (Like all the other legumes, around 20-24 per cent of *mung* is protein). But many legumes have one drawback – they are notoriously difficult to digest and tend to aggravate the digestive system, leading to unsettled tummies and flatulence.

Except for *mung*. Not only is it one of the most nourishing foods, but also one of the easiest to digest. Add to that the fact that its essential nature is alkaline, making it what Ayurveda categorizes as a 'cooling food'. In Chinese medicine as well, mung-bean sprouts are considered to be a cooling food – which also makes *mung* a perfect summer food!

A good sovereign is one who looks after all her subjects, no matter who they are. And that is precisely what makes *mung* the *maharani* of nutrition and health. She offers her healing, nourishing care to one and all. To the elderly, to the sick, and to babies – all of whom need special nourishment that is also easy to digest. To growing children and athletes who need high amounts of protein. To diabetics and heart patients for whom diet is a very important key to managing their diseases. To pregnant and lactating mothers who need extra nutrition – for themselves and their babies. And to anyone who just wants to be healthy.

Last but not the least, like all legumes, *mung* enriches the very soil that she grows in, her roots drawing the life-sustaining nitrogen from the air and 'fixing' it into the soil. Without this nitrogen-fixing action, there would be no nitrogen in the soil and nothing would grow on Mother Earth.

Long Live Queen Mung!

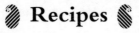 **Recipes**

Cold Roasted Mung Broth (Uppa Hesaru)

(Serves 4–5)

This is an unusual variant of the traditional dal *– because it is never served hot, making it perfect for a sultry summer's day!*

INGREDIENTS

1 ball of tamarind, the size of a marble
¼ kg whole mung *(green gram), cleaned and washed*
7-8 cloves of garlic
1½-2 tsp salt (adjust to taste)
4-5 green chillies
2 tbsp fresh coriander leaves, finely chopped

Tempering
1 tbsp oil
½ tsp mustard seeds
1 dried red chilli, broken into pieces
8-10 curry leaves
1 tbsp lemon juice (optional)
A pinch of asafoetida

METHOD

Soak the tamarind in a quarter cup of water for about 15 minutes. Squeeze and extract the juice and keep aside. Roast the *mung* in a thick pan over a low fire till the *mung* turns brown and gives out a roasted aroma. Allow to cool, then cook in a pressure cooker (8-9 whistles) till very soft.

Roast the green chillies and garlic separately in a heavy pan over low heat for a few minutes till the skins begin to turn brown in places. Grind together the cooked *mung* and green chillies into a thick, coarse paste. Peel the roasted garlic, crush and add this to the *mung* paste along with salt and tamarind juice. Add cold water if necessary to make into a thick, broth-like consistency. Finally add the chopped coriander and mix well.

Heat the oil, add mustard seeds and dried red chilli. When the mustard seeds stop spluttering, add the curry leaves and asafoetida. Remove from heat and add to the *mung* broth. Add lemon juice if you want to increase the tartness.

Serve either with hot rice or *chapattis,* or even with hot toast! (I love eating it by itself, as a sort of in-between-meals hunger-bunger.) You can even chill it for about 30 minutes in the refrigerator.

Variation : If you are feeling lazy, you need not grind the *mung* after you have roasted and cooked it. The end result is just as delicious.

Mung Dal and Coconut Milk Payasam

(Serves 4-5)

This fabulously creamy dessert is such an integral part of the wedding feast in coastal South Karnataka that the politely oblique way of asking someone when they are getting their daughter or son married is, 'When are you giving us payasam?'

INGREDIENTS

Milk extracted from half a coconut (see chapter on Coconut for instructions)
¼ kg whole mung *(green gram), cleaned and washed*
¼ kg jaggery
2 tbsp cashew nuts, chopped
1½ tbsp raisins
5-6 pods cardamom, crushed

METHOD

Boil the *mung dal* in water and the second milk for about 15-20 minutes or till the *dal* grains begin to disintegrate. Now add the jaggery, cashew nuts and raisins and cook again on very low heat for at least 10-15 minutes, stirring every now and then to make sure the *payasam* does not stick to the bottom and burn. (The longer you allow the *payasam* to cook at this stage, the better it will taste.) Now add the first milk and the cardamom and simmer for just another minute or so, stirring all the while. Do not cook for longer than that or else the coconut milk will curdle and the creamy taste will be altered.

This *payasam* keeps very well and tastes as delicious when cold, even refrigerated — a great summer dessert!

Urad Dal: The Other Mung?

She is the less-travelled sister of that Queen of Legumes, the Empress of Good Health, the fabulous green-gold *mung*. But in India, this little legume's empire is no less magnificent, stretching to every corner of the land, and she reigns from a throne no less sumptuous than that of Queen Mung. Like her famous sister, when she is whole, she looks like a tiny bean and because of this she is sometimes called urd bean. And since the skin that covers her is black, she is often called black gram. Also like her sister, when she strips off that black skin and splits into two, her body is a different colour – a beautiful pale cream. In this split avatar, we Indians hail her as *urad dal*, the Princess of Pappads, the Devi of Dals and the High Priestess of Snacks, because without her august presence, the *dosa*, the *idli* and the *vada* would never have been possible.

Needless to say, like her sister *mung* and many others of the illustrious family of legumes, the black gram is an Aladdin's cave of nutrition. But before we explore this wealth, let us first acquaint ourselves with the black gram's ancient lineage.

Worth its Weight in Gold?

In 1485, the Kannada poet, Bommarasa of Terakanambi, thus eulogized a royal feast, 'The kings are relishing a *kadubu* made from black gram; it looked like a full moon, like a mass of mist set together, as if heavenly nectar had solidified into circles or as if a drop of moonlight had hardened…'

But the black gram was in existence in India for thousands of years before that. Remains of it have been found in archaeological sites all over India including Navdatoli in Madhya Pradesh (1300–1600 BC), Paiyampalli in Andhra Pradesh (third to first century BC) and Naikund in Maharashtra (3000–2700 BC).

The black gram appears in several ancient Indian texts dating to the Vedic period – it has been mentioned in the *Brahadaranyaka*, a commentary on the *Rig Veda* (5500 BC), in the *Mahabharata*, and in the *Krishi Parashara,* a treatise on agriculture dating to 400 BC. And from references to it in many other later texts, it is clear that the black gram was used as more than just food. For example, Varahamihira, the great sixth-century astronomer and mathematician and one of the Navaratnas ('nine gems') in King Vikramaditya's court,

---

Low-Cal Vada

You don't have to be a South Indian to have made your acquaintance – nay, to have fallen in love with – those deep-fried, crispy, golden rings of delicious sin called *medu vadas*. But in order to 'sin' a little less and cut down on those calories, all you have to do is soak the black gram for only a couple of hours before grinding it. This makes the batter less 'fluffy' and therefore prevents the *vadas* from absorbing too much oil when you fry them.

mentions black gram in his *Brhat Samhita* as one of the ingredients used to improve the productivity of the soil. So does Suraphala in his treatise on plant disease, *Vrikshayurveda*, dating to around AD 1000.

But the most fascinating use of this little legume in ancient India was as a measure of weight, especially to weigh precious metals like gold and silver. According to the *Manusmriti* (the *Laws of Manu*) and Kautilya's *Arthashastra*, a *masha* – which incidentally, is also the Sanskrit name for black gram – is a unit of weight equivalent to the weight of one grain of black gram, and sixteen *mashas* is equivalent to one *tola* or 11.7 grams!

The black gram's culinary history is a curious one. For example, though the *vataka* – probably an ancestor of the *vada* – is mentioned in Sutra literature (800-500 BC), the black gram also figures in the *Arthashastra* as a fermenting agent – but not to ferment *idli* and *dosa* batter as it is used today, but to make liquor! In fact, the *idli* makes it debut only about 1,500 years later in the *Vaddaradhane* (tenth century AD), considered to be the earliest book of Kannada prose. Here it is called *iddalige* and listed as one of the eighteen items that a lady can offer to a male guest who is a *brahmachari*! Interestingly enough, this early *idli*, as described by Chamundaraya in his encyclopaedia, *Lokapakara* (AD 1025), was not made from a mixture of rice and black gram. Instead, it was a more spicy version, made from black gram soaked in buttermilk, which was then ground to a fine paste, mixed with whey, cumin, coriander, pepper and asafoetida, and steamed.

And if *idli*, *dosa* and *vadas* are synonymous with South Indian cuisine, *pappads* or 'poppodums' have long been one of India's most eloquent culinary ambassadors to the West. As it should be, because we Indians have been making and eating *pappads* for over a thousand years. *Parpatas*, as they were known then, have been mentioned in Buddhist and Jain literature dating to the fourth century BC. In fact, *pappads* were considered such an important part of the meal that documents dating to the fourteenth century describe how professional *papad* makers called *kagal kutas* were an essential part of kings' armies in Rajasthan! Now, there are *pappads* and there are *pappads*, made from everything from jackfruit to horse gram. But the most popular kind of *pappad* was – and still is – made out of black gram!

What's in a Name?

The black gram belongs to the botanical *Vigna* family (also known as the *Phaseolus* family). The family was thus named to honour a seventeenth-century Italian botanist called Dominic Vigni, who in 1625 wrote a commentary on the renowned Greek philosopher, scientist, logician and botanist, Theophrastus.

Many of this legume's Indian names, like the Hindi *urad*, are said to have originated from the Tamil *ulundu*.

Language	Name
English	Black gram, urd bean
Botanical	Vigna mungo, Phaseolus radiata, previously known as Phaseolus mungo
Sanskrit	Masha
Hindi	Urad, urad dal
Gujarati	Arad, arad dal
Bengali	Mashkalai, kalai dal
Marathi	Udid, udid dal
Tamil	Ulundu, ulundu paruppu
Telugu	Minumu, minumu payru
Kannada	Uddu, uddina bele
Malayalam	Uzhinnu, uzhinnu parippu

Nutritionist, Physician and Sexologist

'Men who eat boiled Sasyika rice with ghee *and black gram soup and then drink milk, sleep on those nights with the God of Love; that is, they indulge in sexual congress throughout the night.'*
Varahamihira in the *Brhat Samhita*

Since the black gram is popular only in India, information about its nutritional or medicinal values is very hard to come by – except that like all legumes, it is an excellent source of protein. And like the rest of its leguminous cousins, it is a good source of many of the B vitamins like B1 (thiamine), B2 (riboflavin) and B3 (niacin) as well as of minerals like calcium.

But our ancients knew that this little bean was also packed with an astonishing array of therapeutic powers. So, black gram is used to

treat many digestive disorders like gastritis, dysentery, diarrhoea, even liver disorders. This is curious because as a food, black gram is considered difficult to digest and responsible for causing flatulence! It is also used to treat an impressive list of ailments including nervous disorders, rheumatism, stiff and painful joints and piles. But most significantly, it is used to treat diabetes – both as medicine and as part of the diet prescribed for diabetics. In fact, *idlis* made out of black gram (similar to the one that Chamundaraya described in his encyclopaedia) is considered to be particularly beneficial!

That leaves one other invaluable property of the black gram – as an aphrodisiac. In Ayurveda it is prescribed to increase sperm count. And the sage Charaka, whose *Charaka Samhita* is considered to be a seminal work in the understanding of medicine and medical practice, was so impressed by this legume's ability to enhance a man's sexual performance that he went so far as to say that it would make 'even an old man potent and fertile'.

In Hinduism, of the nine planets, or *navagraha*, Rahu is the dark, dreaded entity, the *asura* (demon) who routinely eclipses the sun and the moon; so much so that no auspicious work is undertaken during that time of the day when he reigns – known as *rahu-kalam*. Therefore appropriately, of the nine grains (*navadhanya*) chosen to propitiate the nine planets, the task of appeasing the mighty, malevolent Rahu is assigned to this little black bean that can manifest itself in such an awesome range of roles – all the way from *pappad* maker to physician to aphrodisiac!

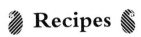

Recipes

Quickie Dosa

(Makes about 10-12 dosas)

It is the black gram content in the dosa *or* idli *batter that causes the batter to ferment and rise. But the reason that the ingredients for the traditional* dosa *or* idli *are soaked for at least four to six hours (often overnight) is primarily because the rice needs that amount of time to soften. So, could there be a short-cut version? In fact there is. Substitute the rice with semolina (*rava *or* sooji*) and you have this delicious version of the* dosa *that can be ready in a couple of hours – which is the amount of time you need to soak the black gram. You can make the* dosas *almost immediately after grinding the batter. Of course, if you let the batter stand for a few hours, it will ferment.*

INGREDIENTS	METHOD
½ cup black gram, cleaned, washed and soaked for about 2 hours	Drain all the water from the soaked black gram and grind it to a very fine, smooth paste – it should feel

¼ kg semolina (rava or sooji)
1 tsp salt (adjust to taste)
Oil

slippery like soap and as smooth as silk to touch. Now mix this paste with the semolina. Add the salt and enough water to make a thick batter of pouring consistency. Allow the batter to stand for about 15-30 minutes.

Heat the *tava*, then grease it with a little oil. When the *tava* is hot, spread the batter in circular motions to make a *dosa*. Dribble a few drops of oil all around and in the centre of the *dosa*. After a few minutes, when the *dosa* starts to turn golden-brown, turn it over and cook till both sides are done. Serve with a dollop of white butter, coconut chutney or pickle.

Variation: Add 1 medium finely chopped onion, ½ teaspoon of cumin seeds, 1 chopped green chilli, 1 tablespoon of chopped coriander leaves and a pinch of asafoetida to the batter.

Sunanda's Gunpowder (Chutney Powder)   (Makes about 1½ cups)

Two ingredients are immutable in mullagai podi *(or 'gunpowder' as it is often respectfully nicknamed), the chutney powder that traditionally accompanies* idlis *and* dosas — *red chillies and black gram. But clever and daring cooks have added to these basics to come up with their own special brand of* podi. *My mother, being one such cook, decided that adding sesame seeds would impart a certain* je ne sais quoi *to this classic. They do — an undercurrent of gentle nuttiness that tones down the pungency of the chillies just a tad.*

INGREDIENTS

1 cup black gram (about 8 tbsp)
1 heaped tbsp black sesame seeds
7-8 dried red chillies (adjust to taste depending on how fiery you like your gunpowder!)
2 pinches of asafoetida
¾ tsp salt (adjust to taste)

METHOD

Roast the black gram in a heavy pan or *tava* till it turns golden-brown and gives out a toasted aroma. Now roast the sesame seeds till they begin to pop and spit. Finally roast the red chillies till they begin to char in places. Allow all the roasted ingredients to cool. Grind the chillies and roasted gram to a coarse powder. Now add the rest of the ingredients and grind to a finer powder, but not very fine — one of the joys of *mullagai podi* is the crunchy bits of black gram that surprise you every now and then.

Store in a dry, airtight jar. Serve with a little oil (purists swear by sesame oil) or melted *ghee,* to be mixed into the powder before eating.

The Other Dals

Apart from *mung*, *urad dal* (black gram), *toor dal* (pigeon pea) and Bengal gram, the 'Big Four' of pulses that are commonly used all over India, there are several others that are also very popular. Like most members of the family, these pulses are excellent sources of protein, many of the B vitamins like thiamine (B1), riboflavin (B2), niacin (B3), pantothenic acid (B5) and folate (folic acid/Vitamin B9), as well as several of the dietary minerals like calcium, iron, magnesium, potassium, phosphorus and sulphur. Here are some of the other *dals*.

Language	Name			
English	Lentil	Cow pea	Horse gram	Lablab bean, hyacinth bean, Egyptian kidney bean etc
Botanical	Lens Culinaris	Vigna unguiculata	Macrotyloma uniflorum, dolichos biflorus, dolichorus uniflorus	Labalab purpureus, Dolichos lablab L, Dolichos purpureus L etc
Sanskrit	Masura, mangalaya	Rajmash, mahamash, chapala	Khatakula, kulattha, vanyakulattha	Nishpava, shimbi, rajshimbi, vallaka
Hindi	Masoor, masoori, masoori dal	Lobia, chowli	Kulti	Sem
Gujarati	Masoor, masoori dal	Chowli	Kulti	Vaal
Bengali	Masoor, masoori, masoori dal	Barbati	Kulti	Shim, rajashimbi
Marathi	Masoor, masoor dal	Chawli	Kulti, hulga	Pavate, vaal
Tamil	Misur paruppu	Karamani, kaattu ulundu, thatta payir	Kollu	Mochai, avari
Telugu	Misur pappu	Alasandulu, bobbarlu	Ulavalu	Anumulu, chikkudu
Kannada	Kesaribele, Channangi bele	Alasande	Hurli	Avare, avarekai
Malayalam	Chuvanna parippu	Payar, vellappayar, kottappayar	Muthira	Avara
Medicinal/ Therapeutic Uses	Nourishing food, blood purifier, removes skin blemishes	Nourishing food, increases lactation	Treatment for urinary stones, obesity, hiccups, and intestinal worms	Treatment for ear and throat infections

Proteins
The Complete Picture

'Protein, the most sacred of all nutrients…'
From *The China Study* by Colin Campbell, physician, scientist and author

We all know that proteins are an inseparable part of a healthy diet and their absence can lead to serious health problems. But there are many misconceptions about this very critical nutrient. For example, one popular belief is that proteins are required for muscle building and so, the people who should really be worrying about their protein intake are athletes and body builders.

Well, it is true that proteins are the body's building blocks and essential for the formation of body tissue – including muscles. But that is only a very small part of why proteins are such a vital part of our diet.

Did you know that insulin is a protein? That the colour of your eyes is determined by proteins? Or that your nose is exactly like your father's because proteins passed on that genetic information from your father's DNA cells to yours? In other words, it is almost impossible to find a part of the body, a stage in a human being's life or a bodily function that does not require the participation of the over thirty thousand proteins in the human body – and often in ways that are not obvious.

Without proteins, we would not have been conceived and our mothers would find it difficult to produce breast milk. We would not be able to grow into healthy adults. Proteins are needed to form new tissue, so without them, wounds wouldn't heal, broken bones wouldn't knit back, our hair and nails wouldn't grow each time we cut them. Our bones, skin and teeth would deteriorate and our organs would collapse. Without proteins, our muscles wouldn't move and our lungs, arteries, ligaments and bladder would lose their elasticity and we wouldn't be able to breathe, swallow, speak or pass urine. There would be no haemoglobin to transport oxygen and no fibrin to clot the blood. And almost all enzymes – and they are too numerous to be counted – and many of the hormones wouldn't exist and without them almost all the biological processes in our body would cease. Without proteins, we would be vulnerable to every possible infection and disease from the common cold to cancer.

And, if you are still not awestruck, proteins account for 20 per cent of the human body weight – the second-largest presence after water.

The Best Source of Proteins – The Whole Nine Yards!
We need to eat proteins every day. Firstly because of the twenty amino acids that generally make up proteins, we humans cannot produce at least nine of them internally and therefore must source them on a daily basis from food. (These nine are called essential amino acids.) Secondly, the body is constantly using up its protein supply – either by breaking it down into amino acids, which are then used for

different bodily processes, or by eliminating them from the body as waste products.

And that brings us to the second popular misconception about proteins – that the best sources are non-vegetarian foods and therefore, vegetarians are typically prone to have protein deficiency.

The truth is very different.

On the one hand, proteins from animal sources are 'complete' proteins, thus labelled because they contain all the essential amino acids. But they are often accompanied by very high levels of saturated fat and dietary cholesterol, especially true in the case of red meat and pork.

On the other hand, protein from plant sources, like legumes, nuts and cereals, are considered 'incomplete' proteins because one or more of the essential amino acids are missing. But this is still the 'incomplete' story because when cereals are paired with legumes or nuts in the right combination they 'complete' or fill in each other's missing amino acids. Further, plant proteins like legumes, nuts and cereals have almost no saturated fats or cholesterol. (In fact, many nuts and seeds like peanut and sesame are rich in the 'good' unsaturated fats.) They also come packaged with other goodies like minerals, vitamins and dietary fibre.

Therefore, when eaten in the right combination and the right quantity, proteins from plant sources are as capable of fulfilling the body's requirements as those obtained from animal sources. In fact, some experts go so far as to say that because plant proteins are synthesized into body protein at a much slower and steadier rate than animal proteins, they are the best kind of proteins to have. The clincher? It's now a fairly well-established fact that a healthy and balanced vegetarian diet leads to lower incidence of hypertension, heart disease, osteoporosis and even cancer.

So here are some of the best combinations of vegetarian foods that will provide you the complete proteins.

Food Combinations	Examples
Whole grain and legumes	*Dal-chawal, idli, dal-roti,* whole-wheat bread with peanut butter
Whole grain and dairy products	Curd-rice, *rava idli*
Dairy products with legumes	*Kadhi-chawal* is a particularly good combination because *kadhi* is made out of buttermilk and Bengal gram flour.
Legumes and seeds	Hummus, sesame-peanut *laddoo*

The protein story would still be incomplete if there were no mention of one more excellent source of protein, this time a 'complete' one. By conventional definition, it is clubbed together with other animal proteins, but it is the only animal protein that vegetarians eat, and in South India, in vast quantities. I speak of course of curd (yogurt) and buttermilk. You're thinking: then why not milk, since both curd and buttermilk are made out of milk. Well, milk is also a good source of protein, but curd and buttermilk contain one other kind of protein that milk does not – whey proteins, found in whey, the 'water' that separates from milk when it becomes curd.

Whey proteins are the only 'complete' proteins that vegetarians can eat – unless of course you are a vegan! (Did you know that over 70 per cent of human breast milk consists of whey protein?) Curds and buttermilk have one more thing in their favour – they are both probiotic foods which have so many other nutritional and therapeutic benefits that they are often dubbed the 'elixirs of life'.

And the best way to eat your curds and whey? Well, according to me, it is the South Indian way – with rice. You see, like *dal-chawal*, curd–rice is another superbly nutritious and delicious combination of two foods that come together to become the complete protein meal!

The word 'protein', coined by the great Swedish scientist Jöns Jacob Berzelius (1779-1848), comes from the Greek *proteios,* meaning 'of prime importance'. An apt name indeed, because without proteins, the magnificent supercomputer that is the human body would simply shut down.

Avatar – Bengal Gram in all its forms

The Royal Beans – Mung, Mung Dal and Urad Dal

Potato: The Much-Misunderstood Tuber

'Only two things in this world are too serious to be jested on, potatoes and matrimony.'
Irish saying

'Pray for peace and grace and spiritual food,
For wisdom and guidance, for all these are good,
But don't forget the potatoes.'
John Tyler Pettee, 'Prayer and Potatoes'

On 25 August 1842, almost fifty years after it became mandatory for the ships of the Royal Navy to carry limes, the *Lancet* published a letter from a certain William Dalton. In the letter, Dalton, a ship doctor, described how every morning the sailors aboard his ship would eat something which they called 'scurvy grass'. Apparently, during that voyage on the high seas, which lasted almost three years, this curious habit ensured that not a single sailor suffered from scurvy! So, what was this wonder food – some kind of greens like spinach, maybe? Not at all. 'Scurvy grass' was nothing but potato, peeled and sliced thinly, and dressed with a little vinegar to make it more palatable!

It is a little-known fact that the potato is one of the best sources of Vitamin C (a deficiency of this vitamin causes scurvy) and this story is a perfect example of how little we know about this most maligned and least understood of Nature's creations. Say 'potato' and the images that it conjures up are almost never wholesome. Most of us think that the potato is one of the Forbidden Unholies – delicious to eat but horribly unhealthy. The fault, however, lies not with the poor potato but with the way in which it is eaten.

Oddly enough, much of the bad press that the potato has received originated from the West, from countries that are some of the largest consumers of this tuber – like America. According to one estimate, an American eats an average of a little over one kilo of potatoes a week! While that may or may not be a lot of potato to eat, the real nub of the problem is in the way it is eaten. For example, there are the ubiquitous French fries, the staple accompaniment to that other American favourite, the hamburger. Then there is mashed potato – usually eaten only after milk, cream, sour cream, butter, cheese, even bits of fried bacon have been lavishly added to it. (Though it was invented in America, mashed potato is eaten all over Europe as well; 'bangers and mash', or sausage and mashed potato, being a British favourite!) Even the healthiest of foods cannot remain healthy after being treated like that… and the fact is that the potato is a very healthy food.

So, what is the real truth about this poor, vilified spud?

Before we find out, let us take a walk back in time because the potato traces its origin back to at least seven thousand years ago…

Staff of Life?

'…yellow, red, blue, purple, violet, pink with yellow spots, yellow with pink spots; round, oblong, twisted, hooked at the end like walking canes or spiralled like spinning tops…'

This is how the *Washington Post* (June 2007) described the more than two thousand varieties of potato that the inhabitants of a Peruvian village had gathered, so that the Lima-based International Potato Center could replenish its potato gene bank. This gene bank is the world's largest and is part of the centre's effort to protect the hundreds of species of potato which may otherwise disappear.

They could not have chosen a better spot because the potato originated in the Lake Titicaca region of Peru and Bolivia between 7,000 and 10,000 years ago. The Incas cultivated at least 200 varieties of it and ate it as their staple food. They made a flour-like substance called *chuno* by first freezing potatoes in the chilly night air, then exposing them to the daytime heat, then soaking them in water and finally drying them. This process – which took several weeks – preserved the *chuno* so perfectly that it could be stored for several years. In fact, the potato was such an integral part of the life of the ancient civilizations of the region that representations of it can be seen on their pottery. Potato motifs have been found in the ceramics of the Moche people of northern Peru (AD 1 to 600), on urns found in the archaeological site of Pacheco in coastal Peru dating between AD 500 and 800, and on later Inca pottery like those of the Chimu people, dating to the fifteenth century.

The potato's journey to Europe began hundreds of years later - some say when the Spanish conquistador Francisco Pizarro arrived on the Peruvian coast in 1524 and made his acquaintance with it. But others believe that the potato actually arrived in Spain accidentally, in a cargo of silver that the Spanish conquerors brought back from the New World. Monks in Seville began to grow it – interestingly enough as nourishment for the sick that they often tended – and the potato soon became a popular food among the poor.

There is much folklore and myth surrounding the potato's arrival in England, but what is clear is that it was through a circuitous route. As one story goes, Sir Francis Drake introduced it to the colonists in the British colony of Virginia in 1586, and they, in turn, brought it back to England. And though it was apparently served at the table of King James I (1566-1625), it took another few hundred years before the potato became a regular part of English cuisine. Meanwhile, according to another popular legend, Sir Walter Raleigh brought the potato to Ireland, where this inexpensive and easy-to-grow tuber was soon embraced enthusiastically, especially by the poor folk.

By the nineteenth century, the potato was well entrenched all over Europe, primarily because it grew easily even in the harshest conditions. The fact that it is a hardy vegetable, able to survive not only natural disasters like long spells of severe winter but also man-made ones like wars (because the potatoes could be hidden in the ground, safe from the enemy's armies), increased the potato's popularity. So, many European rulers like Fredrick the Great of

From Pig Fodder to Food Fit for Kings!

Amongst the world's most enthusiastic potato lovers are the French. But that was not so about 250 years ago when they saw it as a nasty, awful-tasting thing that caused leprosy… in short, food fit only for pigs!

The credit for the potato becoming 'fit for human consumption' in France goes to Antoine Parmentier, a French apothecary who discovered the nutritive qualities of this hated tuber when he survived the Seven Year War (during the course of which he was taken prisoner five times) on a diet consisting only of potatoes! A few years later, when France's wheat crop failed and bread began to disappear from the bakeries, the prestigious Academy of Besançon offered a prize for the best study of 'food substances capable of reducing the calamities of famine'. Parmentier's now-famous work on the potato, *Examen Chymique des Pommes de Terre,* won that prize. When famine did actually strike France in 1785, the potato, already the darling of the French royalty and aristocracy (Marie Antoinette wore potato blossoms on her bosom, and King Louis in his buttonhole), became one of France's best-loved foods! For his efforts, Parmentier was made a baronet and for a while, the potato in France was known as *parmentiere!*

Germany, even King Louis XVI of France (who wore potato flowers as boutonnieres while Marie Antoinette sported them in her hair!) and Tsar Peter the Great of Russia actively promoted potato cultivation.

The potato's journey to America was even more circuitous than the one to England. If the story about the potato and Sir Francis Drake is true, then it left Virginia in 1586 as the 'Virginia potato' and returned only in 1718 to Boston as the 'Irish potato' because it accompanied the Irish immigrants. Ironically, 127 years later, millions of Irish people fled their homeland to escape the Great Irish Famine, caused by the blight that decimated potato crops.

So how did the potato arrive in India? Apparently, it was introduced in India in the early part of the seventeenth century by the Portuguese and was first cultivated in Surat, from where it spread to other areas like Goa that were under Portuguese rule at the time. The earliest-known reference to the potato in India is from an account by Edward Terry, the chaplain associated with Sir Thomas Roe, the British ambassador to the court of Emperor Jehangir from 1615 to 1619. Terry wrote, 'In the northernmost part of the empire... good roots as carrot, potatoes and others like them...are grown.' Some experts feel that this may be a reference to the sweet potato. But there is no doubt that it was indeed a basket of potatoes that was gifted to Sir Warren Hastings around 1780, and, according to WW Hunter in his book, *Indian Empire,* by the first half of the nineteenth century, 'the potato (was) a favourite crop' among the hill tribes of the Himalayas.

Today, the potato is the world's fourth most important food source, after wheat, corn and rice, and India is its third-largest producer.

Will the Real Potato Stand Up?

Let us first understand a few basics about the potato. The potato is rich in carbohydrate, which is a major source of energy for the body. But if your intake of carbohydrate is more than the energy you expend, the extra carbohydrate gets converted to fat and is stored in your body. So, the potato is unhealthy only if you eat too much of it. For that matter, too much of anything is bad, even vitamins or holidays or money! But the question is: how much is too much?

Villagers in Peru — adults and children — eat as much as a kilo of potato at every meal and have done so for thousands of years. Now,

What's in a Name?

'Best black woman', 'best red woman', 'makes the daughter-in-law cry', 'like a deer's white tongue', 'red shadow' and 'like an old bone'. These are some of the many names by which the potato is called in Quechua, the ancient language of the Inca Empire, which is still widely spoken in many parts of South America.

Some experts feel that the English name, 'potato', was probably a result of mistaken identity – the Spaniards who brought back the potato from South America might have confused it with the sweet potato. That is because 'potato' is derived from the Spanish *patata,* which in turn comes from *batata,* which is also part of the botanical name for sweet potato – *Ipomoea batatas.* But others claim that the Spaniards very clearly differentiated between the two tubers.

Batata is what the potato is called in Maharashtra and Gujarat as well. And since this is also the Portuguese name for the potato, it points to the fact that it was the Portuguese who brought the tuber to India. According to KT Achaya in his *Indian Food, A Historical Companion,* both the Hindi and Sanskrit names for the potato – *alu* and *aluka* – are general names given to all tubers.

Solanum, the first part of the potato's botanical name, indicates that it belongs to the *Solanaceae* family, the members of which include the tomato, brinjal, capsicum and tobacco.

Language	Name
English	Potato
Botanical	Solanum tuberosum
Sanskrit	Aluka
Hindi	Alu
Gujarati	Batata
Marathi	Batata
Bengali	Alu, gol alu
Tamil	Urula kalangu
Telugu	Urla gadda
Malayalam	Uralakizhangu
Kannada	Alugedde

that quantity is fifteen times the quantity an average American eats, yet these Peruvian villagers are healthy and fit. Why?

Well, while the potato is considered a high-carbohydrate food, actually as much as 80 per cent of the potato is water. Of the rest, the carbohydrate content is about 85 per cent – hence the perception of it being loaded with carbohydrates. Moreover, the carbohydrates that it contains are complex carbohydrates. These are the best kind to eat since it takes the body much more time to break them down and convert them into energy. The potato is also a good source of dietary fibre. This combination of complex carbohydrates and dietary fibre means that you get your energy the way you should – in a regulated, steady stream rather than in one concentrated burst. And because of this, the other popular misconception about the potato – that it is a no-no food for diabetics – also holds no water. If cooked the right way (boiled or baked) and eaten in the right quantities, potatoes can be as much a part of a diabetic's diet as any other healthy carbohydrate.

The potato is also one of the best sources of vital nutrients like vitamins and minerals. It is so rich in Vitamin C that just one medium-sized potato can have as much as 40-45 per cent of our daily requirement of this vital vitamin. It is also an excellent source of Vitamin B6 (pyridoxine) and choline, and a good source of thiamine (Vitamin B1) and niacin (Vitamin B3). And, like the banana, it is a very good source of potassium as well as other minerals such as copper, iron, magnesium, phosphorus and sulphur. The potato is also a good source of lysine, one of the essential amino acids.

The nutrients in the potato make it a wonderful skin nourisher, particularly its high Vitamin C content which is excellent for lightening skin blemishes and cleaning oily skins. So raw grated potato is popularly used as a facial scrub and cleanser and raw potato slices as eye pads to lighten dark circles around the eyes.

Medicinal Potato?
But perhaps the most surprising fact that is emerging is that the potato has disease-fighting potential as well. In 2007, scientists at the Agricultural Research Service, the research wing of the US Department of Agriculture, identified the presence of phytochemicals in the potato at levels rivalling those in spinach. Of these, quercetin (an important phytochemical in onions) and kukoamines are said to have the potential for lowering blood pressure.

Now that's a real stretch, is it not, that the potato could have therapeutic value? But it does. And again, contrary to popular belief, it is beneficial for many digestive disorders.

The juice of raw potato has been used in traditional medicine to treat stomach disorders such as gastritis, even to relieve chronic constipation. Potatoes are also considered easy to digest by people suffering from liver-related dyspepsia. Perhaps that could be why *Solanum*, the first part of the potato's botanical name, *Solanum tuberosum,* is derived from a Latin word meaning 'soothing'!

So, the fault is not in the poor potato but in what we do to it before eating it. Deep-frying potatoes is probably the worst way to treat them because frying kills many of the heat-sensitive nutrients like potassium and Vitamin C. It also dries up most of the water (so that we end up with much more carbohydrate for the same weight of potato), robs it of most of its nutrients and loads it with the potential to make us sick. Dousing it with butter and cream or adding cheese or pouring thick, rich gravies over it as they do in the West has much the same effect. Then, after eating these unhealthy versions, we go back to our sedentary couch-potato lives and blame the resultant flab and ill health on the poor undeserving potato.

The healthiest way to cook a potato is to bake, steam or boil it in its skin and preferably eat it with the skin. This is because most of its nutrients are concentrated in a thin layer beneath the skin, which is also a very good source of dietary fibre. Of course, it is important to wash the potatoes thoroughly before cooking them, especially if you are not going to peel them.

One of my most vivid childhood memories is that of my mother making rice-flour *rotis* on a coal-fired *sigri* (stove). As she cooked the *rotis*, she would pop a few potatoes into the hot coals. When the *rotis* were ready, so were the potatoes, their skins hard and charred black in places, while their insides would be soft, moist, perfectly cooked, and infused with a heavenly, smoky aroma that no electric oven could ever replicate.

So, if cooked and eaten in the right way, the potato is truly a delicious, inexpensive boon of good health. It can be stored for long periods of time, can be cooked in hundreds of ways, and converted into everything from bread to salad, and is even recommended as baby food. So perhaps the words of Louisa M Alcott say it all: 'Money is the root of all evil, and yet it is such a useful root that we cannot get on without it any more than we can without potatoes.'

Potato Protection
Never store raw potatoes in the refrigerator because the cold temperature will convert the potato's starch to sugar.

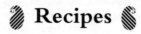

Recipes

Alu Chaat   (Serves 4–5)

This is a wonderfully versatile dish that can be served as a salad, snack, hors-d'oeuvre, or even as a light meal on a hot summer's day. Serve plain, or with sweet tamarind chutney or hot pudina (mint) chutney.

INGREDIENTS

4-5 medium-sized potatoes, washed, boiled, peeled and cut into large cubes (The potatoes should not be hot, otherwise they will disintegrate when they are mixed with the other ingredients)
The juice of a small lemon (adjust to taste)
1-2 tsp chaat masala (adjust to taste)
2 tbsp finely diced onion (optional)
1 tsp fresh mint leaves, finely chopped (optional)
1 tbsp fresh coriander, finely chopped

METHOD

Place the potatoes in a large bowl, add all the other ingredients and mix gently but well, making sure that the potato cubes are well coated. Serve.

Variation: You can add any of the following ingredients in whatever combination you prefer. My favourite are peanuts because they give a delicious crunchiness to the dish!

1–2 tbsp roasted peanuts

2 tbsp boiled chickpeas (*kabuli channa*)

1 tbsp pomegranate seeds

Cheater Potatoes   (Serves 4)

With this ingenious dish you can have the best of both worlds – potato fries that are low in calories! The only downside is that you have to watch the potatoes constantly while they are being cooked and the cooking time is slightly long, but the delicious end result makes it all worthwhile.

INGREDIENTS

4-5 medium-sized potatoes, washed, boiled, peeled and cut into thick fingers or rounds (The potatoes should not be hot, otherwise they will disintegrate when you repeatedly turn them over while cooking.)
2 tbsp vegetable oil
Salt and pepper to taste

METHOD

Apply a coating of oil on a heavy *tava* (a non-stick pan is a good option) and place over low heat. Now place the potato fingers on the *tava* so that they don't touch each other. Dribble a few drops of oil around and on each piece. Turn over gently after a few minutes. Continue to do this till the pieces are golden-brown. Remove from the *tava* and season. Serve hot with tomato sauce or chutney.

Variation: You can substitute the pepper with red chilli powder or substitute the salt and pepper with *chaat masala*.

Arvi: Nature's Raincoat

The Lotus Effect. No, it does not refer to the stupor that the mariners fell into after eating lotuses in Alfred Tennyson's poem *Ulysses*, but to a very curious trait that the leaves of some plants display when water falls on them. Instead of wetting the leaves' surface, the water immediately turns into 'beads' and rolls off, taking along with it all the dirt particles and leaving the leaves not only completely dry but also immaculately clean!

The German scientists at the University of Bonn who first studied this astonishing phenomenon called it the Lotus Effect because it occurs most impressively with lotus leaves. (Incidentally, this had already been documented in ancient Sanskrit texts and given as one reason why the lotus is regarded as a symbol of purity!) The water-resistant quality of these leaves is so remarkable that the race is on to mimic it in everything from non-stick coatings and paints to aircraft windshields and computer hard disks.

There is another plant whose magnificent, arrowhead-shaped leaves behave in a similar manner. Perhaps this is the reason why the first part of its botanical name, *Colocasia esculenta*, is derived from the Greek word *kolokasion* which, according to the first-century Greek physician and herbalist Dioscorides, was what the lotus was once called. In many parts of India, it is known as *arvi* (or *arbi*).

But being super-hydrophobic (the botanists' term for this trait) is only one of the *arvi*'s many amazing qualities – because not only is every part of it edible but it is also one of the most nutritious foods.

'Divine' Arvi

To the Hawaiians, *arvi* (or taro, as it is known in Hawaii) is much more than just food. It is believed to have been born from the union of the earth and sky before the advent of man, and therefore it is considered superior to the human race, and accorded with an almost godlike status. So, like *annam* in Sanskrit, which means both 'rice' and 'food', *ai* in the Hawaiian language is a word used both for *arvi* and food; and the *arvi*'s ancient and deep-rooted association with Hawaii has given rise to the commonly held belief that it originated there.

Some varieties (Hawaii has at least 300) might indeed have come from this area but the *arvi*'s true birthplace is said to be in the Indo-

---

Immaculate Wrapper

If you buy flowers from a flower seller in Mysore, it is more than likely that you will get it wrapped in an *arvi* leaf. Apart from the fact that these leaves are freely available, their 'super-hydrophobic' nature makes sure that they are always both dry and clean. Perfect for wrapping!

Malayan region, somewhere between eastern India, Bangladesh and Malaysia. In India, the *arvi* probably grew in the wetland areas where rice would later be grown, making it one of the earth's oldest cultivated crops. Remains of domesticated *arvi* found in the Kilu Cave on the Buka Island and in the Solomon Islands, east of New Guinea indicate that the *arvi* was cultivated as far back as 23,000 years ago, at least 8,000 years earlier than rice! From its centre of origin, the *arvi* began to circle the globe, going eastwards and reaching Indonesia and China where burial records date its presence to the Han Dynasty (206 BC–AD 220). In fact, one of the *arvi*'s many names is *dasheen*, from *de Chine*, which is French for 'from China'. From Indonesia, it travelled to New Zealand and Polynesia and arrived in Hawaii only around AD 450, thousands of years after it first appeared on this planet!

Simultaneously, it journeyed west to Egypt, and through the Middle East to Europe. So when the great Roman naturalist Pliny the Elder compiled his *Naturalis Historia* in AD 77, he wrote, 'In Egypt, next to the colocasia, it is the cichorium (chicory) that is held in the highest esteem…' By the time Jesus Christ was born, it had reached the east coast of Africa, from where it travelled across the African continent to hop on to slave ships and reach the Caribbean. Thus, the globetrotting *arvi* had truly become a citizen of the world. Today, *arvi* – leaves and root – is eaten by millions of people and is ranked fourteenth among the staple foods of the world.

The Bill Gates of Nutrition

Now we all know how nutritious green leafy vegetables are but did you know that the three of the most nutritious greens originated in India? They are the leaves of the drumstick tree, *agathi* (*Sesbania grandiflora*) and… *arvi* leaves.

So, what makes *arvi* leaves so special? Let us look at the lesser-known reason first. Of late, much has been written about Omega-3 fatty acids because they are the good guys of the fat story, as their presence helps prevent many serious diseases including cardio-vascular disease, asthma and rheumatoid arthritis. What is perhaps not so well known is that these fatty acids are brain food, vital for the cognitive process and for keeping depression at bay. One of the most critical of the Omega-3 fatty acids is alpha-linolenic acid or ALA. But, like Vitamin C, the body cannot manufacture ALA and we have to get all our supplies externally, mainly from food. Now,

---

Arvi in Your Garden…

Nancy's Revenge. Black Magic. Yellow Splash. These are the names of the varieties of *arvi* that are grown purely as ornamental plants. Though not edible, these spectacular plants, growing up to eight feet tall and sporting enormous leaves in a beautiful range of colours and variegation, are gardeners' favourites.

Itch Guard!

Most edible varieties of *arvi* contain an organic acid called oxalic acid, present in both leaves and corm, which can cause the insides of your mouth and the skin on your hands to itch. To relieve the itching, wash the leaves or corms thoroughly before cooking and cook them well. Adding the juice extracted from tamarind to the leaves while cooking also helps. If you still experience itching, wash the affected area thoroughly with lots of water.

among the foods rich in ALA, the most obvious are nuts like walnuts and almonds, but green leafy vegetables such as *arvi* leaves are an equally good source of ALA.

Like all greens, these leaves are also loaded with minerals, vitamins and antioxidants. They have three times as much calcium as spinach and nine times as much iron. Also, they are a rich source of beta-carotene, Vitamin C, riboflavin (Vitamin B2), magnesium, iron, potassium and dietary fibre.

The roots of the *arvi* plant are equally nutritious. Actually, though they look like roots and grow underground, they are corms – the short, thickened, underground part of the stem in which many plants store food to survive adverse conditions like drought and severe winters or summers.

When Captain Cook discovered it in Hawaii on his third and last voyage in 1778, he found that *arvi* was to the Hawaiians what rice and wheat were to the rest of the world – staple food. The native people living on the islands (there were about three hundred thousand of them at the time) lived chiefly on *poi* (fermented or unfermented *arvi* paste), sweet potato, fish, seaweed and some vegetables and fruits. Although most of them consumed up to five pounds of *poi* a day, and their diet included no grain, no milk and almost no meat, they were in excellent health! This is not at all surprising if we look at the nutrition the *arvi* packs in. Dietary fibre, protein, complex carbohydrate, vitamins C and E, several minerals like potassium, magnesium and iron, and many of the B vitamins including thiamine (B1), riboflavin (B2) and niacin (B3). In fact, *arvi* has more B vitamins than whole milk, and, along with wheat, Bengal gram, amaranth and cluster beans, it is one of the

Arvi, MD

The *arvi's* nutritional wealth and its versatility as a food is well known all over Asia. But the lesser-known fact is that in Hawaii and other parts of Polynesia, almost all parts of the *arvi* plant are also used as medicine. For example, the raw *arvi* corm is used to treat constipation and indigestion and its juice is sipped to alleviate fevers. *Poi*, or the *arvi* paste that is such an integral part of Hawaiian cuisine, is used to treat diarrhoea and as a poultice to cure infected sores. The stems of the *arvi* leaves are used to stop the bleeding of wounds and ease the swelling and pain caused by insect bites and stings, while the leaves are used to treat asthma.

What's in a Name?

The associations of the colocasia family with the elephant are many. For one, the huge arrow-shaped leaves of the *arvi* plant (often measuring up to three feet in length and two feet in breadth) are reminiscent of an elephant's ears – a family trait that it shares with other members of the colocasia family. And this is the reason why it is sometimes also called the elephant's ear yam, even though it is not a yam. The resemblance to the elephant's anatomy doesn't stop with the ears. A close relative of the *arvi,* because of its likeness to the pachyderm's foot, is called the elephant's foot yam (*Amorphophallus paeoniifolius*) or the elephant yam. And this 'yam' is not a yam either!

Language	Name
English	Taro, dasheen, eddo, elephant's ear yam, cocoyam
Botanical	Colocasia esculenta
Sanskrit	Aaluki, alukam, alupam, kachchi, kachu
Hindi, Gujarati	Arvi, arbi
Marathi	Arukudya
Bengali	Kochu
Tamil	Chembu, cheppankizhangu
Telugu	Chamagadda, chamadumpa
Kannada	Kesavinnagedde
Malayalam	Chembu

best sources of folate or folic acid (Vitamin B9). The Nutrition Foundation of India classifies *arvi* as a micronutrient-rich food, but looking at its nutritional profile, one could say that it is not just rich but the Bill Gates of micronutrient-rich foods…

But what makes its nutritive wealth so much more significant is that *arvi* is one of the most easily digestible foods because it is rich in amylose, a starch that breaks down easily when mixed with saliva. This makes *arvi* particularly suitable for people with digestive problems, lactose and gluten (wheat) intolerance and, of course, for babies! So *arvi* is among the vegetables recommended as the baby's first solid food, and a popular ingredient in packaged infant formulas and canned baby foods.

Around the World with Arvi…

The Chinese New Year is perhaps the most important and longest of the Chinese festivals and lasts the entire first fortnight of the first lunar month of the Chinese calendar. The last day is celebrated as the Lantern Festival, an ancient tradition dating back to Emperor Han Wu of the Han Dynasty (156-87 BC) during which beautiful lanterns are lit and taken out in spectacular parades. One of the many customs during this festival is for the family to gather at midnight and eat boiled *arvi* under a lantern. The belief is that by doing so one can see into the future, or then, perhaps more realistically, that it will improve the eyesight. A kind of sweet cake or pudding made out of *arvi* is one of the traditional foods made during the fortnight-long festivities.

All over Asia, *arvi* is a popular vegetable, used in a myriad delicious ways. In Japan it is used for making their famous miso soup. Stewed *arvi* is used as an ingredient in curries and it is also fried to make tempura. In Cambodia and Vietnam, the leaves are used to flavour soups. In Thailand, Indonesia and Malaysia, *arvi* is cooked with rice, used in soups and curries, added to salads and made into desserts, even ice cream!

Its flavour is considered so delectable that it has even found its way into the repertoire of Italian ice cream makers, long considered masters in this art! In India, both the leaves and the corm of the *arvi* are popular, particularly in Kerala where it is cooked in all manner of ways and is one of the eight ingredients used to make a special festive dish called *thiruvathira puzhukku*, during Thiruvathira, a festival celebrated by women. In south coastal Karnataka and Gujarat, the leaves are made into rolls which are steamed and then used for making a variety of curries and snacks.

In Hawaii, the *arvi* is also called *haloa*, which means 'everlasting breath'. And in an ancient tradition still practised in many homes on the island, when the bowl of *poi* (fermented *arvi* corm paste) is uncovered at mealtime, it is a signal to end all quarrelling and arguments. One by one, everyone present eats some of the *poi* from the bowl. By doing this, they reaffirm their bonds with each other and with life. It is a beautiful tradition and a befitting tribute to the *arvi*.

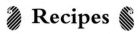

Recipes

Arvi-Leaf-Rolls Curry   (Serves 6-7)

This delicious curry is a traditional favourite in south coastal Karnataka, where my mother comes from. Though usually eaten with plain steamed rice, it tastes just as good with chapattis.

INGREDIENTS

For the arvi *rolls*

¼ kg rice, washed and soaked for 6-8 hours
1 tbsp coriander seeds, roasted (optional)
Tamarind, the size of a large marble
1 tsp grated jaggery
4 dried red chillies, roasted
6-8 large arvi leaves
2 tsp salt (adjust to taste)

For the curry

½ coconut
1 tbsp coriander seeds, roasted
1 tbsp urad dal, roasted
2-3 red chillies, roasted
½ tsp jeera, roasted
1 tbsp jaggery
Tamarind, the size of a large marble

Tempering

1 tbsp oil
1 tsp mustard seeds
1 dried red chilli, broken into pieces
7-9 curry leaves
A pinch of asafoetida

METHOD

To make the rolls

Grind the soaked rice, coriander seeds, tamarind, jaggery, chillies and salt into a thick, coarse paste. Wash and wipe the leaves, slicing off the veins in the centre if they are too thick. Now smear about a quarter-inch-thick layer of the rice paste on one of the leaves. Place another leaf on top and smear this too, in the same way. Repeat till you have used half the leaves. Now make the leaves into a roll, pressing firmly so that it does not open. Repeat till all the leaves are used. Steam the rolls for about 30 minutes. Allow the roll to cool, then slice into ½-inch thick slices.

To make the curry

Grind the coconut with all the roasted ingredients, jaggery and tamarind, adding water to make a paste of thick, chutney-like consistency. On low heat, bring this paste to a boil, stirring all the time. Gently add the sliced *arvi*-leaf rolls. Simmer for a few minutes. To temper, heat the oil, then add the mustard seeds and red chillies. When the mustard seeds stop spluttering, add the rest of the tempering ingredients. After a few seconds, remove from heat and add to the curry. Serve with steamed rice or *chapattis*.

Variation: The *arvi*-leaf rolls make a great snack by themselves. Just slice the rolls and temper them as you would the curry and serve with chutney or sauce.

Arvi Chips

A great snack for a rainy day!

INGREDIENTS

½ kg arvi, *washed thoroughly*
Vegetable oil for deep frying
Salt and chilli powder

METHOD

Boil (15-20 minutes) or pressure-cook (3 whistles) the *arvi* till cooked but not too soft. Peel and allow it to cool completely. Now, cut into thin slices and deep fry in hot oil. Remove and allow the oil to drain, then sprinkle with salt and red chilli powder.

Fenugreek: A Girl's Best Friend

'Fortunate are the feet that tread on the earth on which grows the helbeh (fenugreek)'
Egyptian Proverb

In ancient Egypt, it was an ingredient in an incense called *kyphi* that was used both to embalm dead bodies and to fumigate homes. In the Middle Ages, a paste of it was recommended as a cure for baldness, but the smell was found to be so offensive that they began to call it 'Greek excrement'! To some, it is a spice that adds flavour to breads and pickles, and an indispensable ingredient in all kinds of *masala* powders from the Bengali *panch phoran* (five-spice powder) and the South Indian *sambar* powder to the Ethiopian *berbere*. To others, it is a green leafy vegetable and a veritable powerhouse of nutrition. Many consider it an ancient and potent healer, used for treating everything from diabetes to dandruff. But perhaps few of us know that fenugreek – or *methi* as it is popularly called in India – is a legume, a member of the vast family of *dals*, grams, beans and peas.

Though it has been cultivated in India for thousands of years (references to it date back to AD 200) and is used in Ayurveda, most experts say that fenugreek probably originated somewhere in North Africa or the Middle East. The charred remains of fenugreek seeds have been found in archaeological sites in Iraq dating back to 4000 BC, in the remains of the Bronze Age city of Lachish in Israel and in the fabulous tomb of the Pharaoh Tutankhamun (1341-1323 BC).

Fenugreek was used as both spice and medicine by the ancient Greeks and Romans, but it was the Benedictine monks who introduced and popularized it in Europe during the ninth century, growing it in herb gardens in their monasteries. Around the same time, in AD 812, Emperor Charlemagne issued the *Capitulare de Villis*, one of the many acts that were formulated to define proper governance of his empire. At the end of it was a long list of plants and herbs that were to be cultivated in all imperial gardens – and fenugreek was one of them.

Fenugreek was introduced in Asia by the ancient spice traders of Arabia. This is borne out by the fact that the Arabic name for

Weapon of War?

Fenugreek is probably the only spice or herb to be used as a defensive weapon! In ancient warfare, the standard strategy to deter the enemy from scaling the walls of a city or fort was to pour boiling oil or water on enemy soldiers scaling the walls. But during the Roman siege of Jerusalem (AD 70), the Jewish defenders added fenugreek to the oil before pouring to make it even more slippery!

fenugreek – *hulbah* – is very similar to the names by which it is known in many Asian languages. It is *uluva* in Malayalam, *uluhal* in Sinhalese, *halba* in Malay and *hu lu ba* in Chinese. Fenugreek was brought to India by the Arab traders who first landed on the Kerala coast around the second century AD, towards the end of the reign of the Chera dynasty. And while the exact date of its arrival in China is not available, records show that fenugreek was used as medicine during the Sung Dynasty (AD 960-1279).

Today, fenugreek is consumed the world over – from the United States where it is used to flavour maple syrup to Egypt where it is brewed into a tea and served in coffee shops during winter.

Physician of Yore
In 1874, the Egyptologist, George Ebers, acquired a sixty-five-foot-long Egyptian papyrus at the site of the ancient Egyptian city of Thebes. The papyrus, one of the oldest preserved medical documents in the world (dating back to about 1550 BC), contains detailed information about medical practices prevalent in Egypt at the time. And among the over five hundred medicinal herbs listed in it was the fenugreek.

The first-century Greek physician and herbalist Dioscorides recommended fenugreek as a treatment for gout and headaches. Pliny (AD 25-79), the great Roman philosopher and naturalist, prescribed it for deafness, and Hippocrates mentioned it in *The Epidemics,* a massive medical treatise consisting of seven books.

But it was the Arabs who prized and intensively studied the therapeutic qualities of fenugreek. Avicenna (Ibn Sina), the founder of the Unani system of medicine, in his monumental work, *Al-Qanun fi'l Tibb* (*The Canon of Medicine*) listed it as one the hundreds of plants that have great medicinal value. And Arab physicians researched its medicinal properties at the Scuola Medica Salernitana, the famous ninth-century school of medicine in Salerno, Italy. This institution, where ancient Roman and Greek medicine came together with Arabic medical practices, had such a reputation for excellence that people from all over the world went there, both to be healed and to study.

Fenugreek entered into the Ayurvedic pharmacopoeia late, several centuries after the sages Charaka and Sushruta had compiled their *Samhitas*, and its use as medicine was probably first recorded when

What's in a Name?

In his essay on agriculture titled 'De Agri Cultura', considered the oldest surviving work of Latin prose and written in 160 BC, Cato the Elder recommended that fenugreek leaves be used as cattle fodder. There are differing opinions about the reason for this — some say it was to camouflage the smell of mouldy or inferior-quality hay, while others think that it was to improve the milk yield. Whatever the reason, this practice is probably how fenugreek got its Latin name — *Trigonella foenum graecum*. *Foenum graecum* means 'hay' in Greek and *trigonella* is from the Greek *trigonon* meaning 'triangle'. Some experts explain that this is a reference to the formation in which fenugreek leaves grow — three leaves forming a triangular shape. Others say it refers to the shape of the flowers.

Language	Name
English	Fenugreek
Botanical	Trigonella foenum graecum
Sanskrit	Methika, chandrika
Hindi, Bengali, Marathi, Punjabi	Methi
Gujarati	Methro, methini
Tamil	Vendiyam
Telugu	Mentulu
Kannada	Menthe
Malayalam	Uluva

it was mentioned in the sixteenth-century Ayurvedic text, *Bhavaprakash Nighantu*, written by Pandit Bhava Mishra, Emperor Akbar's court physician.

It is amazing that so many ancient systems of medicine knew and used fenugreek as a potent and multitasking medicine. (The leaves were used to treat flatulence, indigestion, colic, dysentery, diarrhoea and sluggish livers and because of their 'cooling' nature, as poultices for burns and inflammations; the seeds to treat diabetes, respiratory disorders and digestive ailments and to increase lactation.) But equally astonishing is that modern medical research confirms these curative powers in treating the very same ailments!

Little Brown Giants

In the impressive list of things that the little, brown, innocuous-looking fenugreek seeds can do — apart from spicing up both your

sambar and your sex life (they are also considered to be an aphrodisiac) – the most well known and important is in the treatment of diabetes. To understand how they work, soak some fenugreek seeds in a few tablespoons of water for a few hours. You will find that the seeds will become coated with a thin layer of a gummy, jelly-like substance. This substance – called mucilage – constitutes 20-30 per cent of the fenugreek seed and acts as a sponge, absorbing blood sugar and thus lowering it. Studies have shown that just five to six grams, or approximately one teaspoon, of fenugreek seeds can significantly lower fasting and post-prandial blood glucose levels.

The mucilage also makes fenugreek seeds a very efficient purifier, mopping up and ridding the body of toxins, allergens and hardened mucus. So fenugreek seeds are used to soothe and clean out inflamed digestive tracts and are especially effective for treating peptic ulcers, flatulence, dysentery and diarrhoea as also respiratory tracts inflamed or clogged as a result of infections like bronchitis and influenza.

Fenugreek Garden

One of the best ways to eat fenugreek is in the form of fresh sprouts. The seeds sprout very easily and you can wait till the shoots are long and cook them the same way as fenugreek leaves. You can even add them raw to salads, but do so sparingly because they have a slightly bitter taste. Fenugreek is also ridiculously easy to grow – just scatter the seeds in loose, damp soil and water regularly.

Fenugreek seeds are a woman's best friend. For one, they help to reduce the symptoms of menopause. This is because they contain diosgenin, which belongs to a group of plant chemicals called saponins, some of which mimic female hormones. And even though there is little in the way of documented research to support this, perhaps this is also the reason why since ancient times, in many parts of Asia and North Africa including India and Egypt, various concoctions made from fenugreek seeds are given to breastfeeding mothers to promote lactation. Interestingly enough, it is a practice also recommended by many modern-day Western doctors as well as organizations promoting breastfeeding. In fact, a popular herbal tea by the name of Mother's Milk Tea has fenugreek seeds as a key ingredient! Needless to say, fenugreek seeds, like the leaves, are rich in nutrients including iron, Vitamin A, Vitamin B1 (thiamine) and Vitamin C. And their protein content confirms their identity as a legume because like so many other members of the legume family, as much as 25 per cent of a fenugreek seed is made up of protein!

Mother Methi

There is perhaps no better testimonial of a food's nutritive value than if it is recommended for a lactating mother, since what she eats impacts every aspect of her baby's development. For example, the development of a newborn baby's brain is partly influenced by the presence of fatty acids in the mother's breast milk.

The brain is a circuit board of millions of neurons (nerve cells) connected to each other by synapses, which are the 'wires' of the brain. How these wires are connected to one another determines everything, from our ability to read to our capacity to sustain relationships. Within the first twelve to fourteen months of a child's life, the final wiring of the brain is done. And the fatty acids in breast milk are critical for this.

The question then is, what has that got to do with fenugreek… aren't fatty acids found mainly in nuts and oil? Yes, but it is a little-known fact that green leafy vegetables – like fenugreek leaves – are also excellent sources of Omega-3 fatty acids. In India, poverty often makes it difficult for people to incorporate the required amount of fats in their daily diet. A recent survey carried out in ten Indian states showed that, in rural areas, the dietary intake of fat is less than 25 per cent of what a lactating mother needs. In such a scenario, fenugreek leaves are particularly important because they cost very little (or nothing, if grown in your backyard!) and yet, are very rich in nutrition. And along with those all-important fatty acids, fenugreek leaves are also loaded with folate (folic acid/Vitamin B9), Vitamin C, Vitamin A, riboflavin (Vitamin B2), magnesium, iron, potassium and dietary fibre.

And if fenugreek seeds are a woman's best friend, so are the leaves. Firstly, as one of the best sources of iron, they provide a simple solution to the problem of the anaemia that plagues 60-70 per cent of adolescent girls in India even today. Secondly, they are an excellent source of calcium, a mineral that is especially important for women because it helps prevent osteoporosis (women are four times more likely to suffer from this disease than men) and also reduces menstrual pain and premenstrual tension.

With such therapeutic and nutritional wealth in it, it is surprising that the fenugreek is not considered sacred or offered to the gods as so many other such foods are. But in Yemen, according to popular folklore, eating fenugreek makes a woman plump and fertile. In fact, in Arabic, fenugreek is also called *helbeh* or *hulbah*, which translates into 'be fruitful and multiply'. It could well be the blessing that the fenugreek bestows on us every time we eat it!

Recipe

Sunanda's Methi Lemon Rice (Serves 4-5)

Adding fenugreek leaves to almost anything, especially dals, *or even to* chapatti *dough, is a great way to perk up both taste and nutrition. This recipe is my mother's creation and so named after her.*

INGREDIENTS

¼ kg rice, cleaned and washed
2 tbsp oil
1 dried red chilli broken into pieces
A pinch of asafoetida
1 tsp mustard seeds
1 tsp urad dal
1 tsp channa dal
3 green chillies, chopped (adjust to taste)
8-10 curry leaves
3-4 small bunches methi *leaves, washed, cleaned and finely chopped*
½ tsp turmeric powder
1-1 ½ tsp salt (adjust to taste)
The juice of one medium-sized lemon

METHOD

Cook the rice and allow it to cool completely. Heat the oil. Add red chilli, mustard seeds and asafoetida. When the seeds begin to splutter, add the two *dals,* green chillies, and curry leaves and fry till the *dals* turn golden-brown. Now add the *methi* leaves and cook for about 3-4 minutes, stirring constantly. Then add turmeric and salt and stir-fry till the fenugreek leaves are cooked. Before removing from the heat, stir in the lemon juice. Add the fenugreek leaves mixture to the rice and allow it to cool. Mix well, taking care not to mash the grains of rice.

Brinjal: The Other Apple?

'I could look down into the vegetable garden enclosed within its tall pale of reeds – rich chocolate earth studded emerald green, frothed with the white of cauliflowers, jewelled with the purple globes of eggplant and the scarlet wealth of tomatoes…'
Doris Lessing

George Bernard Shaw was eighty-seven years old when his wife, Charlotte, died. Shaw was devastated by her death. She had been his beloved companion for forty-five years and had also painstakingly put together and cooked a large repertoire of vegetarian dishes for her husband, whose ardent advocacy of vegetarianism was well known. So, it was fortunate that Alice Laden, the young widow who nursed Mrs Shaw through her last illness, agreed to stay on as Shaw's housekeeper after Charlotte's death and continued to cook Charlotte's vegetarian recipes for him.

In 1971, twenty-one years after Shaw's death, Mrs Laden collaborated with RJ Minney to write and publish *The George Bernard Shaw Vegetarian Cookbook*, featuring more than 180 of Shaw's favourite recipes, laid out as a six-act play. The blurb on the back cover announces, 'Starring Walnut Soufflé and Vegetable Charlotte, featuring Savory Eggplant!', and among the long list of main dishes in the section called 'Sitting Room Only' are Eggplant Au Gratin and Stuffed Eggplant. So it seems that the eggplant was quite a favourite with George Bernard Shaw!

In India, we know this rather oddly named vegetable as the brinjal.

Hamara Brinjal Mahaan!
Even though all its other relatives like the tomato, potato, chilli and tobacco originated in South and Central America, there is little doubt about the brinjal's Indian origins. The *Rig Veda* mentions it and that fact that the brinjal's many Sanskrit names originated from the Munda languages – which are so old that the date of their origin is not known – is a further testimony of its antiquity.

From India, the brinjal spread to many parts of Asia. There is some confusion about when it appeared in China – some say that it had been growing there since 500 BC, but a reference to it in a fifth-century Chinese record on agriculture called the *Ts'i Min Yao*

Shu indicates the brinjal's presence in China for at least the last 1,500 years.

In Middle Eastern cuisine, the brinjal has been a favourite for hundreds of years. Avicenna (Ibn Sina), founder of the Unani system of medicine, mentioned the brinjal in his great work, *Al-Qanun fi'l Tibb* (*The Canon of Medicine*). There is a recipe featuring it in the tenth-century cookbook by the poet-prince, Ibn Al-Mahdi, a brother of the fifth and the most famous Caliph of Baghdad, Harun al-Rashid (763-809 AD). And so, naturally there is a reference to the brinjal in the *Arabian Nights* because many of its stories may have been inspired by the splendour of this Caliph's fabulous court.

There are no ancient Greek and Roman names for or references to the brinjal and that is because its entry into Europe was much later, when the Moors invaded Spain in the eighth century. The Spaniards fell in love with the 'invader', incorporating it enthusiastically into their cooking – and into their sex lives, because they believed it to be a powerful aphrodisiac. They even christened it *berenjena* or 'the apple of love'! (Perhaps they weren't too off the mark because the brinjal is also mentioned in the *Kamasutra*!) The brinjal insinuated itself similarly into the hearts and the kitchens of the Greeks and Italians, and by the time Shakespeare was born in 1564, it had become an integral part of Mediterranean cuisine.

Other Europeans weren't so enthusiastic however. The fact that the brinjal is a relative of the deadly nightshade, an extremely poisonous plant also known as belladonna, made them view this vegetable with great suspicion. Many believed that it caused insanity if eaten and Albert of Cologne, the thirteenth-century Dominican friar, scholar and theologian rather uncharitably called it *mala insana* or 'mad apple', which is how it became known all over Europe!

However, with the passage of time, the fear of the 'mad' brinjal faded and by the French Revolution, it was grown and eaten all over Europe. Thomas Jefferson held the brinjal in high regard and introduced it in the United States in 1806. In fact, even today, a prickly white variety is grown in Monticello, Jefferson's beautiful estate in Virginia.

Meanwhile, in India, the brinjal remained a firm favourite over the ages, especially in Bengal and South India. Dishes made from brinjal

The Caliph's Wife and Baingan ka Bharta

As the story goes, it was one of the most lavish weddings in the history of Arabia – when Al Ma'mun, the seventh Caliph of the Abbasid dynasty, married Buran, the daughter of his Wazir. At the fabulous wedding feast, among the hundreds of dishes served, was one created by the bride herself – and the main ingredient was brinjal. It was so delicious and became so famous that it was named *buraniyyat,* in honour of its creator. Over the centuries, different versions of it became equally popular in other parts of the world including India – some say that *baingan ka bharta* is a descendant of this ancient dish!

are mentioned in South Indian literature as far back as the third and fourth century AD. The brinjal also graced many a kingly table – in 1485, the Kannada poet, Bommarasa of Terakanambi described a royal feast (probably in the palace of a Vijayanagar king) in which '…the women served an unfried brinjal *bajji*, which contained coconut shreds, curry leaves and cardamom mixed well and flavoured with citrus juice and a little camphor…'

Bahubali's Brinjal

But Karnataka's ancient association with the brinjal goes much beyond gracing the tables of its great kings. Shravanabelagola, a town in the state's Hassan district, is of great archaeological importance and one of the most holy pilgrim centres for Jains. Here, a magnificent 57-foot-high statue of Lord Bahubali stands atop the nearby Vindyagiri hill. It is considered to be the largest monolithic statue in the world and was commissioned by Chamundaraya, the commander-in-chief and minister of King Gangaraya of the Ganga Dynasty.

When it was completed in AD 981, all arrangements were made for the very first 'head anointing' ceremony, or *mahamastikabhisheka*, of the statue. As the story goes, when the ceremony began and Chamundaraya poured milk on the statue's head, for some reason the milk would not flow beyond the navel. The distraught Chamundaraya tried to pour the milk again and again, but in vain.

Then a poor old woman turned up. In her hand was a small *gulla kayi* (a special variety of round, green brinjal that grows only in south coastal Karnataka) whose insides had been scooped out to make a bowl. Inside that 'bowl' was a little milk, and she asked to be allowed to pour that milk on the statue's head. Chamundaraya laughed in derision at the temerity of the poor old woman who thought she could achieve what he, the great minister and general, could not. But he allowed her to pour from her pathetic little 'bowl' of milk anyway.

What happened next was amazing. Not only did the milk flow beyond the navel and drench the statute from head to toe, but it is said to have gushed down in such great quantities that it created a beautiful white pond at the foot of the hill. (Apparently, Belagola, the short form of the town's name, originates from this event since *bela* means 'white' and *kola* means 'pond' in Kannada.) It was then that Chamundaraya realized that it was his own conceit about being the creator of this magnificent statue that had been the obstacle to the *abhisheka*.

Who was the old woman? Some say she was Goddess Padmavati, others that she was the celestial nymph Kushmandini. But whoever she was, a stone statue of the old woman holding a *gulla kayi* in her hands stands exactly opposite the main entrance to the statue complex as a befitting reminder of the importance of humility.

The *gulla* has another divine connection.

One of the luminaries of the Haridasa devotional movement in Karnataka and head of one of the eight Udupi *maths*, Sri Vadirajatirtha (1480-1600) was a great philosopher, reformer and poet. He created the *paryaya* system by which the Sri Krishna Temple in Udupi is managed in rotation by each of the heads of the eight Udupi *maths* for a period of two years. He is also said to have gifted the seeds of the *gulla* to the people of Mattu (or Matti) in Udupi district and thereafter, the *gulla* growing in this area became famous as *Mattu gulla*. Ever since, during the Paryaya festival, when the head of the Udupi Sri Krishna Temple hands over charge to the next incumbent, it has been a tradition for the people of Mattu village to bring offerings to Lord Krishna from the year's very first harvest of *gulla*.

Purple Potentate

Purple — a beautiful, brilliant colour, worn since ancient times by emperors and kings, so much so that the word itself is used to mean 'royal' or 'of high rank'. In fact, in the Christian church, the rank of a cardinal or bishop is called purple. The word 'purple' originates from the Latin word *purpura*, which in turn is derived from the Greek *porphura*, the name of the ancient purple dye made from the mucus secretion of a species of marine snail. The process of extraction was so expensive that the cost of the dye was several times the price of gold and so, only kings and noblemen could afford to wear purple clothes! So, over time, the colour has come to symbolize power, nobility and luxury.

But more recently, purple has also become a colour of health because we now know that it is one of the many shades with which Mother Nature paints her fruits and vegetables, not just to make them look beautiful but also to indicate that they contain important

What's in a Name?

The nomenclature of the brinjal is an excellent example of how the world is round and how everything comes full circle!

Let us start with its Sanskrit names since the vegetable's birthplace is India – *vatingana, vartaka* and *vrntaka*. From *vatingana* came the Persian *badinjan* and the Arabic *al bathinjan* or *al badhinjan*, from which came the Spanish *alberenjena, alberginia* or *berenjena*, from which came the French *abergine* or aubergine. And aubergine is what the British call this vegetable! Many of the brinjal's Indian names also originated from Sanskrit – including the Hindi and Gujarati *baingan,* the Oriya *baingana,* the Bengali *begun* and the Kannada *badanekai.*

Which leaves us with 'brinjal' and 'eggplant'. The latter is what the Americans called the brinjal because the varieties they first made acquaintance with were white or yellow and shaped like eggs. Of course, 'eggplant' later became popular in England as well. Brinjal is the Anglo-Indian corruption of the Portuguese *berinjela*, which in turn is from the Spanish *alberenjena, alberginia* or *berenjena* and so on and so forth, taking us back to where it all began – India!

Incidentally, in the West Indies, 'brinjal' has been further corrupted to 'brown-jolly'!

Language	Name
English	Eggplant, aubergine, brinjal, Guinea squash
Botanical	Solanum melongena
Sanskrit	Vatingana, vartaka, vrntaka
Hindi, Gujarati	Baingan
Marathi	Vangi
Bengali	Begun
Tamil	Katrikai
Telugu	Vankaya
Kannada	Badanekai
Malayalam	Vazhuthininga

nutrients. And the colour of those lovely, fat, shiny purple brinjals signals that they are packed with a remarkable group of antioxidants called anthocyanins. (The word is derived from the Greek words *antho* for 'plant' and *cyan* for 'blue'.) Actually, anthocyanins are cued by any shade of blue, red or purple. So plums, purple grapes, onions, red radish, beetroot, *jamun*, figs and, of course, brinjals are the colour they are because of the presence of anthocyanins.

And like all antioxidants, their disease-fighting abilities are very impressive indeed.

The anthocyanin that makes the brinjal purple is called nasunin and research has shown that it inhibits the production of LDL or 'bad' cholesterol, prevents formation of blood clots and generally improves the flow of blood by relaxing the arterial walls. Nasunin is also a powerful brain food because it protects the brain cell membranes from damage.

This antioxidant plays another very important role. Iron is a vital nutrient especially because it helps the blood to transport oxygen. But too much iron (like a surfeit of many other dietary minerals) is harmful for the body. And if left to accumulate in the body, it can, over time, even increase the risk of heart disease and cancer. Nasunin removes the excess iron in the body.

King of Hearts

But brinjals come in many colours other than purple, ranging from pale green and white to orange and lavender, and all of them are as beautiful and as healthful as their purple siblings. That is because all brinjals contain two other nutrients that are very important to keep the heart healthy – potassium and dietary fibre. Potassium helps the heart to beat regularly and helps lower high blood pressure, which also lowers the risk of stroke. And a cup of steamed brinjal contains as much potassium as half a banana (the best natural source of this vital mineral). Dietary fibre is vital for a healthy heart. It binds itself to the 'bad' (LDL) cholesterol and helps eliminate it from the body. It slows down the digestive process, keeping those hunger pangs at bay (thus making it the dieter's friend) and also controls the release of blood sugar. A cup of steamed brinjal contains as much as 10 per cent of your daily requirement of dietary fibre.

Perhaps this is why, in South India, the brinjal is called 'the king of vegetables'. (In the Arab world, they call it *sayyid al-khudaar*, 'lord of vegetables'!)

The brinjal is one of the most under-rated and misunderstood vegetables in the world. Not many of us associate it with nutrition, yet it is packed with nutrients. Not many would say that it is one of the most delicious vegetables; yet it is eaten in every part of the globe. In fact, it is the main ingredient in some of the world's most famous dishes – moussaka from Greece, ratatouille from France,

'Colouring' Tip!

You may have noticed that the flesh of a brinjal starts to discolour and turn a dark brown as soon as it is cut. Actually, the discolouration is a very good sign because it signals the presence of certain plant chemicals called phenolic acids that are potent antioxidants. When you cut a brinjal, an enzyme called polyphenol oxidase in it makes the phenolic acids react with air and form a brown pigment. To stem the discolouration, put the brinjal pieces in water as soon as you cut them. Drain the water well before cooking.

eggplant parmigiana from Italy (Frank Sinatra had his own special recipe for it!), and, of course, so many Indian favourites like *bagara baingan*, *baingan ka bharta* and *vangi bhath*! It is also one of the most inexpensive vegetables, is available throughout the year and cooks in a jiffy.

No wonder then that the brinjal is called the poor man's caviar.

The Brinjal and the Fainting Imam

There is a popular Turkish dish of stuffed brinjals with a very curious name – *Imam bayildi*. It literally means, 'the Imam fainted'. Now there are several versions of the story as to why the Imam fainted. One version says it was when he got to know how much olive oil (which was very expensive at the time) was used to make the dish. Another claims it was because he was so delighted that the shopkeeper's wife could quickly rustle up such a delicious dish when he paid an unexpected visit. Yet another states that after observing a daylong fast, he was so taken with the delicious aroma of this dish that he fainted.

But one version seems to combine all these versions into a most entertaining tale, and it goes like this…

A long time ago, a Turkish Imam (Muslim priest), known for his love of good food, surprised his friends by announcing his engagement to the young daughter of a wealthy olive-oil merchant. The friends did not know if she was a good cook but they presumed that the lady's dowry would definitely include olive oil. They were right because her father presented the groom twelve jars – each large enough to hold a person – of the precious oil.

The Imam's bride proved to be an excellent cook and every day, she prepared a special dish for her epicurean husband. One of them, eggplant cooked in olive oil, became his favourite, and he ordered that his wife make it every night for dinner. This she did for twelve consecutive days. On the thirteenth night however, the dish was missing from the meal. When asked about its absence, the bride replied, 'Dear husband, I do not have any more olive oil. You will have to purchase some more for me.' The Imam was so shocked that he fainted. And since that day, this dish has been known as *Imam bayildi*!

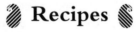 # Recipes

South Indian Roasted Brinjal Bharta (Serves 3-4)

This recipe is from south coastal Karnataka – the land of the gulla *– and is one of my maternal grandmother's specialities! The original name in Tulu is* sudu bajji, *which literally means 'roasted chutney' and that is because the brinjal is roasted on a wood or coal fire.*

INGREDIENTS	METHOD
1 large gulla *or brinjal* 3-4 dried red chillies A marble-sized ball of tamarind	Soak the tamarind in about half a cup of hot water for about 20 minutes. Then remove the soaked tamarind from the water and squeeze well to extract the juice.

¼-inch piece ginger, diced
1 tsp salt (adjust to taste)
1 tsp jaggery, crushed (this is optional and you
can adjust the quantity depending on how sweet
you like the dish)

Tempering
1 tbsp oil
¾ tsp mustard seeds
½ a dried red chilli, broken into pieces
A pinch of asafoetida
7-8 curry leaves

Keep the juice aside. Roast the whole brinjal/*gulla* over the gas burner or steam it in a pressure cooker till well cooked and very soft. Cool, peel and discard the skin, remove the stem and mash the brinjal well. Now gently roast the red chillies in a *tava* over a slow fire till they begin to char and you get a roasted aroma. Allow to cool, then coarsely crush the chillies and add to the mashed brinjal/*gulla* together with the rest of the ingredients and mix well. (Add only about a tablespoon of the tamarind juice at first, then add the rest if required after tasting.)

To temper, heat the oil, then add the mustard seeds and red chillies. When the mustard stops spluttering, add the rest of the tempering ingredients. After a few seconds, remove from heat and add to the brinjal mixture. Serve with hot rice or *chapattis*.

Tip: *Finely chopped raw onions make a great accompaniment.*

Phatafat Brinjal Cutlets   (Serves 3-4)

Breathtakingly quick, these cutlets are a great way to 'dress up' a simple dal-chawal *meal or to feed surprise guests. They are also an excellent way to get kids to like brinjal.*

INGREDIENTS

2 brinjals (large variety)
1 heaped tbsp wheat flour or rice flour
1 tsp red chilli powder
A pinch of asafoetida
½-¾ tsp salt (adjust to taste)
Oil for frying

METHOD

Mix the flour, chilli powder, salt and asafoetida well. Cut the brinjal into ¼-inch thick 'rounds'. Press both sides of each round into the flour mixture, making sure it is well coated. Place on a non-stick *tava* or a shallow, flat frying pan, dribble a little oil around each slice and fry over very low heat till the coating is browned and crisp and the brinjal tender. (You can dribble more oil while frying if necessary.) Great with *dal* and rice!

White Pumpkin: The Goddess Gourd

He was a scion of the famous Medici family and was called Cosimo the Great. It is said that during his reign as the Duke of Florence from 1537 to 1574, and then as the very first Grand Duke of Tuscany from 1569 to 1574, the fortunes of his family were restored to their earlier brilliance. In keeping with the family tradition, Cosimo was a great patron of the arts, nurturing many famous painters, architects and sculptors. He commissioned the fabulous Boboli gardens in Florence and the magnificent Uffizi Gallery which, to this day, houses works by Renaissance masters like Michelangelo, Leonardo da Vinci and Raphael. Cosimo also commissioned the Orto Botanico di Pisa, or the Botanical Garden of Pisa, in 1544. It was Europe's very first botanical garden and it soon became renowned as a centre for the study of plant sciences, housing many plants of medicinal and pharmacological importance.

Relocated three times, it found its final and current address in the city of Pisa in the same year that Shakespeare wrote his very first play – 1591. By that time, the director of the garden was a Flemish botanist called Josef Goodenhuyse who took on the Italian name Giuseppe Benincasa. This name later acquired a special significance because it became part of the botanical name of a vegetable of great nutritional and medicinal value – *Benincasa hispida*, or the white pumpkin.

But the origin of its botanical name belies the white pumpkin's antiquity, because it goes back to thousands of years before the Renaissance. It most probably originated in Malaysia, and its rind and seeds have been found in the Kana archaeological site of Papua New Guinea, where some of the world's staple food plants were first cultivated about seven thousand years ago.

Its association with India is equally ancient, going back to the *Puranas*; it is mentioned in the *Kalika Purana* as one of the offerings to the Devi. Actually, the white pumpkin's association with the goddess is a very special one. Of the nine manifestations of the Goddess Durga, the fourth one is as Kushmanda Devi. She is worshipped on the fourth day of Durga Puja and of the various offerings that are made to her during this time, the most important

---

Did You Know That...

The white pumpkin is actually a fruit but is commonly referred to as a vegetable because it is cooked and eaten as one.

one is considered to be the white pumpkin. So it comes as no surprise that one of the white pumpkin's Sanskrit names is *kushmanda*!

The white pumpkin is also mentioned in Ayurvedic texts like the *Charaka Samhita*, the *Ashtanga Hridaya Samhita* (considered the third most important work on Ayurveda and written by Vagbhata around 700 AD) and the *Raja Nighantu* written by Naraharipandita in the eighteenth century.

Brain Food, Tonic or Aphrodisiac?

You wouldn't think that a food that is more than 96 per cent water (another one of the white pumpkin's Sanskrit names is *kumbhaphala*, meaning 'waterpot fruit'!) would be able to pack in much in the way of nutrition. But like many other members of the gourd family (cucumber, watermelon, bottle gourd, etcetera) to which it belongs, the white pumpkin is loaded with nutrients. It is an excellent source of thiamine (Vitamin B1) and a good source of niacin (Vitamin B3) and Vitamin C. It also has good amounts of many minerals like calcium and potassium. And the fact that it has almost no calories makes it both the nutritionist's and the dietician's dream.

Needless to say, the ancient wise men of the East knew about the white pumpkin's amazing nourishing qualities and so in many traditional systems of medicine, it is used as a general tonic, restorative, pick-me-up and even brain food – and often in ingenious ways!

Take for instance the 'winter melon urn', a well-known Chinese soup, thus named because it is made by scooping out the inside of a white pumpkin (also called winter melon) to make an 'urn'. This 'urn' is then filled with the scooped-out pulp and various other ingredients like Chinese cured ham, mushrooms and warming herbs like ginger. Then the 'urn' is closed with its own 'lid' and steamed for at least two hours. When the 'urn' is finally brought to the dinner table, it is a spectacular sight. The outside of the pumpkin is often elaborately carved with intricate designs (which include dragons!). Inside, the delicious, nourishing soup, suffused with the pumpkin's mild, subtle flavour, is no less impressive. Soups in China are considered not just as food but also believed to have healing and medicinal properties and this soup is no different.

And closer home, the white pumpkin's most famous avatar, a traditional North Indian sweet called *petha*, is another example of this gourd's restorative powers. It is rare for a sweet dish or a dessert to have therapeutic qualities as well, but *petha* is one such exception. Made by preserving chunks of white pumpkin in sugar syrup, it is considered a general tonic, brain food, even an aphrodisiac and is one of the main tourist attractions in at least two cities in North India. In Amritsar, there is an entire bazaar in the walled city named after it – the centuries-old Pethawala Bazaar. And in Agra, many locals boast that it is almost as famous as the Taj Mahal. Naturally, both cities claim that theirs is the better *petha*! Incidentally, in North India, since *petha* is the most popular and often the only way that the white pumpkin is cooked, in Hindi, it is often called *petha kaddu* or even just *petha*!

Dr Pumpkin

When my mother's favourite cousin started suffering from a kind of paranoia, characterized by bouts of a nameless fear, he began to regularly visit Ayurvedic doctors in Kerala. And among the various treatments prescribed to him was a *lehyam* (a thick, sweet, jam-like medicinal preparation) in which one of the main ingredients was the white pumpkin! (Apparently, the *leyham* was also very delicious and so my uncle rather looked forward to his visits.) You see, in Ayurveda, the white pumpkin is used to treat various kinds of nervous disorders and mental illnesses – one well-known Ayurvedic preparation made from it is used for the treatment of epilepsy, even insanity!

The white pumpkin's essentially alkaline and 'cooling' nature has a neutralizing effect on stomach acids and so it is also used for a whole host of digestive ailments like dyspepsia, hyperacidity and biliousness, even ulcers. In fact, a popular remedy for peptic ulcers is white pumpkin juice, which is also used to treat diabetes. Piles, respiratory disorders like asthma, blood-related diseases, and urinary diseases like kidney stones are some of the other ailments that the white pumpkin helps to heal.

And it is not just the flesh of the white pumpkin that is such potent medicine. The leaves are rubbed on bruises, the ash obtained from burning the rind is applied to ease the discomfort of painful swellings and the seeds used for expelling intestinal worms. And the ash made from burning the seeds and the peel is mixed with

What's in a Name?

Many of the white pumpkin's names come from the appearance and texture of its rind. For example, the *hispida* in its botanical name refers to its faintly fuzzy texture, which is also the reason why it is sometimes called hairy melon. The ash-like and waxy covering on the rind has prompted two of its most popular names in English (wax gourd and ash gourd), its original botanical name *Benincasa cerifera* – *cerifera* means 'wax-bearing' – and many of its names in Indian languages. For example, *boodhi*, both in Kannada and Telugu, means 'ash'.

Language	Name
English	Ash gourd, wax gourd, winter melon, fuzzy melon, hairy melon, Chinese preserving melon, Chinese squash, white gourd, white pumpkin, etc
Botanical name	Benincasa hispida, earlier known as Benincasa cerifera
Sanskrit	Kushmanda, kumbhaphala, brihatphala, kumbhanda, kunjaphala, valliphala, etc
Hindi	Petha, petha kaddu, safed kaddu, golkaddu, etc
Marathi & Gujarati	Kohala
Bengali	Chal kumro
Tamil	Vellai pooshnikaia, neer pooshnikai, pooshnikai, etc
Telugu	Booddida gummadi, boodigummadi
Kannada	Boodhi kumbalakai
Malayalam	Kumbalanga, elavan

coconut oil and used to promote hair growth and as a treatment for dandruff!

In fact, the white pumpkin's curative powers are so wide-ranging that Ayurvedic practitioners of Kerala use a special variety of white pumpkin for their formulations, appropriately called *vaiyda kumbalam*, or 'medicinal pumpkin'.

A Refrigerator in Your Pumpkin?

In my grandmother's house – and most other houses in south coastal Karnataka – if you looked up at the ceiling of the storeroom, you'd see a curious sight: vegetables wrapped in 'cradles' woven out of strips of dried coconut palm, hanging from the wooden rafters of the storeroom ceiling. They would hang there for months on end, to be 'plucked' and cooked whenever needed. And amazingly, they would neither rot nor deteriorate in spite of the hot and humid climate of the region. Among the vegetables thus hung was the white pumpkin. The secret of the white pumpkin's longevity is the white, chalky wax on its skin, which prevents micro-organisms from attacking it and so acts as a preservative, allowing the pumpkin to be stored for as long as a year without refrigeration.

The white pumpkin has much to recommend itself as a vegetable. Its crunchy yet succulent flesh cooks in a jiffy, and it mingles well with other foods, infusing them with a delicate but singular flavour. And it is inexpensive and versatile, transforming into a wide range of dishes, all the way from soup to desserts! (A famous Chinese delicacy is a traditional pastry filled with white pumpkin and almond paste. As the story goes, an impoverished farmer who sold his wife as a slave to pay for the treatment of his ailing father bought her back by making and selling these cakes. So ever since, they are called sweetheart cakes or wife cakes!)

In India, this gourd is particularly popular in South India, especially in Kerala, where it is an integral part of a variety of traditional favourites like *aviyal* (a mixed vegetable dish), *pulinkari* (a tamarind-based curry), *olan* (a curry that is always part of the *sadhya* or 'festive meal') and even a traditional chicken curry called *kozhiyum kumbalangayum*! In Karnataka, it is the star ingredient in *dhamroot* (a kind of *halwa*, served especially at weddings) while in Bengal, it is dipped in batter and fried to make *chal kumro bhaaja*.

In other words, the white pumpkin is no ordinary vegetable. But its extraordinariness is also in the diverse variety of roles that it plays – from sacred offering to the gods to medicine, from brain food to aphrodisiac, from banquet food in China to wedding fare in India. The protective wax coating on its skin is even used to make candles! It is also one of the largest members of the gourd family, known to grow to a weight of 35 kilograms!

But then, you wouldn't expect any less from one that is the favourite food of a goddess. It is said that worshipping the Goddess Kushmanda Devi frees you from sorrow and disease and bestows you with long life and health. So, like the goddess that it is named after, the white pumpkin always blesses us with nourishment and good health.

Cinderella's Coach...

What was it that the fairy godmother waved her magic wand over to turn into Cinderella's fabulous coach? A pumpkin, of course! This close relative of the white pumpkin comes in many varieties (at least twenty-six) and goes by a whole host of names including winter squash, Bohemian squash, turk's cap gourd, spaghetti squash and of course fairytale pumpkin! The name pumpkin originated from *pepon*, the Greek word for 'large melon'. The French changed that into *pompon* which the English made into 'pumpion'. American colonists altered the term 'pumpion' to its current form – 'pumpkin'.

In fact, the Americans are the pumpkin's most ardent fans, growing and eating over 1.5 million tonnes of it annually. Pumpkins take on a special importance during the October festival of Halloween when their insides are scooped out and their outsides carved to make spectacular lanterns called jack-o'-lanterns.

We know this gourd in India as the red or yellow pumpkin, though unlike the white pumpkin, it originated in South America almost ten thousand years ago – the people of the Mayan civilisation grew it in their cornfields, using the stalks of the corn plants as support for the vines of the pumpkin plants.

But even though this pumpkin originated thousands of miles away, its several Sanskrit names indicates that it made the journey to India fairly early on in its history. Some of these names also signal this vegetable's amazing wealth of nutrition. For example, *pitaphala* and *pitakushmanda* both refer to the distinctive colour of the flesh because *pita* means 'yellow' in Sanskrit, a colour that indicates the presence of beta-carotene, the plant raw material that the body converts to Vitamin A. And like its 'white' relative, it is also a very good source of many of the B vitamins like thiamine (Vitamin B1), niacin (Vitamin B3) and folate (folic acid/Vitamin B9), as well as Vitamin C and minerals like potassium, manganese and copper.

Pumpkin seeds rival the flesh in terms of both nutrition and protection against disease. Rich in dietary minerals like zinc, magnesium, manganese and iron, they are also an excellent source of Omega-3 fatty acids and phytosterols, plant chemicals that help to lower cholesterol.

The red pumpkin shares another remarkable property with the white pumpkin – long shelf life. Its thick, hard rind allows it to last as long as six months without refrigeration.

Language	Name
English	Winter squash, acorn squash, butternut squash, pumpkin, red pumpkin, etc
Botanical name	The most popular varieties are Cucurbita maxima, Cucurbita pepo L, Cucurbita mixta, Cucurbita moschata
Sanskrit	Punyalatha, dadiphala, pithaphala, etc
Hindi	Mitha kaddu, kaddu, lal bhopla, kashiphal, etc
Marathi	Lal bhopla, tambada bhopla
Gujarati	Pilu kohala
Bengali	Lal kumra, mitha kumra
Tamil	Parangikai, nalla pusini, etc
Telugu	Gummadi, gummadikai, erra gummadikai, etc
Kannada	Chinikai, sihi kumbalakai
Malayalam	Chakkera kumbalan, mathanga

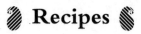

Recipes

White Pumpkin Khadi (Serves 3-4)

Perfect for a delicious, cooling lunch on a hot summer afternoon, this dish cooks in a jiffy!

INGREDIENTS

½ kg white pumpkin, peeled, deseeded
and cut into large cubes
½ litre curds, beaten till smooth
¼ tsp jeera (cumin) powder
2-3 peppercorns, freshly ground
1 ½ tsp salt (adjust to taste)

Tempering
1 tbsp oil
¾ tsp mustard seeds
1 dried red chilli, broken into pieces
7-10 curry leaves
A pinch of asafoetida

METHOD

Boil the pumpkin in about one cup of water till cooked. Keep aside the liquid till it cools down. Now add the liquid and about a cup of water to the beaten curds, so as to get a thick buttermilk consistency. Add the cooked pumpkin, *jeera* powder, pepper and salt. Heat the oil, add red chillies and mustard. When the mustard stops spluttering, add the asafoetida and curry leaves. Remove the tempering from the fire and add it to the curry. Serve with plain steamed rice.

Quickie Red Pumpkin Bhaji (Serves 3-4)

This is one of the fastest, simplest, yet most wonderfully delicious of dishes. It can be served hot as a side dish with dal and chapattis or rice and can even be eaten after it has cooled down as a salad, with bread or with some leftover cooked rice gently mixed in – perfect for a dieter's lunch box!

INGREDIENTS

½ kg red pumpkin
2-3 green chillies, finely chopped
1½ tbsp oil
¾ tsp mustard seeds
1 dried red chilli, broken into pieces
A pinch of asafoetida
6-7 curry leaves
½ tsp turmeric powder
1 ½ tbsp fresh coriander, finely chopped
1 tsp salt (adjust to taste)

METHOD

Remove the rind from the red pumpkin and cut into ½-inch cubes. Heat the oil, add the mustard seeds and red chillies. When the seeds stop spluttering, add the asafoetida and the curry leaves and after a few seconds, add the red pumpkin and green chillies. Over low heat, stir-fry for a few minutes, then add the salt and turmeric powder and finally close the pan with a lid. The pumpkin will release its own juices and cook in them. Stir occasionally so that the pumpkin doesn't burn and stick to the bottom of the pan, but do so very gently because at this stage the pumpkin has a tendency to disintegrate. Add the fresh coriander, stir for another few seconds, then remove from heat and serve.

The Devi – White Pumpkin

Supermum and her Lil' Giants – Fenugreek Leaves and Seeds

The Other Gourds

The gourds are a massive family numbering in the hundreds (according to one estimate – seven hundred!) and include a fabulous variety of fruits and vegetables. But what makes them unique is that not only are they very nutritious (the cucumber is an excellent source of Vitamin C and the watermelon and melon of Vitamin A) and exceptionally therapeutic (the bitter gourd is a well-known treatment for diabetes), but they are also easy to cultivate, inexpensive and transform into a vast variety of delicious dishes.

And while the most well-known gourds are cucumber, watermelon, bitter gourd and pumpkin, there are others, though no less healthful and therapeutic than their more famous relatives, that are known mainly in India. Here is a summary of the more popular of these gourds.

Language	Name				
English	Ridge gourd, towel gourd, sponge gourd*	Snake gourd	Pointed gourd	Ivy gourd	Bottle gourd, calabash
Botanical	Luffa acutangula	Trichosanthes anguina, Trichosanthes cucumerina	Trichosanthes dioica	Coccinia grandis, coccina indica, cephalandra indica	Lagenaria siceraria
Sanskrit	Koshataki, jhingaka, dhamargava	Chichinda	Patola	Bimbika, vimbaja, tundika	Katu tumbi, tumbini
Hindi	Thorai	Chichonda, chachinda, padwal	Parwal	Kundru, bimba	Lauki, dudhi, ghiya
Gujarati	Gisoda, turiya	Pandola, padavali	Parwal, potala	Tindora	Dudhi
Bengali	Jhinga	Chichinga	Potol	Telakucha, kundri	Lau
Marathi	Dhodaka, ghosale	Padwal	Parwar	Tondli	Dudhi bhopla, ran bhopla, dudhi
Tamil	Pirkangkai	Pudalanga	Kombu pudalai	Kovakka	Suraikkai, sorakai
Telugu	Beera kaya	Potla	Kommu potla, adavi potla	Dondakaya	Sorakaya
Kannada	Hirekai	Padval kai	Kahi padvala	Tondekai	Sorekai
Malayalam	Peechinga	Padvalanga	Kattu potolam, patolam	Kovakka	Churakai
Common Medicinal/ Therapeutic Uses	In treatment of bleeding piles, as a diuretic	As a tonic, in treatment of heart disease, liver problems, fever	As a tonic, in treatment of biliousness, jaundice and other liver problems, fever, skin problems	In treatment of diabetes, skin eruptions and diseases like ringworm and psoriasis	As a diuretic, in treatment of cough, bronchitis, skin diseases

Refers to the fact that when the gourd is dried, it yields a fibrous frame or skeleton that makes an excellent bath sponge, body scrubber etc, popularly known as the loofah.

Vitamins
Pluck Yourself Some Health

*'We are living in a world today where lemonade is made from artificial flavours
and furniture polish is made from real lemons.'*
Alfred E Neuman, fictional mascot of *Mad* magazine

In February 2009, an article appeared in *The New York Times* titled 'Vitamin Pills: A False Hope?' In it was the apparently shocking revelation: 'Several high-quality studies have failed to show that extra vitamins, at least in pill form, help prevent chronic disease or prolong life.'

Actually, we shouldn't be surprised because the article only reiterates what countless studies of the healthiest and the longest-living people in the world have already told us. That good health and a long life depend on a complex network of hundreds of factors, all interconnected. And one of them certainly is a lifelong habit of eating balanced meals, laden with fresh fruits and vegetables, whole grains and good fats. And popping vitamin pills doesn't figure anywhere in this scheme of things. Why should it? If you can get your Vitamin A from a luscious mango or your Vitamin D from an early-morning bask in the sun, why would you even consider swallowing a boring, tasteless pill?

That specific foods can make the difference between good health and disease was known to the great men of medicine thousands of years ago. Both the *Ebers Papyrus* and Hippocrates prescribed animal liver for night blindness, even though it was not known that it was the Vitamin A content in the liver that did the trick! In fact, the first glimmer of insight into the connection between vitamins and good health came much later – during the fifteenth century, when hundreds of sailors on long sea voyages began to die of scurvy. The reason – discovered only much later – was that the sailors' diet was completely lacking in fresh fruit and vegetables, the most important sources of Vitamin C. And scurvy is a disease caused by the deficiency of this vitamin. It was even later, towards the end of the nineteenth century, that the first real work on understanding the role of vitamins in health began.

In 1912, based on his own studies and the pioneering work of scientists like Christiaan Eijkman, Fredrick Gowland Hopkins, Gerrit Grijns and others, Casimir Funk put forth a hypothesis that many diseases like beriberi, rickets, pellagra and scurvy were caused by the deficiency of certain substances in diet and could be cured when these substances were reinstated in the required quantities in the diet. He called these substances vitamines – 'amine' meaning 'containing nitrogen' and 'vita' meaning 'life'. This was later changed to 'vitamins' since they do not contain nitrogen.

The meaning of the word 'vita' is a pointer to the importance of vitamins. They are required in the tiniest of quantities and though, unlike other nutrients, they don't constitute any part of the body, they are vital catalysts without which life itself will cease. Vitamins also demonstrate the interconnected nature and functioning of nutrients. And that the best source is always from Nature.

Vitamins at a Glance

Name	Other Names	Solubility	Key Functions	Primary Food Sources
A	Retinol, carotenes★	Fat	Ensures normal vision, builds immunity	All green leafy vegetables, yellow or orange fruits and vegetables, herbs and spices like curry leaves and red chilli
B1	Thiamine	Water	Needed for carbohydrate synthesis and proper functioning of the nervous system	Banana, jackfruit, legumes, whole grains, sprouts, green leafy vegetables, white pumpkin, coconut, mustard, *arvi,* sesame, curry leaves, fenugreek seeds, curd
B2	Riboflavin	Water	Antioxidant, needed for synthesis of carbohydrate and functioning of other B vitamins	Whole grains, legumes, green leafy vegetables, *arvi,* jackfruit, jaggery, curry leaves, fenugreek seeds and dairy products like curd
B3	Niacin, Nicotinic acid	Water	Maintains skin health, lowers LDL and increases HDL cholesterol, needed for synthesis of sex hormones	Whole grains, legumes, peanuts, potatoes, sprouts, green leafy vegetables, *arvi,* white pumpkin, curry leaves, coconut, mustard and curd
B5	Pantothenic acid	Water	Keeps blood healthy, builds immunity, helps reduce stress (the 'anti-stress vitamin')	All foods, but the highest amounts are in whole grains, especially whole wheat, and in legumes, nuts and curd
B6	Pyridoxine, pyridoxal, pyridoxamine	Water	Needed for proper functioning of the nervous system, regulating mood (the 'happiness vitamin'), synthesis of carbohydrates and fats and functioning of over 100 enzymes, and protects the heart	All foods but highest amounts are in whole grains especially whole wheat, legumes, nuts and curd.
B7	Biotin	Water	Synthesis of fats and carbohydrates, regulation of blood sugar	Whole grain, legumes, walnuts, peanuts, milk
B9	Folate, folic acid, folacin	Water	Ensures proper functioning of the nervous system, normal development of the foetus, vital for healthy blood, protects the heart	Whole grain, legumes, green leafy vegetables, *arvi,* cucumber, white pumpkin, coconut, curry leaves, fenugreek seeds

Vitamins at a Glance

Name	Other Names	Solubility	Key Functions	Primary Food Sources
B12	Cobalamin, methylcobalamin, cyanocobalamin	Water	Regulates functioning of the nervous system, vital for healthy blood, is heart protective	Milk and dairy products like curd
Choline**		Water	Helps proper functioning of the liver, nervous system and brain (so called the 'memory vitamin'), keeps blood healthy, is heart protective	Peanuts, potatoes, sesame seeds, legumes, whole grain, banana
C	Ascorbic acid	Water	Antioxidant, immunity builder, helps in repair and maintenance of skin, cartilage, bones and teeth	Green leafy vegetables, cucumber, white pumpkin, potato etc
D	Four variants – D1, D2 (ergocalciferol), D3 (cholecalciferol) and D4 ***	Fat	Vital for bone health, immunity builder, antidepressant	Though certain foods like fish and other seafood, milk and dairy products are good sources of this vitamin, the best source is sunlight
E	A group of eight variants – 4 tocopherols and 4 tocotrienols. Alpha tocopherol is the most active.	Fat	Antioxidant	Vegetable oils like peanut, sesame, palm etc, green leafy vegetables, whole grain
K	Two variants – K1 (phylloquinone or phytomenadione) and K2 (or menatetrenone)	Fat	Vital for bone health and clotting of blood	Green leafy vegetables, vegetables from the *Brassica* family like mustard, radish, cabbage etc

* Retinol, found only in animal foods, is the only dietary form of Vitamin A. Carotenes are found in fruits and vegetables and is converted into Vitamin A by the human body.

**Though not a vitamin, declared 'an essential nutrient' and included in B family of vitamins in 1998.

*** Plants convert a plant chemical called ergosterol into Vitamin D2. But the most active form of Vitamin D is Vitamin D3, produced when the ultraviolet rays in sunlight act on a type of cholesterol in the skin's cells.

The Power of Purple – Brinjals

Hot Stuff – Red Chillies and Powder

Chillies: Good Li'l Demons

'The pungent taste gives us stimulation, invigoration and awakens our interest in pursuing life's challenges.'

Maya Tiwari, renowned Ayurvedic practitioner, in *Ayurveda – Secrets of Healing*

Spicy food. For so many of us, it is yet another one of life's forbidden pleasures. We crave for it and feel as guilty about our 'lapses' into it as an alcoholic would about falling off the teetotalling wagon. And that's because we are constantly told that 'spicy food' is the arch enemy of our digestive systems, making us burn and burp, and causing everything from acidity to ulcers, even cancer.

But the facts point quite to the contrary.

'Spice' is a word that describes any plant-based ingredient that is used to flavour and/or preserve food and does not in any way allude to pungency. By this definition, even curry leaves and turmeric are spices. More importantly, all spices used in Eastern cooking are healers acknowledged both by the traditional systems of medicine as well as by Western medicine. Turmeric, for example, an ingredient without which most self-respecting *masala* powders would refuse to be thus dubbed, could probably play a significant role in the treatment of a whole host of diseases from Alzheimer's to cancer, while fenugreek (*methi*) has proven effective in helping to control both diabetes and high cholesterol.

But, unfortunately, both the words 'spice' and 'spicy' have acquired misleading baggage over time. 'Spicy' is mostly used to describe food that is overly pungent (sometimes even greasy!) and has thus acquired unhealthy associations. And of all the spices judged so harshly, the one that is the most maligned and regarded as anathema to healthy, nutritious food is the poor, undeserving chilli. It is time to set the record straight.

And what better place to start than the chilli's botanical curriculum vitae?

Fruit, Vegetable or Spice?
Bernardino de Sahagún, the Spanish Franciscan friar, in his chronicles about the life of the native Indians in sixteenth-century

Mexico, observed that in the marketplace, the chilli vendor sold 'mild red chillies, broad chillies, hot green chillies, yellow chillies, cuitla chilli, tenpil chilli, chinchioa chilli, water chilli, conchilli, smoked chillies, small chillies, tree chillies, thin chillies, those like beetles; green chillies, sharp-pointed red chillies…'

And if Sahagun had come to India, the litany would have been something like this – *Kashmiri mirchi, Pusa jwala, lavangi mirchi, Guntur sannam, Ellachipur chilli, Hindpur chilli, Byadgi chilli, gundu milagai, oosi milagia, Warnagal chatpatta…*

What I mean to say is that there are chillies and there are chillies: some slim, elegant stilettos, others wickedly curved like a villain's moustache; some large, fat, round ladies, others tiny as marbles; some shaped like bells, others like mushrooms; some spewing their fire at the merest touch, other barely whispering their piquant secrets. Each kind of chilli has its own unique signature of pungency and flavour, and even though botanically speaking, there are only five cultivated species of chillies, over the centuries these have evolved to include hundreds of varieties – some say four hundred, others say thousands!

Add to that the various ways in which we eat chillies – dried, raw, powdered, ground, pickled or tempered in hot oil – and we have a Continent of Chillies more varied than the states of India!

Whatever their denomination, chillies belong to a vast genus of pod-like berries that go by the family name *Capsicum*. That makes the chilli a fruit and so, like many fruits, when it is unripe it is green. Then, as it ripens, it changes colour and most varieties turn a glorious fiery red. In fact, the word 'chilli' traces its origin to Nahuatl (a group of ancient South American languages that include the one spoken by the Aztecs), in which it means 'red'. But some chillies remain stubbornly green even to a ripe old age, others prefer to mature into a golden-yellow and one variety even turns a deep royal purple instead of red!

In India (where we know a thing or two about chillies, being both the world's largest producer and consumer) and in many parts of South America (the chilli's birthplace), the honour of being called a chilli is bestowed upon only the fiercest, fieriest members of this berry-clan. And in these places, there is no doubt that the chilli is a

Hot, Hotter, Hottest!

The pungency of a chilli is measured in Scoville units. The hottest chilli in the world was the Red Savina Habanero at a searing 580,000 Scoville units! Till the *naga jolokia* or the 'chilli of the Nagas' was discovered in 2000 near Tezpur in Assam. With a pungency of 1,001,304 Scoville units, it is twice as hot as the Habanero and so, this chilli has since acquired a few more names in Assamese – *bhut jolokia* or 'demon chilli' and *bih jolokia* or 'poison chilli'. Naturally, there are plans to use the blistering 'heat' of this scorcher in anti-mugging weapons like pepper sprays and for riot-control purposes! In comparison, the Kashmiri chilli, popularly used in its dried, red form in Indian cooking, is just 40,500 units.

spice, to be treated with the utmost of respect and used in the most judicious way as all spices must be.

But in many Western countries, the chilli terminology is confusing because it is variously called chilli pepper or cayenne pepper or paprika or sometimes, just pepper – even though the chilli is no relation of the pepper. And to make things even more confusing, the chilli's milder siblings, which are used only as vegetables, are called sweet peppers or bell peppers… or then, just peppers! (In India we know them by the family name – capsicum.)

Naturally, the question is – if chillies are not peppers, why are they often called so?

Blame it on Columbus…

Well, we can blame it all on that great explorer and discoverer of more than just continents – Christopher Columbus. Actually, going by what one bunch of experts says, it was Diego Alvarez Chanca, a physician accompanying Columbus on his second voyage to the West Indies in 1494, who brought the chilli back to Spain and later wrote about its medicinal effects. (Oh yes, shocking but true – the chilli is no mean nutritionist and healer, but more on than later.) But another lot of experts says that it was Columbus himself who stumbled upon a plant with exotic-looking, shiny, red fruit that mimicked the taste of pepper. So he called them red peppers and took them back home. Soon 'the fire' spread all over Spain and Portugal and then, travelling aboard the ships of Spanish and Portuguese explorers, it reached Africa and India. And we embraced this pungent foreigner so ardently and enthusiastically that today it is inconceivable that any Indian food can be cooked without chillies.

So curiously enough, though Indian cuisine has an overpowering and often not very complimentary reputation for fieriness (we are after all the people who introduced the world to the 'joys' of curry), the chilli came into India just a few centuries ago. Before which, our primary 'hot stuff' was the black pepper, a native of India.

But that is just about 500 years of history of a spice that traces its origins back to thousands of years before that. Remains of the chilli have been found in archaeological sites in the Tehuacan Valley in Mexico dating back to between 5,500–7,000 years ago as well as in other sites of later dates in Peru and El Salvador. Research done by the Smithsonian Institute also indicates that the domestication of the chilli began around the same time in south-western Ecuador at the sites of Loma Alta and Loma Real. So, by the time Montezuma II became the emperor of the Aztec Empire in AD 1502, the chilli had been in use in South America for thousands of years. And the emperor himself was rather partial to it because as legend has it, his favourite tipple was a drink that is probably the ancestor of hot chocolate: it was made from a fruit called cacao (or cocoa), whose seeds are made into cocoa solids and cocoa butter – the main ingredients in chocolate. It is said that he drank fifty goblets of this drink a day, flavoured with vanilla… and chillies!

But coming back to India, our love affair with the chilli has been no less passionate, no less unwavering in its intensity. In many parts of India all that accompanies the *chapattis* in a poor man's meal is a raw onion or two and a few green chillies. And there are perhaps two reasons for this. One is that chillies are often the only things he can afford to perk up otherwise dull fare. The other is that the very thing that makes the chilli so fiery on the tongue also makes it a remarkable health food and healer.

Hot Healer!

It may sound incredible but the chilli is one of Nature's most potent healers. What is even more incredible is that all these medicinal powers can be attributed to the very thing that also makes the chilli pungent – an alkaloid called capsaicin! So here is a look at what this amazing phytochemical can do…

Painkiller

The way capsaicin tackles pain is a bit like fire fighting fire. You see, the burning sensation that we call as the 'chilli taste' is actually pain caused by capsaicin. This pain induces the body to release substance P, a chemical that transmits messages of pain from nerve endings to the brain. But, amazingly enough, if capsaicin is present in the area long enough, it actually depletes the substance P and thus gives relief from pain! So scientists are hoping to harness the chilli's 'burning' powers in the treatment of pain, especially in arthritis, psoriasis and diabetic neuropathy. In fact, capsaicin is already a key ingredient in a plethora of topical creams that are prescribed for pain relief.

Bird Food

That chillies are a parrot's favourite food is a well-known fact. The reason for this is a happy symbiotic relationship between the two. Birds don't experience the 'burning' sensation when they come in contact with capsaicin the way we mammals do. And so, chillies make a delicious, nutritious bird meal. In return, the birds disperse the chilli seeds either by dropping the seeds while eating or when they pass them undigested through the digestive tract!

What's in a Name?

Kith and kin of the tomato and the brinjal, the chilli clan consists of about twenty wild species and five cultivated ones. Of these five, the one to which most of the Indian chillies belong goes by the botanical name of *Capsicum annuum,* whereas *Capsicum chinense* is the one that has the hottest chilli.

The chilli's names in all Indian languages are a variation of the word for pepper. For example, the Hindi *mirchi* can be traced to *maricha,* the Sanskrit name for pepper. And *marichi* is the Sanskrit name for chilli, which is also the name of a great Indian *rishi* and means 'ray of sunlight' – a rather diplomatic reference perhaps to the chilli's fieriness!

Language	Name		
	Generic	**Green Chilli (Unripe)**	**Red Chilli (Ripe)**
English	Chilli, chilli pepper	Green Chilli	Chilli pepper, cayenne pepper, paprika, red chilli
Botanical	Capsicum pubescens, Capsicum annuum, Capsicum baccatum, Capsicum chinense and Capsicum frutescens	Capsicum pubescens, Capsicum annuum, Capsicum baccatum, Capsicum chinense and Capsicum frutescens	Capsicum pubescens, Capsicum annuum, Capsicum baccatum, Capsicum chinense and Capsicum frutescens
Sanskrit	Ujwala, katuvira, marichi phalam	Marichi phalam	Rakta marichi
Hindi	Mirchi	Hari mirchi	Lal mirchi
Gujarati	Marcha	Lila marcha	Lal marcha
Bengali	Lanka	Lanka	Lal lanka, shunko lanka
Marathi	Mirchya	Hirvya mirchya	Lal mirchya
Tamil	Milagai, molagai	Pachai milagai	Sigappu milagai
Telugu	Mirapakaya	Pachi mirapakaya	Pandu mirapakaya, yendu mirapakaya
Kannada	Menasina kayi	Hasi menasina kayi	Menasinakai, kempu menasina kai, vona menasinakai
Malayalam	Mulaga	Paccha mulaga	Chuvanna mulaga

Heart Protector

Preliminary studies show that capsaicin may play a role in improving blood flow to the heart and therefore in the treatment of atherosclerosis, where blood flow to the heart is restricted or even blocked by the hardening and narrowing of arteries.

Capsaicin's ability to stimulate blood circulation, lower cholesterol and dissolve fibrin, the chemical that causes blood to clot, is borne out by the fact that in regions of the world where chilli is liberally used in food, there is a much lower rate of heart attack, stroke and pulmonary embolism.

Researchers have also found that chillies could help in both the prevention and treatment of diabetes. This is because of two reasons. Firstly, it has been found that the amount of insulin required to regulate blood sugar after eating food that contains chillies is less than that required for food that contains none. Secondly, capsaicin induces the pancreas to secrete more insulin.

Hot Comfort for Cold Misery
Remember that old grandma's remedy for a cold — a cup of steaming -hot, spicy *rasam* laced with pepper and chilli — and how it seemed to magically clear up your clogged nasal passages? Well, this happens because capsaicin has the ability to stir up secretions that help to thin and move that thick, stubborn mucus from the nose or congested lungs. Its action is similar to the way many cold remedies work, but with one big difference: capsaicin works much faster. That combined with the fact that the chilli also has some amounts of Vitamin C makes it a perfect cold remedy — faster, healthier and delicious to boot!

Cancer Killer?
Capsaicin may also prove critical in the treatment of prostate cancer. In 2006, researchers at the Cedars-Sinai Medical Center and the University of California Los Angeles School of Medicine found that the size of the prostate cancer tumours in mice that were given capsaicin were about one-fifth that of tumours in mice that did not get any capsaicin. This was because capsaicin induced approximately 80 per cent of prostate cancer cells growing in mice to — as they put it — 'commit suicide' or self-destruct!

Ulcer buster
Anybody will tell you this. If you have any kind of trouble with your digestion, avoid chillies in any form. Right? Actually, wrong! Recent research findings seem to have acquitted chillies from the charge of being one of the primary causes of ulcers and heartburn. Not only that, there also seems to be reason to believe that chillies, if consumed judiciously, can actually have a beneficial effect on

stomach ulcers – by not just helping to treat them but perhaps even helping to prevent them!

How 'Hot' is your Vitamin Pill?

Many associate the colour of the red chilli with its 'fiery' taste. But the chilli is red for the same reason that the insides of pumpkins are orange and mangoes are yellow – it indicates the presence of a very high amount of beta-carotene, one of Nature's most powerful antioxidants and the substance that the body converts into Vitamin A. Red chillies are also rich in that other mighty disease-fighter – Vitamin C.

And green chillies aren't lagging behind in nutritive value just because they are a different colour. They are also a very good source of Vitamin C and contain a fair amount of Vitamin A.

That brings us to the end of this chilli story and leaves just one question that needs to be answered.

How much chilli?

It is an important question because while it is true that chillies are great nutritionists and healers, it is also true that excessive consumption of chillies on a regular basis can do serious harm to your health.

Perhaps the answer lies in a plant with beautiful pink trumpet-like flowers called the foxglove. Its botanical name – *Digitalis purpurea* – alludes to the presence of a plant chemical called digitalis. In 1785, William Withering, a British doctor, discovered the life-saving properties of digitalis in treating patients suffering from congestive heart failure – but only if administered in the right dose. Otherwise, digitalis is one of Nature's deadliest poisons. No wonder then that it has been a favourite murder weapon of the writers of mysteries and thrillers – including the great Agatha Christie!

So, there are many things that are wonderfully beneficial, but only when used in the right quantities and ways. Otherwise they can do grievous harm, even kill. So use chillies like make-up – with a light hand. And allow these little green and red pods to enhance and highlight the flavours of your food without drowning or killing it, thereby perking up not just your meal but also your health!

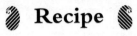

Recipe

Hot 'n' Sweet Chilli Chutney

(Makes about 1 ½ cups)

This fabulous chutney goes with anything from dosas and idlis to curd-rice and works even as sandwich spread!

INGREDIENTS

100 gm dried red chillies (the Kashmiri variety is more flavourful and less pungent)
A ball of tamarind the size of a small lemon
5-6 medium-sized garlic cloves (optional)
½ cup copra (dried coconut), cut into small pieces
¾ cup grated jaggery (adjust to taste)
½-¾ cup oil (if you use coconut oil, it gives a distinctive, delicious flavour to the chutney!)
¾-1 tsp salt (adjust to taste)

METHOD

Grind all ingredients except the garlic and oil to a coarse paste. Now add the garlic and grind to a smooth paste. Remove from the blender and dribble in the oil, stirring all the time, till the oil is completely absorbed into the chutney. Store in a dry jar.

Variation: You can substitute the garlic with a tablespoon or so of roasted sesame seeds (*til*) – the black variety are the most flavourful. Toast the seeds gently and grind them together with all the other ingredients.

Curry Leaves: Currying Flavours

A few years ago, in a flurry of astounded 'oohs' and 'aahs', researchers of the Department of Pharmacy at King's College in London announced that curry leaves may prove to be the next wonder herb in the treatment of diabetes. Surprise, surprise, I muttered to myself – because in India, we had cottoned on to this about a few thousand years ago. You're thinking: are we talking about those innocuous little leaves that the vegetable seller often throws in gratis with the rest of the veggies? The stuff that we toss into seasonings and chutneys and pickles? That ingredient without which no South Indian cook worth his/her weight in curd-rice would be seen in the kitchen? Those little greenish-brown bits that we pick out of the *upma* or the *sambar* and throw away?

Absolutely!

Actually, the clue to the curry leaf's staggering nutritional and therapeutic credentials lies in the fact that it is a close relative of that other great healer, the lemon. And like the lemon, it is a native of India. Its ancestry is at least a few thousand years old, but unlike its citrus kin, information about the curry leaf's history is scanty – though apparently there are references to it in early Tamil literature dating back to the first to fourth centuries AD. This includes a passage in the *Perumpanuru*, one of the ten anthologies in the collection of Sangam poetry called *Pathu Pattu*. The fifteenth-century Kannada poet, Bommarasa of Terakanambi, also mentions curry leaves as one of the ingredients in dishes served at a royal feast.

What a Little Bitterness Can Do…

So what is it about the curry leaf that could make it so important in the treatment of diabetes? The findings of the King's College study indicate that the curry leaf slows down the action of a digestive enzyme called pancreatic alpha-amylase, which is involved in the breakdown of dietary starch to glucose. This in turn regulates the release of glucose into the bloodstream, a function that diabetics are unable to do efficiently. Or as Professor Houghton, the scientist heading that research team, put it, the action of the curry leaf on blood sugar is 'like restricting people coming out of a station gate in the rush hour so that they come out one at a time rather than seven at a time'!

Of course, in Ayurveda, the curry leaf – along with bitter gourd and fenugreek – is used in the treatment of diabetes for two important reasons. The first is that in Ayurveda, the 'bitter principle' is used to counteract the effects of an excess of 'sweetness' in the body. So ingredients that are bitter in taste – like the curry leaf – are used in the treatment of diabetes, which is essentially an excess of blood sugar due to the inability of the body to control the absorption and synthesis of glucose. The second reason is that Ayurveda also considers the curry leaf to be an insulin stimulant. As it is estimated that by 2030 there will be about 370 million diabetics in the world, 80 million of them in India, these two reasons alone could catapult the curry leaf to the kind of medicinal star status that turmeric and *neem* currently enjoy.

Cool Relief for 'Burning' Problems!

The clue to another one of the curry leaf's famed curatives powers is in the strong, unmistakable but refreshing aroma that fills the air when you gently crush a curry leaf. You see, crushing the leaf releases its essential oils – and research has shown that these oils have strong antibacterial and anti-fungal action. Also, according to Ayurveda, the curry leaf is essentially 'cooling' in nature. So the leaf is used to treat ailments where it is important not only to fight infection but also to alleviate inflammation, and includes minor burns, skin eruptions and skin conditions like allergic rashes from insect bites. And the curry leaf's soothing properties might be the reason why it is also said to improve the voice! The curry leaf is even recommended to provide relief from the burning sensation that many diabetics experience on the soles of their feet.

The combination of its antibacterial property and the fresh, citrus-like fragrance of its essential oils also make the curry leaf an excellent breath freshener. The antibacterial action destroys the bacteria that cause bad breath, and the fragrance makes your breath smell great!

Your Digestion's Little Helper

It seems that there is little that the curry leaf cannot do to help your digestive system function properly – from kick-starting a listless, dull appetite to working as a gentle laxative to nudge those

What's in a Name?

It is a curious fact that though the curry leaf is no relation of the *neem*, its names in almost all the Indian languages allude to the *neem*. For example, the curry leaf's Sanskrit name is *krishnanimba*, a derivative of *nimba* which is the Sanskrit name for *neem*. In Kannada, it is called *karibevu*, meaning 'black *neem*', and in Hindi, though the more popular name is *karipatta*, it is also known as *meetha neem*, meaning 'sweet *neem*'. Perhaps this is because the flowers and fruits of the tree, but especially the leaves, closely resemble the flowers, fruits and leaves of the *neem* tree.

The curry leaf's botanical name honours two distinguished pupils of the famous Swedish naturalist and physician, Carolus Linnaeus. *Murraya* is inspired by the Swedish botanist Johann Andreas Murray (1740-1741) while *koenigii* is in memory of the Polish botanist, Johann Gerhard König (1728-1785).

Language	Name
English	Curry leaf
Botanical	Murraya koenigii
Sanskrit	Krishnanimba, surabhinimba
Bengali	Karipatta
Gujarati	Mitho limdo, kadhilimdo
Hindi	Karipatta, meetha neem
Marathi	Kadhi limb, karhi limb
Tamil	Kariveppilai, karuveppilai
Telugu	Karepeku, karivepaku
Kannada	Karibevu
Malayalam	Kariveppila, kariveppu

laggardly bowels to get moving. Now you know why South Indian dishes are always so liberally flavoured with curry leaves!

But apart from this, the curry leaf is also an excellent remedy for several common digestive problems and ailments. Ayurveda uses it to treat diarrhoea and dysentery and to expel intestinal worms. It is also used to treat all varieties of nausea – like that caused by overindulgence and eating too much fried food, or by biliousness, morning sickness or even the more serious kind of nausea and vomiting caused by cholera.

Little but Mighty Healthy

You wouldn't think so looking at it, but this little leaf also packs in an astounding amount of nutrition. It's loaded with vitamins – Vitamin C and four of the B vitamins (thiamine – B1, riboflavin – B2, niacin – B3 and folate or folic acid – B9). The leaves are also rich in beta-carotene (the raw material that the body converts into Vitamin A) and packed with minerals like iron, calcium and phosphorus, the iron content high enough for it to be used in diets for people suffering from anaemia. No wonder then that curry-leaf powder has been included in the mid-day meals given to children in *anganwadis* as part of the Puratchi Thalaivar MGR Nutritious Meal Programme in Tamil Nadu!

Great…But How Many Leaves?

Naturally, the question that springs to mind is – considering that only a handful of them are normally used to flavour food, does this mean that we will now have to chomp on sheaves and sheaves of these little green leaves? Of course not. But start by making three things a habit. First, season your dishes with curry leaves frequently and lavishly, preferably by cooking them along with the dish rather than frying them in a tempering (*tadka*). So, for example, chuck in a handful of leaves into the *dal* or the *sambar* while it is cooking. This is because while fried curry leaves lend a delicious flavour to the food, the frying process destroys or drastically reduces many of the nutrients, especially heat-sensitive vitamins like Vitamin C. Second, the next time you find curry leaves in your food, don't pick them out and throw them – eat them! Third, check out the Complete Curry Leaf Guide (see page 117) to see how you can make curry leaves a regular part of your diet and your medicine chest!

Which finally brings me to share with you a small but almost infallible thumb rule that comes in handy in figuring out the healthfulness of a food. If you find that it is traditionally grown in every backyard and if your mother or grandmother tends to liberally use it in all kinds of things from chutneys to home remedies, you can be sure that it's one of Mother Nature's most trusted healers. And what better example of it than the little green curry leaf?

The Complete Curry Leaf Guide

It's all very well to say that the curry leaf is good for everything from diarrhoea to dandruff but the question is how exactly are you supposed to have it? Paste, poultice, potion, powder, *pulao* or pudding? Well, here's the Complete Curry Leaf Guide to answer all your questions.

Condition	Formulation	Ingredients	Method
Diabetes	Chutney powder	5 gm dehydrated curry leaves (dried in the shade or lightly roasted on a *tava*) 20 gm lightly roasted *methi* seeds 40 gm soya bean 40 gm *mung dal* A pinch each of rock salt and black salt (adjust to taste) ¼ tsp chilli powder 2 tsp dehydrated tamarind powder or small piece of tamarind	Grind together all ingredients except salt to a fine powder, add salt to taste and store in a dry, airtight jar. Can be eaten with everything from *chapattis* to rice, as a sandwich spread or even mixed into curd to make a spicy *raita!*
Diarrhoea, dysentery	Curry-leaf paste	30-40 fresh curry leaves	Wash the leaves well, dry and grind to a paste. Mix ½ teaspoon of the paste in 5 tablespoons of buttermilk and drink. You can also eat the paste directly.
Nausea	Fried curry leaves	5-6 fresh curry leaves, washed and dried ½ teaspoon *ghee* made from cow's milk	Fry the leaves in the *ghee* till crisp. Cool and eat. (You can also crush the fried leaves, add to about 2 tablespoons of buttermilk and drink the mixture.)
Bad Breath	Fresh curry leaves	5-7 curry leaves	Keep the leaves in the mouth for about 7-10 minutes. Chew gently if you can, then spit out and rinse your mouth with water.
Worms	Curry-leaf paste	20-25 curry leaves	Wash thoroughly and grind to a smooth paste. Have 1 teaspoon first thing in the morning on an empty stomach.

With grateful thanks to Dr CS Anil Kumar, BAMS, MD (Ayurveda, Kayachikitsa), DNY; Physician Consultant in Ayurveda, Yoga and Naturopathy; Associate Professor, Department of Kayachikitsa, JSS Ayurveda Medical College, Mysore; Director, Dixit Health Clinic & Research Centre, Mysore

Leafy Beautician

If the curry leaf's therapeutic and nutritional benefits are not so well known, it is even lesser known as a beautician. But the fact is that the presence of nutrients like vitamins and minerals as well as antimicrobial essential oils makes it the perfect skin and hair food/tonic. So, no surprise then that curry leaves are excellent for treating dry skin and dandruff and are used as skin softener, hair conditioner, even hair wash!

Condition	Formulation	Ingredients	Method
Dandruff, eczema, allergic skin rash, burning sensation and dry, dull skin. This oil apparently also prevents premature greying and even helps restore pigmentation to grey hair.	Coconut-curry leaf oil	100 ml fresh coconut oil 20-25 curry leaves, cleaned and dried	Heat the oil till it boils, add the curry leaves and immediately remove from heat. Do not cover, and allow to cool. Store in a clean, dry bottle. Massage the scalp with this oil. Leave for about 30-60 minutes. Shampoo thoroughly. For the skin, gently apply on affected area and allow the oil to stay on for a few hours.
Dry, dull hair	Hibiscus-curry leaf hair wash	20 gm curry leaves 20 gm hibiscus leaves	Wash the leaves well. Grind to a paste. Massage into the hair and scalp well like a shampoo. Rinse thoroughly.

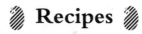 # Recipes

Coconut and Curry Leaves Chutney Powder

(Makes about 2 cups)

This chutney powder is a versatile accompanist. It's a great toast/sandwich/chapatti spread and combines superbly with curd to be eaten with puris or chapattis. It is an excellent companion for curd-rice and dal-chawal, and sprinkled lavishly on hot rice and mixed with a dash of melted ghee, it takes you straight to heaven!

INGREDIENTS

½ copra (dry coconut), cut into small pieces
1 ½ tbsp urad dal
3 dried red chillies (adjust to taste)
2 tbsp sesame seeds (the black variety is the most flavourful)
1 cup curry leaves, washed, cleaned and dried
2 thumbnail-size pieces of tamarind
¾ tsp salt (adjust to taste)

METHOD

Roast the *urad dal*, red chillies, sesame seeds and curry leaves separately on a very low flame till they release a roasted aroma. (Be particularly careful while roasting curry leaves, because they will char and burn in seconds.) Grind together with the tamarind, copra pieces and salt till you get the consistency of a coarse powder. If stored in a dry, airtight jar, this chutney powder will keep for weeks, but it is tastiest when freshly ground.

Tomato-Curry Leaves Rasam

(Serves 3-4)

This rasam *has many things going for it, in terms of both taste and nutrition. The abundance of tomato makes it almost soup-like in taste and colours it a glorious shade of red. The lashings of curry leaves impart a wonderfully subtle 'Southie' flavour. The* toor dal *(pigeon pea) ensures that there is sufficient protein in your meal, and the fact that it is made without a single drop of oil makes it a dietician's dream!*

INGREDIENTS

½ cup toor dal, *cleaned and washed*
4-5 medium-sized tomatoes, each cut into two
1 heaped tsp rasam *or* sambar *powder*
1 ½ tsp salt (adjust to taste)
25-30 curry leaves
A pinch of asafoetida

METHOD

Pressure-cook the *toor dal* and the tomatoes (4 whistles) – the *dal* and the tomatoes should be almost disintegrating. Allow to cool, then take out each tomato half, peel off and discard the skin, mash well and add back into the cooked *dal*. Now add about 1½ to 2 cups of water and the rest of the ingredients and bring to a boil. Simmer for another minute or so.

(If you want to increase the sourness, add some lemon juice.)

Serve with plain steamed rice, lots of *pappads* and melted *ghee!*

If you leave the *rasam* standing for a while, a clear liquid will separate and come to the top. Serve this liquid with a dab of butter as a clear soup – it's wonderful in winter or in the monsoons and is a great start to dinner parties.

Variation: 3-4 peppercorns crushed and added to this *rasam* imparts a lovely zing and makes it an excellent remedy for colds.

Mustard: Sarson ka Saag-a

'Him I call indeed a Brahmana who does not cling to pleasures, like water on a lotus leaf, like a mustard seed on the point of a needle.'
Buddha's teachings according to *The Dhammapada*

To a South Indian, cooking without mustard seeds is like asking a ship to sail on dry land.

Unthinkable.

Everything savoury begins or ends with that classic South Indian tempering – mustard seeds spluttering and chattering excitedly in hot oil or *ghee*, accompanied by a few red chillies and curry leaves, and laced with a judicious pinch or two of asafoetida. The resulting aroma is so delicious, it's guaranteed to kick-start the most sluggish appetite – the only thing that could probably compete with this wake-up call is the aroma of freshly brewed coffee!

But, it's not just South Indians who are so madly in love with this spice. It is said that the word *raita*, which is the name of a North Indian dish made with curd, originates from *rai*, which is the Hindi name for mustard. In America, 'to cut the mustard' means to achieve something or succeed – naturally, since the Americans are the largest consumers of mustard in the world. According to one estimate, more than 1,600 gallons and 2 million individual packets of mustard paste are consumed every year at New York's Yankee Stadium alone!

From Beijing to Bhatinda, from Yokohama to Yorkshire. Roasted and toasted, fried or raw. Ground to paste, pounded to powder. Pickling spice, seasoning or salad dressing. Leaf, seed or oil. *Panch phoran* or mayonnaise or chutney. *Tatsoi, mizuna, juk gai choy* or *sarson ka saag*, the mustard's reign is all-pervasive.

Ancient Spice... or Medicine?

When the most famous portion of the Great Wall of China was being built by Emperor Qin Shi Huang (also known as Ch'in Shih Huang) of the Qin Dynasty in the second century BC, the coolies who were working on the wall needed all the fortifying food that they could get. So part of their daily diet consisted of many fermented vegetables, including greens – probably the same greens

that is one of the Punjabis' favourite winter vegetables. *Sarson ka saag*, or mustard greens!

In other words, the mustard started its innings thousands of years ago as a weed growing wild in central Asia. From there, it evolved into the three variants that are consumed all over the world – black, brown and white mustard.

The Indian variant, brown mustard, most probably originated somewhere in the Himalayan region around 4,000 years ago. We know this because carbonized seeds were found in the Indus Valley civilization site of Chanhu Daro (located about 130 kilometres south of the Mohenjodaro site in the Sindh province of present-day Pakistan) which was inhabited between 4000 and 1700 BC. References to the mustard have been found in innumerable ancient Indian texts, religious and temporal, including in several Buddhist scriptures like the *Lotus Sutra*, in the *Devi Bhagavatam*, the *Laws of Manu*, the *Arthashastra*, and the Jain *Acaranga Sutra* (500 BC) which has the earliest reference to *sarson ka saag*.

The last two texts also make references to the white mustard. This is the mildest mustard variant and is of equal antiquity, originating in the Mediterranean region. Some experts feel that its culinary use began primarily to improve the taste of meat. (Since these were the days before refrigeration, meat tended to perish quickly and required constant camouflaging.) But it seems that initially, the ancient Greeks and Romans used the white mustard more as a medicine than as a spice. Pythagoras employed it to treat scorpion stings, Hippocrates used it in a variety of medicines and poultices. According to Pliny the Elder, the list of ailments that the mustard could treat was a long and impressive one and included 'maladies of the stomach', 'all deep-seated pains in any part of the body', toothache, asthma, epilepsy and lethargy. He also recommended it to resuscitate 'hysterical females', probably because of the mustard's sharply pungent aroma about which he said, 'there is none to be found to be more penetrating to the brain and nostrils'!

It was the Romans who introduced black mustard to Gaul (a region that is now part of Western Europe) somewhere during the fourth century AD. Black mustard is considered to be the strongest in aroma and flavour and is the variety of mustard that is used to make the famous Dijon mustard that is relished by epicures the world over. Originating somewhere in the Middle East, this mustard was cultivated in Sumer in Southern Mesopotamia (current-day Iraq), said to be the earliest human civilization, which flourished from the sixth to the second millennium BC.

Black mustard must have also reached India fairly early on because the mention of *rai* and *rajika* found in several ancient Indian texts are considered to be names for black mustard. By the Middle Ages, this variety of mustard was prized in Europe both as spice – no self-respecting dinner table would do without it – and as medicine, used to treat sciatica and gout. Among its many aficionados were at least two popes, of which Pope John XXII was such an ardent fan that he created the post of *Grand Moutardier du Pape* for his good-for-nothing nephew. The title translates to 'the Great Mustard-Maker to the Pope'!

Tiny But Power-Packed!

The mustard seed is a very strange seed. Left whole and un-disturbed, it is completely innocuous and odourless. But crush one even slightly and it transforms into a spice whose pungent odour can be quite ferocious in its intensity. (Incidentally, this 'smelly' trait is something that mustard shares with other family members like cabbage, horseradish and cauliflower that also start giving off very strong – and often unpleasant – odours when they are chopped, chewed, crushed, broken or cooked.) And this transformation happens because the crushing causes a chemical reaction between an enzyme called myrosinase and a compound of sulphur and nitrogen called glucosinolate present in the mustard, which produces and releases a volatile, strong-smelling chemical called allyl isothiocyanate (AITC).

But AITC is responsible for more than just the mustard's straight-up-the-nose-to-the-brain pungency. Scientists stumbled on its anti-carcinogenic properties in 1931, when they found that rabbits fed with cabbage leaves survived lethal doses of uranium. It took many years of research to figure out that it was AITC and other such plant chemicals in the cabbage that protected those rabbits. We now know that AITC helps prevent many types of cancer, particularly cancers of the gastrointestinal tract.

Mustard seeds are also excellent nutritionists. For two reasons. First, they contain very high amounts of two very important minerals – selenium and magnesium. (Other important minerals present in

Filmi Mustard

Mustard fields in full bloom are one of the most spectacularly beautiful sights in the world. Acres and acres of breathtaking, sunshine-yellow mustard flowers – the ideal setting for a hero to romance his heroine! So mustard fields are veterans in Hindi films, vying with Kashmir as a favourite location for romantic numbers. And the most famous 'mustard scene' in Hindi cinema is filmed to the song, '*Tujhe dekha to yeh jana sanam*' in *Dilwale Dulhaniya le Jayenge!*

good amounts in mustard seeds are iron, zinc and manganese). The second reason is because as much as 30 per cent of mustard seed is oil…

Pehelwan Oil

Mustard oil is so rich in unsaturated or 'good' fatty acids (both polyunsaturated and monounsaturated) that there is almost no place for the saturated or 'bad' fats. (The percentage of saturated fats in mustard oil is the lowest among all vegetable oils, even lower than in that darling of Western nutritionists, olive oil!) Unsaturated fatty acids play a vital role in preventing a whole range of ailments including depression, asthma and rheumatoid arthritis, but most importantly in preventing and managing cardiovascular disease. And the oil present in just two teaspoons of mustard seeds yields as much as 8 per cent of your daily requirement of these fatty acids.

There has been some controversy about the high levels of a monounsaturated Omega-9 fatty acid called erucic acid in mustard oil and its possible adverse effect on the heart. (This is the reason why this oil is not considered suitable for human consumption in the USA, Canada and the European Union.) But the findings of a 2004 study conducted by a team consisting of researchers from the Harvard School of Public Health, the All-India Institute of Medical Sciences, Delhi and St John's Medical College, Bangalore revealed something quite to the contrary. They indicated that the use of mustard oil as a cooking medium actually lowered the risk of heart attack by 71 per cent!

In India, mustard oil is an old friend. Mustard is one of the sixty oilseeds listed in the *Sushrutha Samhita*, one of Ayurveda's oldest and most authoritative texts, and mustard oil's reputation as massage oil is amply evident in the fact that it is the oil favoured by Indian wrestlers! They use it not just to relieve sore muscles but also liberally slather it on before a wrestling match to make their bodies slippery and therefore difficult for the opponents to grip!

In winter, for millions of poor people in North India, it is also an inexpensive way of keeping the skin soft and the body warm because a rub-down with mustard oil is considered to be invigorating and warming. Naturally therefore, it is also a treatment for rheumatism. And since mosquitoes find its pungent odour unbearable, mustard oil also acts as a mosquito repellent!

What's in a Name?

There are differing opinions about the origin of the English word 'mustard'. The most popular is that it is a contraction of the Latin *mustum ardens* meaning 'burning wine'. This refers to the spicy 'hotness' of the crushed mustard seeds and the French practice of mixing the ground seeds with *must*, the freshly pressed fruit juice used for making wine.

Language	Name		
English	White mustard	Black mustard	Brown mustard, Indian mustard
Botanical	Brassica alba, Sinapis alba	Brassica nigra	Brassica juncea
Sanskrit	Siddhartha, gaura sarshapa	Sarshapa	Rajika
Bengali	Shaada sharshe	Kalo sharshe	Sharshe
Gujarati	Safed rai	Rai	Rai, sarsva
Hindi	Safed rai	Banarasi rai	Rai, sarson
Marathi	Mohori pandari	Mohori	Pivali siras
Tamil	Kadugu	Kadugu	Kadugu
Telugu	Avalu	Avalu	Avalu
Kannada	Sasivey	Kari sasivey	Sasivey
Malayalam	Vella kadugu	Kadugu	Kadugu

Mustard oil is also popular as a cooking medium, especially in many parts of North and East India. In fact, in Orissa and Bengal, mustard oil is to the local cuisine what coconut oil is to Kerala and south coastal Karnataka – indispensable. And like coconut oil, it is relished for the very thing that makes many other people dislike it – its strong, unmistakable flavour. In fact, many Bengalis will swear that if Bengali food is not cooked in mustard oil, it loses its 'Bengali-ness'. The famous economist and Nobel Laureate Amartya Sen said in an interview that he never fails to replenish his stock of mustard oil every time he comes to India!

The Saag-a of Nutrition

There is a very good reason why those Chinese coolies labouring on the Great Wall of China thousands of years ago made mustard greens (the leaves of the mustard plant) a part of their daily diet. It is also the reason why these pungently delicious greens are such a

favourite with the Punjabi farmer. Actually it is not one but eight very good reasons because these greens are packed with eight vitamins! Of these, five are B vitamins – B1 (thiamine), B2 (riboflavin), B3 (niacin), B6 (pyridoxine) and folate or folic acid (B9). The other three are beta-carotene, the raw material that the body converts to Vitamin A (one cup of these greens has as much as 60 per cent of your daily requirement), Vitamin C (one cup has your entire daily requirement!) and Vitamin E.

Did I say eight reasons? Make that fifteen, because mustard greens are also loaded with seven important minerals – magnesium, calcium, potassium, iron, copper, phosphorus and manganese. They are also an excellent source of dietary fibre. And like the seeds, mustard greens are powerful disease fighters because they are loaded with a chemical called sulphoraphane, a compound of sulphur. Studies have shown that this compound has anti-carcinogenic properties; so much so that in the information on cancer-fighting foods listed on the official website of the John Hopkins School of Health, sulphoraphane is described as triggering 'enzymes that block carcinogen damage to your cells' DNA'. The website goes on to say, 'Population studies show that the more cruciferous vegetables (like mustard) you eat, the lower your risk of cancer in several sites, especially lung, stomach, colon and rectal cancers.'

Need I say any more?

Mustard the Mediator

Hyperaccumulators. No, it is not a term to describe people like Imelda Marcos! Hyperaccumulators are plants that absorb toxic heavy metals like chromium, lead, cadmium and zinc from the soil. And the process of using plants and trees to clean up and rejuvenate the environment is called phtyoremediation. The Indian mustard plant is one such hyperaccumulator, used regularly to gobble out toxic matter from areas that would otherwise have to be abandoned because they were so unsafe for human inhabitation. Consider this – in 1989, three years after the Chernobyl disaster, the Soviet government asked the International Atomic Energy Agency (IAEA) to assess the damage from radiation and the resultant health risks in the area surrounding the power plant. One of the findings was that radioactive metals were contaminating the soil, posing serious health hazards to humans. And it was mustard plants that

> **Mustard and Menopause**
>
> Mustard greens are especially good for women going through menopause. This is because they are an excellent source of calcium, magnesium as well as Vitamin B6 and folic acid (folate/Vitamin B9), all vital in the prevention of the bone loss and osteoporosis that usually occurs at this stage of life. Magnesium has also been shown to play a part in reducing stress and restoring normal sleep patterns. The Vitamin E in the greens helps to decrease the occurrence of hot flashes.

came to the rescue, ridding the soil of many toxic metals such as caesium and strontium.

So much residing inside such a tiny seed… you could say it is almost a universe. Which is why, in the famous parable of the mustard seed in the Bible (Mark 4:30–2), Jesus says, 'Whereunto shall we liken the kingdom of God? (It is) like a grain of mustard seed, which when sown in the earth, is less than all the seeds that be in the earth. But when it is sown, it groweth up, and becometh greater than all herbs…'

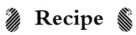

Recipe

As-You-Like-It Mustardy Curry

(Serves 4-5)

This is a simple delicious mustardy 'base' to which you can add raw or steamed vegetables or fruit and serve either as a side dish or a main curry, with rice or chapattis.

INGREDIENTS

3 cups diced vegetables or fruits of your choice

Base

2 large cups curds, beaten to a smooth consistency
½-¾ tsp mustard seeds
2-3 green chillies, finely chopped
1 tbsp fresh coriander, finely chopped
1 tsp salt (adjust to taste)

Tempering

1 tbsp oil
¾ tsp mustard seeds
1 dried red chilli, broken into pieces
A pinch of asafoetida
7-10 curry leaves

METHOD

Crush the mustard seeds till you get a coarse powder and add to the curd with all the other ingredients. To this base, you can add finely chopped or grated raw cucumber, diced banana, pineapple or steamed vegetables like *doodhi* (bottle gourd), white pumpkin, red pumpkin, cucumber and so on. The proportion is approximately 1 ½ cups of vegetable or fruit to 1 cup of the base – you can adjust the quantities according to your preference.

For the tempering, heat the oil, add the mustard seeds and the red chilli pieces. When the mustard seeds stop spluttering, add the asafoetida and the curry leaves. Remove from heat and add to the curry. Mix well.

Variation: You can substitute the curd with about a third of a fresh coconut, grated and ground to a chutney-like paste along with 2-3 dried red chillies and a tiny piece of tamarind. Add the mustard seeds and grind again, but only as long as is needed to crush the seeds. (Grinding for too long will alter the flavour of the mustard.) If you use this variation for the base, do not use diced bananas or fresh coriander while making the curry.

Turmeric and Ginger: The Gemini of Health

The plant kingdom is an infinitely dazzling – and confusing – masquerade. There are fruits pretending to be vegetables (brinjal, white pumpkin and tomato) and berries that are 'false' (watermelon), and still others that are not only false berries but also masquerading as vegetables (cucumber)! What you thought of as grain is actually the fruit of grasses (wheat and rice) and what you believed to be nuts are not nuts at all – some are a kind of fruit called drupe (coconut and almond) while others are actually legumes (peanut).

If you thought bananas grew on trees, think again – because they grow on what are actually giant herbs that are mistaken to be trees. (Incidentally, the banana is yet another of those false berries!) And the cabbage is actually a collection of leaves. You may think you're looking at just one pineapple (or for that matter, one fig) but it is actually a collection of many little fruits (or drupelets) that are conniving with each other to look like one fruit. Then there are flowers posing as vegetables – though in all fairness, in the case of the cauliflower, the name does give you a hint about its true identity. There are even leaves purporting to be flowers – for example, bougainvillea and anthurium.

But it seems that it is the stems that are the most cunning and clever impersonators of them all and some of their finest acts of subterfuge are played out when they go underground. For this is where, often aided and abetted by the leaves, they swell up and become bulbs (onion, garlic). Or they morph into things that are sometimes mistaken to be roots, but are not roots at all – like tubers (potato) and corms (colocasia). Or rhizomes, of which two are superstars of healing and nutrition – ginger and turmeric.

Sisters of the Orient

'Vasco da Gama, a gentleman of your household came to my country, whereat I was much pleased. My country is rich in cinnamon, cloves, ginger, pepper and precious stones. That which I ask of you in exchange is gold, silver, corals and scarlet cloth.'

Message from the Zamorin of Calicut to King Manuel I of Spain, which Vasco da Gama carried with him when he returned to Spain from India in 1499.

'I allow you, O bhikkhus, the use of roots as medicine — turmeric, ginger, orris root, white orris root, ativisa, black hellebore, usira root, bhaddamuttaka and whatsoever other roots are used for medicine and impart an appetizing flavour to foods…'

From the second book of the *Vinaya Pitaka*, the Buddhist scripture about monastic rules for monks and nuns.

The reason why ginger and turmeric are so similar in appearance is because it is a family resemblance — they both belong to the *Zingiberaceae* family. In fact, the ginger's botanical name — *Zingiber officinale* — is a derivative of this family name. And both *Zingiber* and *Zingiberaceae* provide the clue to the birthplace of the two siblings because these names are said to be derived from the ancient Tamil name for ginger — *injiver*.

Now both ginger and turmeric have been around on this planet for so long that some experts say that they originated even before recorded history. And though the broad region of their origin is said to be somewhere in South Asia or East Asia, the exact locations are the subject of much debate. Some experts say that it is almost certain that turmeric originated in India. Others are of the opinion that ginger may be a native of China — it was certainly known in China since the tenth century BC and is mentioned in the writings of Confucius (551-479 BC) as both medicine and spice. Its etymology however seems to point to South India as a possible birthplace.

Auspicious Twosome

In rural Tamil Nadu, during the harvest festival of Pongal, fresh turmeric and ginger saplings are tied to the neck of the *pongal panai* (the earthenware pot in which the *pongal* — a traditional dish made by boiling rice with green gram — is cooked). It is said that the turmeric is auspicious while the ginger represents the spice of life!

But irrespective of whether they are native Indians or not, both ginger and turmeric permeated the very fabric of life in ancient India. Ginger was hailed as *visvausadha* ('medicine of the world') and turmeric was of such importance as medicine, spice and in religious rituals that it is mentioned in the *Garuda Purana*, the *Devi Bhagavatam*, the *Vishnu Sutra*, the *Jaina Sutras*, in Tantric texts and in the Buddhist scripture called the *Vinaya Pitaka*. Of course, the two rhizomes were featured prominently in several Ayurvedic texts all the way from the *Charaka Samhita* and the *Sushruta Samhita* to the sixteenth-century *Bhavaprakash Nighantu*, compiled by Emperor Akbar's court physician, Pandit Bhava Mishra

And like many spices of Indian origin, both ginger and turmeric travelled aboard the ships of ancient Arabian spice merchants, reaching faraway lands in the Middle East and Europe. So they are

mentioned in the *Assyrian Herbal*, a botanical encyclopaedia compiled during the reign of King Ashurbanipal (668-633 BC) of Assyria, and were among the sixty-four varieties of herbs, spices and vegetables grown in the royal gardens of King Merodach-Baladan II who ruled Babylon from 721 BC to 710 BC.

In Europe, they found favour with the ancient Greeks and Romans as spice and as medicine. But though both ginger and turmeric figured in *De Re Coquinaria* (*The Art of Cooking*), said to be the world's oldest cookbook and compiled around the first century AD by Apicius, ginger was by far the more popular spice.

By the time the Crusades began at the end of the eleventh century, ginger was so popular in Europe that the street in the Swiss town of Basel which was the centre of spice trade was named *Imbergasse*, meaning 'ginger alley'! And it was a precious spice, less expensive than only pepper and a pound of it costing as much as the price of one sheep.

In comparison, turmeric – even though it was used in biblical times to make perfume – remained a relatively obscure spice in Europe, and was popular only in Spain. But in all of Asia and the Middle East, it reigned supreme not only in the kitchen and the medicine chest but also in the temple!

Turmeric – India's Other Gold

It is an ironic reality that we in India often begin to take our indigenous medicines seriously only when the West starts to do so – and turmeric is a perfect example. For thousands of years, it has been a mighty healer in Indian, Chinese and Unani systems of medicine. Yet it has moved to centre stage only in recent times, after modern medicine 'discovered' its astonishing therapeutic powers.

According to a 2005 article in the *Wall Street Journal* titled 'Common Indian Spice Stirs Hope', 256 research papers on turmeric had been published in the space of just that one year. Actually, this should not come as a surprise because the list of diseases that turmeric can both prevent and help to treat is breathtaking. To name only a few: Alzheimer's disease, cystic fibrosis, rheumatoid arthritis, Crohn's disease, ulcerative colitis. And cancer. The active ingredient responsible for this wealth of healing is also responsible for the beautiful golden-yellow pigment that turmeric yields and it is called curcumin.

Studies show a link between the frequent use of turmeric and the lower rates of childhood leukaemia and cancers of the breast, prostate glands, lung and colon. In fact the significantly lower rates of childhood leukaemia and prostate cancer in Asia (in India, prostate cancer is a rare occurrence), has been attributed to the regular and frequent consumption of turmeric. Equally important is the finding that, in the treatment of breast cancer, turmeric can augment the effects of chemotherapy and may prove to play an important role in slowing down the tumours spreading to the lungs.

The evidence is also compelling that regular consumption of turmeric offers protection against heart disease, for two reasons. First because it lowers bad cholesterol (LDL) while raising the levels of good cholesterol (HDL). Second, turmeric is a very good source of Vitamin B6 (pyridoxine), which plays a vital role in lowering the risk of the hardening of arteries and therefore of heart disease. Turmeric also improves the functioning of the liver and is a great brain food and experts think that perhaps the reason why the incidence of Alzheimer's disease is much lower in Asian countries is because of the regular consumption of turmeric.

Perhaps the ultimate certificate of turmeric's health-protective powers is that fact that turmeric tea is a very popular drink in Okinawa. This chain of islands in Japan shot to fame in 2001 when the results of a twenty-five-year-long study of the islanders showed that not only did they have life expectancy that was among the longest in the world, but that they also live happy, healthy lives. Compared to Westerners, they have an 80 per cent lower chance of heart disease, 60 per cent fewer hip fractures, much lower risks of dementia and hormone-dependent cancers such as breast and prostate cancer. One of the main factors that contributed to this was… yes, their diet!

Holy Haldi

Kanchani, meaning the Golden One. Varavarnini – one of the many names of the Goddess Kali. Gauri – one of the names of the Devi. And all these are also the Sanskrit names of turmeric – a very good indication of its importance in Hinduism. Like the Devi, the presence of turmeric is all-pervading. It is the symbol of purity, fertility and prosperity and because of its colour, also of the sun. (Perhaps one reason why turmeric is associated with purity is

---

Did You Know…

- That the bright-yellow colour in American mustard is because of the presence of turmeric?
- That in five thousand pages of elaborate notes that he wrote on everything from airplanes to painting techniques, Leonardo da Vinci recommended the combining of turmeric and verdigris to get 'a fine green'. (Verdigris is the green coating or patina that forms on copper, brass or bronze when they are exposed to air or seawater over a period of time.)

because long before Western medicine discovered them, our ancients knew of its antiseptic and antibacterial properties!)

So turmeric is one of the ingredients most often used in Hindu rituals. It is used to anoint the deities and is an integral part of the *puja* offerings. Rice grains that are used during religious ceremonies are often stained with turmeric.

It is also used to bless and consecrate almost every auspicious Hindu occasion or celebration, especially weddings. For example, it is a popular custom to stain the four corners of the wedding invitation card with turmeric paste. In South Indian weddings, you could say that turmeric is almost as important as the priest. In Tamil Nadu, the *pallav* of the bride's sari is filled with symbols of prosperity and fertility. These include fruits, betel nuts… and turmeric. The *thaali* – a traditional gold pendant that married women wear in South India – is strung on a thread dipped in turmeric. It is the practice in some communities that during the wedding ceremony, this thread, accompanied by a plate of turmeric-stained rice, is passed around. Every guest touches the *thaali* with both hands as a blessing for the couple and then takes a handful of the rice to throw over the couple's heads after the ceremony is over.

In many parts of India, especially the North, the bride is given a ritual bath before the wedding, during which she is first anointed with a paste made of *haldi* (turmeric), *besan* (Bengal gram flour) and milk, and then bathed. It is said that the purpose of using turmeric is twofold. The first is to bless the bride – since turmeric is considered auspicious. And the second is to make her look beautiful, since turmeric is said to be very good for the skin.

And almost always in these ceremonies and rituals, turmeric partners with another avatar of itself. Called *kumkum* (or *kumkuma*), this is turmeric powder treated with slaked lime (calcium hydroxide) to turn it into a brilliant vermilion red. Together, they are smeared on the divine and the human alike. The offering of *haldi-kumkuma* is also a popular tradition in South India. On festive occasions (or sometimes even at the end of an ordinary visit), the lady of the house offers *haldi* and *kumkum* to the female guests just as they are about to leave. It is said to symbolize the hostess's parting wishes of good fortune and prosperity for her visitors.

Turmeric Tips

- Never add turmeric directly to hot oil. It will immediately burn and lose all its flavour. So, if you are adding turmeric to a tempering *(tadka),* do so after taking the oil off the fire.

- Turmeric stains are the most stubborn stains to remove so tackle them immediately by liberally dousing the area with lemon juice.

- Turmeric powder is a good repellent for ants. Just sprinkle a line of turmeric powder to cordon them off.

- Gold jewellery will sparkle if boiled for a couple of minutes in water to which half a teaspoon each of turmeric powder and detergent have been added.

What's in a Name?

The turmeric's botanical family name – *Curcuma* – is said to come from its yellow colour. In many parts of the world like the Middle East, this colour was reminiscent of a more familiar spice, saffron. (In fact, in English, turmeric is sometimes also called Indian saffron.) So the word *Curcuma* is said to be a derivative of *al kurkum*, which was once the Arabic name for saffron. The word 'turmeric' is considered to be a derivative of the French *terre-mérite* which in turn is derived from the Latin *terra merita*, meaning 'meritorious earth'. Again, experts believe this is a reference to yellow ochre, the mineral pigment in clay.

There is some debate about the origin of ginger's botanical name – *Zingiber officinale*. (The English 'ginger' and its name in almost all European languages is derived from this.) Some feel that *Zingiber* is from the Sanskrit *shringavera* as well as the Pali *singivera*, which both mean 'shaped like a horn'. But others think that *shringavera* and *singivera* are themselves from the much older Dravidian word for ginger – *inji*.

Language	Name		
	Turmeric	Ginger (fresh)	Ginger (dried)★
English	Turmeric, Indian saffron	Ginger, fresh ginger	Dried ginger
Botanical	Curcuma longa, Curcuma rotunda	Zingiber officinale	Zingiber officinale
Sanskrit	Harida, nisha, gauri, kanchani, aushadhi.	Adraka	Katugranthi
Bengali	Halud	Ada	Sont
Gujarati	Halad, haldar	Adu	Sunth
Hindi	Haldi	Adrak	Saunt, sont
Marathi	Halad	Aale, shuntya	Sunt
Tamil	Manjal	Inji	Shukku
Telugu	Haridra, pasapu	Allam, allamu, allamu chettu	Shonti
Kannada	Arshina, arshana	Shunti, hasi shunti	Vona shunti
Malayalam	Manjal	Inchi	Chukku

★ *In many parts of India especially the North, dried ginger is used for certain dishes and as medicine. Hence, different names are used to differentiate between dried and fresh ginger.*

Ginger – The Great Medicine

'And they shall be served round with vessels of silver and goblets that are as flagons, flagons of silver which they shall mete out! And they shall drink therein a cup tempered with Zingabil (ginger).'

Description of Paradise in the Holy Quran.

Ginger's many Sanskrit names sound like a grand drum roll, as if they are heralding the arrival of a mighty emperor or a great queen. *Adraka, anupama, apakrishnaka, chandrakhya, cukku, gulmamula, kandara, katubhadra, mahaushadha, sringavera, sringveradrakam, sunti, sushakaka, vishwabeshaja, visvausadha.* And among these names, two are of particular significance: *mahaushadha*, or 'the mighty medicine' and *vishwabeshaja* or 'the universal medicine'. They indicate the importance of ginger's medicinal properties in the ancient systems of medicine.

According to the renowned Ayurvedic practitioner, Maya Tiwari, ginger carries in it the power of the earth's fires. Because of this it is used in Ayurveda to stoke digestive fires, stimulate dispirited appetites and to treat all kinds of digestive disorders such as flatulence, dyspepsia, colic and nausea resulting from biliousness. It is also used as a cardiac tonic and to treat respiratory problems such as coughs and colds and bronchitis, and in treating inflammatory disorders like arthritis and rheumatism.

In Unani and Chinese systems of medicine, ginger occupies a place of equal importance. It is listed as a special drug in *The Canon of Medicine,* compiled by Avicenna (or Ibn Sina), the eleventh-century Arab doctor, poet, philosopher-scientist and astronomer. Ginger is mentioned in the *Shennong Bencao Jing*, the herbal pharmacopoeia compiled by the Emperor Shen Nung around 3000 BC, considered to be the foundation stone of Chinese medicine. Even the physicians of ancient Rome used ginger as medicine – Dioscorides (AD 40-90) listed it in his *De Materia Medica* as an antidote to poisoning and as a digestive.

Not surprisingly, modern research corroborates all of ginger's therapeutic properties. And according to these studies, the active ingredients responsible for these healing powers are also responsible for that unmistakable 'gingery' taste and smell. They are a group of phytochemicals called – what else but gingerols!

The reason why these chemicals are such potent disease fighters is because they have anti-inflammatory properties. Inflammation is the body's defensive and protective response to a harmful stimulus, which could be anything from a physical injury like a burn or a cut to the intrusion of foreign bodies, toxins, chemical irritants or pathogens like disease-causing bacteria or viruses. And inflammation can manifest itself in anything from a simple blister or boil to tuberculosis, rheumatoid arthritis, ulcers and other disorders of the digestive tract, or even heart disease. Studies have shown that ginger is amazingly effective in reducing the crippling pain, swelling and muscular discomfort experienced by people suffering from osteoarthritis or rheumatoid arthritis. There are also indications that ginger may help in treating heart disease by lowering cholesterol.

Gingerols impart two other important curative powers to ginger. The first is its ability to both prevent and treat nausea, vomiting and dizziness, caused by a whole host of conditions ranging from motion sickness to pregnancy. Because the Chinese knew this thousands of years ago, sailors on Chinese ships carried ginger plants and chewed on ginger to prevent seasickness! Research suggests that ginger could even reduce the severity and duration of nausea experienced during chemotherapy. Gingerols are also powerful antioxidants, and studies indicate that they may prove to be significant allies in the treatment of ovarian cancer and the prevention of colon and rectal cancers.

But the final word on these twin divinities of nutrition and healing is this. Yes, lace your *dals* and curries with turmeric because it is brain food and it will help you build a powerful force field against ill health. But do it also for the colour that will flood your curries – a glorious golden-yellow, which must surely have been stolen from the sun. Yes, add slivers of ginger in your buttermilk and brew a fine ginger tea because both are true protectors of your stomach and your heart. But also do it for that moment when your knife slices through a piece of ginger and the sharp, fresh, fabulous gingery aroma bursts forth and rushes up to delight your senses.

It is wise to eat to be healthy. But while doing so, take a detour to remember the other reason why we eat. (And cook!) So that we can touch, taste, smell and joyously exult in Nature's dazzling wealth.

Grandma's Pharmacy

The 'medicinal twins' have made their place not just in the great pharmacopoeias ancient and modern, but also in grandma's little pharmacy of home remedies. She has used them for everything from discouraging the growth of facial hair (turmeric) to easing menstrual cramps (ginger). Here are three of the more popular of those remedies.

Golden Nightcap

This is an excellent remedy for coughs, colds and especially for sore throats. It is best had just before going to bed. (You can also have it about 2-3 times during the day.)

The warm milk, sweetened with honey, is soothing and calming while the turmeric does its bit as an antiseptic, tackling all those microbes in your irate, infected passages. (Makes 1 cup)

Ingredients
1 cup milk
¾ tsp turmeric powder
(If available, whole turmeric is best. Substitute turmeric powder with a ½-cm piece of whole turmeric, crushed)

1-1 ½ tsp honey or sugar (honey is recommended because apart from being healthier than sugar, it is also anti-bacterial, acts as an expectorant and promotes sleep)

Method: Boil the milk and then lower the heat to simmer. Add the turmeric. Bring to boil again. If you are using sugar, add it now. Stir and remove from heat and allow to cool a little. If you are using honey, stir it in just before drinking.
This milk should be drunk as hot as possible for best results.
Variation: A quickie version is to mix about ¼ teaspoon of turmeric in a spoon of honey and have it 2-3 times a day.

Ginger Tea

Try this simple tea to alleviate nausea, calm that heaving stomach and to get relief from arthritic pain. (Makes 1 cup)

Ingredients
1 tsp grated ginger
1 tsp honey
1 cup hot water

Method: Steep the ginger in the hot water for 10-15 minutes, covering the cup with a lid or saucer. Stir in the honey just before drinking.

Ginger Digestive

This is a simple and effective way to tackle both indigestion and lack of appetite.

Ingredients
2 tsp ginger juice
2 tsp lemon juice
A few pinches of rock salt

Method: Mix the ginger juice, lemon juice and rock salt and have a teaspoon of this mixture just before meals. If you find it a little strong, you can dilute it with about half a cup of water.
To extract ginger juice: Peel and grate about a 1 ½-inch piece of ginger. Then place the grated ginger in a clean piece of thin cloth (like muslin), tie the cloth into a pouch and squeeze well over a small bowl.

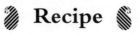 Recipe

Sweet and Sour Ginger Relish   **(Makes about 1 ½ to 2 cups)**

Called puli-inji *(tamarind-ginger), this relish from Kerala is regulation fare at* sadyas, *the traditional feasts served during festive occasions like Onam and weddings.*

As is often the case with such things, there are as many versions of this dish as there are fish in the sea — I have chosen the simplest one. Also, the quantity of chillies, ginger, jaggery and tamarind should be adjusted according to your preference, so I suggest that you experiment a couple of times before freezing on your own favourite version of this recipe.

INGREDIENTS

Tamarind, the size of a medium lemon, soaked in a cup of hot water for about 15-20 minutes
1 tbsp oil
¾ tsp mustard seeds
1 dried red chilli, broken into pieces
1 tsp urad dal
A pinch of asafoetida
½ teaspoon fenugreek seeds
8-10 curry leaves
5-6 green chillies, chopped
50 gm fresh ginger, finely diced
½ tsp turmeric powder
2-3 tbsp grated jaggery
1-1½ tsp salt (adjust to taste)

METHOD

Squeeze the tamarind well and extract the juice. (Make about 1½ to 2 cups, by adding more water.) Keep aside. In a pan, heat the oil and add mustard seeds and the red chilli. When the mustard seeds stop spluttering, add the *urad dal*. When it begins to turn golden-brown, add the asafoetida, fenugreek seeds and curry leaves. Now add the chopped ginger, chillies, turmeric powder and salt. Fry for about a minute or so, till the ginger and chillies begin to turn brown and crisp. Then add the extracted tamarind juice and the jaggery and allow this to boil till it turns thick.

The relish keeps for about a week in the refrigerator.

Jodi No.1 – Ginger and Turmeric

Hail the King – Mangoes

Antioxidants
Colour Me Healthy!

Did you know that the more the number of colours of fruits and vegetables on your plate, the more disease-resistant and healthier you are likely to be?

The reason is that fruits and vegetables are coloured the way they are because each colour is an indicator of the presence of potent disease-fighting phytochemicals called antioxidants.

And what is an antioxidant?

Well, let's first understand something called free radicals. Oxygen is essential for the survival of the human body and oxidation is the process during which the body's cells utilize oxygen. But there is a by-product of this process – unstable molecules of oxygen called 'free radicals'. (Free radicals are also created from environmental pollution, certain industrial chemicals and smoking.). The state of instability is because each of these molecules has an electron missing, which also makes them scavengers, on the hunt to fill that electron gap. So, they 'attack' other molecules and thus set off a 'chain reaction' causing more and more free radicals to be formed. The ensuing damage to the body's cells is known to be associated with hundreds of diseases, including heart disease, cancer and age-related diseases.

Antioxidants function as the body's bomb-disposal squads because they 'defuse' these free radicals by interacting with them, thus rendering them harmless and ending the chain reaction. Now, though there are enzyme systems in the human body that are antioxidants, they can function only with outside assistance, primarily from nutrients like vitamins (vitamins C and E) and minerals (selenium) or plant chemicals like beta-carotene, all of which must be acquired through food.

Antioxidants help combat virtually every chronic disease. In fact, studies increasingly indicate that antioxidants may be the new frontier in the fight against cancer, heart disease, diabetes, dementia, cataract and several age-related diseases like Alzheimer's disease, Parkinson's disease and the degeneration of the retina.

Antioxidants are present only in natural foods like fruits, vegetables, herbs, grain, nuts and seeds and they indicate their presence with the most breathtaking spectrum of colours. Hundreds of gorgeous shades of green, from the palest jade of the flesh of cucumbers to the deepest emerald of green leafy vegetables. A myriad of reds from the jewel-crimson seeds of a pomegranate to the vermilion of ripe chillies. Yellows all the way from the sun-kissed blonde of lemons to the deep gold of mangoes. Purples richer than a king's robes, pinks more delicate than a baby's lips, oranges picked out from a sunset sky. In other words, there are thousands and thousands of antioxidants.

The discovery and understanding of antioxidants is just a few decades old. And so it will be a while before we know even a small percentage of them, but we are already acquainted with some of the most

Antioxidants at a Glance

Colours	Primary Food Sources	Dominant Antioxidants	Health Benefits
All shades of red and pink	Tomatoes, apples, watermelon, pink grapefruit, pomegranate, guava (the variety that is deep pink inside)	Beta-carotene – the most well-known member of a family of over 500 anti-oxidants called carotenoids. Along with alpha-carotene and gamma-carotene, it is one of 50 carotenoids known as 'provitamin A' compounds. The human body converts them to Vitamin A.	Vital for good eyesight, reduces the risk of age-related cataract and deterioration of the retina. Also reduces the risk of certain cancers and helps prevent cardiovascular disease. Vital for female reproductive health since the highest concentration of it in the human body is found in the endocrine structure in the ovaries that produces progestogen.
		Lycopene – another carotenoid	May help prevent many kinds of cancer including cancers of prostate, pancreas, stomach, breast, cervix and lung. Also helps prevent heart disease, cataracts, and age-related macular degeneration.
		Vitamin C	Enhances the body's immunity to many diseases including infectious disorders and many types of cancer. It also promotes the healing of wounds.
Orange or deep yellow	Papaya, banana, apricot, peach, pineapple, orange, sweet potato, carrot, pumpkin, mango, jackfruit, corn etc	Beta-carotene	See above
		Lutein (also present in green vegetables, especially green leafy vegetables)	Along with another yellow antioxidant called zeaxanthin, is vital for protecting the eyesight of the elderly and help prevents cataracts and macular degeneration.
Green	Green vegetables and green leafy vegetables	Beta-carotene	See above
		Lutein	See above
All shades of purple, maroon, crimson, magenta etc	Purple grapes, plums, purple brinjal, *jamun* fruit, beetroot, some varieties of onions etc	Anthocyanin – members of a family of antioxidants called flavonoids	Anti-carcinogenic, lowers bad cholesterol (LDL) and increases good cholesterol (HDL), reduces the risk of stroke and heart disease, reduces the risk of age-related neurological disorders

powerful ones. We also know that a particular family of colours signals the presence of a particular group of antioxidants. (Though the same antioxidant can be present in more than one colour group.) But there are exceptions. Like Vitamin C – the chameleon among antioxidants – because it can be present in fruits and vegetables of almost any hue and often it prefers to cue its presence by tickling our taste buds with a sour taste.

Naturally, the question is how many colours does one need to eat to keep the body well stocked with antioxidants? Well, the current thumb rule is to try and have at least five colours of fruits and veggies in your diet. This would cover almost all the major antioxidants your body needs.

So, tank up your diet with fruits and vegetables. And look at it like this. Besides all those boring reasons that your mother gave you to eat up that spinach and beetroot, there is one other great reason. Just think how brightly and happily coloured your meals will be!

Mango: Superfruit!

How does that saying go? You can take an Indian out of a mango but you can never take a mango out of an Indian. Actually, there is no such saying, but there could well be. Let's say that you are traipsing across the Arctic wastes of Alaska, and you bump into one – an Indian, I mean. Don't say, 'Helloji!' or '*Namaste*', don't mention your fourth cousin from your mother's side to whom you think he/she might be related, don't even swap *gotrams*, ancestral village names or the best place to buy *mullagai podi* in Outer Alaska. Just utter this magic word. Mango. In a flash, you will see a strange light pop up in the stranger's eyes – the same one that was in Sir Galahad's when he sighted the Holy Grail, in Romeo's when he spotted Juliet at yonder window, and in Scrooge's when he spied a dime on the rubbish heap. And in a flash, you will be embraced like a long-lost fourth cousin. From your mother's side.

It's not for nothing that the mango is the national fruit of India and almost as much a nationwide passion as cricket and movies. The thing is, you can't get more Indian than the mango, a fact that is evident in its botanical name – *Mangifera indica*. *Indica* means 'originating from India' and *mangifera* is derived either from *mankai* or *mangai*, the Tamil word for mango, or the Malayalam word, *manga*.

The ancestors of the current-day mangoes grew wild on the north-eastern hills of Indo-Burma. Palaeobotanists at the Birbal Sahni Institute of Palaeobotany (BSIP), Lucknow found a sixty-five-million-year-old fossil of a mango leaf in the hills of Meghalaya, much older than the earlier fossil records of mango – also found in the same area – which were twenty-five to thirty million years old. So you could say that the mango is as old as the hills – literally!

Palaeobotany apart, it is said that that Lord Shiva made the mango tree appear on earth to please the cravings of his beloved Parvati. Another story goes that Lord Shiva and Goddess Parvati had quarrelled during a game of dice and Shiva, whose rage is legendary, put a curse on Parvati that she would lose her beauty. A desperate Parvati turned to Lord Vishnu for help. Vishnu advised her to appease her enraged beloved by doing penance under a mango tree on the banks of the Kampa River at Kanchipuram. Parvati followed

A King for Kings…

In the days of yore, mango orchards were almost mandatory in kingdoms and empires as a sign of prosperity. But of all the monarchs who patronized this fabulous fruit, the most besotted was Akbar. So much so that he had one lakh mango trees planted in an orchard that stands to this day as the famous Lakhi Bagh near Darbhanga in Bihar. When his son Jehangir lifted the ban on the grafting of fruit trees anywhere other than in the royal gardens, one of the first fruits to be grafted was, of course, the mango.

Lord Vishnu's advice and this not only helped her regain her beauty but also made her eyes so dazzlingly lovely that she earned herself the name Kamakshi or 'The Beautiful-Eyed One'. Goddess Kamakshi became the main deity of the centuries-old Kamakshi Amman temple in Kanchipuram.

Of course, Parvati's penance also ended the lover's tiff and she was once again united with her beloved Shiva who subsequently became known as Ekamranatha or Ekambareswarar, meaning 'Lord of the Mango Tree'. And it is as this avatar that he reigns as the main deity in the ancient Ekambareswarar Temple built by the Pallava kings – also in Kanchipuram. In the compound of this temple stands a mango tree which, according to the plaque near it, is 3,500 years old. It is said that the four branches of the tree represent the four *Vedas*, which is why each branch bears fruit of a completely different taste!

Buddha and the Mango

Nobody knew who her parents were or where she came from but because the little baby girl was found under a mango tree in a mango grove, they named her Ambapali or Amrapali. She grew up to be a beauty of great accomplishment and when she became a royal courtesan in Vaishali in Bihar, the capital of the ancient kingdom of Licchavi, the city was as renowned for the enchanting Amrapali as it was for the dazzling splendour of its royal court.

At the height of Amrapali's fame, a visitor came to Vaishali. He was an eighty-year-old man and they called him the Buddha. All the princes of Vaishali and the neighbouring kingdoms vied to invite him to their house. But he accepted only one invitation – that of Amrapali. So influenced was she by the Buddha's teachings that she renounced the world and became a *bhikku*. She also gifted the Buddha a mango grove, which still exists in a village called Amvara on the outskirts of Vaishali. And according to popular legend, so do many of the mango trees under which the Buddha might have rested around 2,500 years ago!

The Buddha's associations with the mango are many. At Sravasti in Uttar Pradesh, where he spent twenty-five years of his life, the Buddha is said to have made a mango tree burst forth in blossom. He also created a white mango tree. Both events are depicted in stone sculptures in Bharhut in Madhya Pradesh dating to the mid-second century BC and in Sarnath dating to AD 6.

King of Nutrition

We know that the mango is called the King of Fruits, but would it be correct to call it the King of Nutrition? Absolutely, even though not many of us associate the word 'nutritious' with mangoes, especially the ripe ones. In fact, the natural tendency to gorge on them brings on stern warnings that your gluttony might be punished with skin eruptions. Perhaps one reason for this could be that Ayurveda classifies the mango as a 'hot' food and recommends that it be eaten with milk to 'cool' things down! But in spite of all this, Ayurveda also considers the ripe mango to be calming, nourishing and full of *prana* or 'life energy'.

In fact, the mango is quite a 'hottie' even according to modern nutritionists. In 2009, Dr Paul Gross, popularly known as the 'berry doctor' because of his authoritative work on the nutritive value of fruits, published a book called *Superfruits*. As the title indicates, the book is a compilation of twenty fruits that are loaded with nutrients and disease-fighting phytochemicals like antioxidants. And topping this list is none other than our beloved mango!

The most obvious sign of the mango's superfruit status is the golden colour of its delicious, juicy flesh. This colour indicates the presence of very high levels of beta-carotene -- the mango is one of the richest sources of this all-important phytochemical. So much so that one medium ripe mango (about 100 grams) can provide up to 100 per cent of your daily requirement of beta-carotene!

The mango is also an excellent source of Vitamin C -- in fact, weight for weight, some varieties of mango have equal or more Vitamin C than an orange! The mango is also rich in many of the B vitamins including Vitamin B6 (pyridoxine), needed for the production of serotonin, the 'thermostat' that regulates mood. So, you could say that the mango makes you both healthy and happy! And its calcium content almost equals that of the orange, while its potassium content rivals the banana's!

There is also one other thing that the mango is loaded with -- fructose, because of which it is traditionally considered a forbidden food for both diabetics and weight watchers. But in fact, studies have found that certain phytochemicals in the mango can actually

Is the Mango a Nut?

If the mango is a cousin of the cashew and the pista – all members of the *Anacardiaceae* family – shouldn't it also be a nut? Well, the botanists say no. For the mango – apart from being a fruit – is also a 'drupe', which means that it is a fruit that has just one large seed ('pit' or 'stone') surrounded by an outer fleshy part. (Some of the other drupes are olive, coffee, plum, cherry, peach, apricot, almond and coconut.) Anyway, this much is for sure – even if the mango isn't a nut, there are millions of us who are nuts about it!

help protect against the onset of diabetes (see 'Mango the Medicine' section). Equally surprisingly, mango figures in the list of foods permitted for diabetics on the websites of the American Diabetes Association and the Mayo Clinic! Perhaps it is to do with the fact that mango is rich in dietary fibre, always a boon for diabetics.

Mango the Medicine

Maybe we can now accept that the mango is a wonderfully nutritious fruit. But it is still difficult for many of us to believe that it has medicinal properties. Well, Dr KM Nadkarni's *Indian Materia Medica*, an authoritative treatise on ancient systems of medicine like Ayurveda and Unani, has an astounding list of the mango's healing qualities. The fruit (ripe and unripe), seed, root, bark, leaf and even the smoke from the burning of mango leaves are used as cures for a whole host of ailments, minor and major – cracked heels, asthma, chronic dysentery, piles, excessive menstrual bleeding, gonorrhoea, diabetes, burns, even loss of voice, to name just a few. And Dr Nadkarni says that 'a confection prepared out of the juice of the ripe fruit with the addition of sugar and aromatics is a nice restorative tonic'. If you are still not impressed, the powder of dried mango flowers can even be used as a fumigant to get rid of mosquitoes!

Modern medicine is also waking up to the therapeutic benefits of the mango. A study conducted in 2006 at the University of Queensland, Australia indicates that ripe mangoes contain chemicals that act in a manner similar to the drugs used for treating diabetes and cholesterol. And the presence of a plethora of antioxidants (including twenty-five different kinds of carotenoids, according to Dr Gross) in the mango makes it a mighty powerful ally in the fight against a host of serious ailments including coronary disease, age-related eye diseases like cataract, and cancer.

In the Raw!

It's not just the ripe mango that is such a nutritional superstar. The tart, perky, unripe or 'raw' mango, such an integral part of Indian cuisine, is no different. It is rich in pectin, the soluble dietary fibre that helps reduce cholesterol. It is also an excellent source of Vitamin C – the sour taste will tell you that – so much so that, like the lemon, it is used to treat scurvy. In addition, according to Ayurveda, the raw mango is very effective in treating gastro-intestinal disorders. That is the reason why dried raw mango

---

A Dentist in Your Mango Tree?

You wouldn't find toothbrushes and toothpaste in my grandmother's bathroom. (Except when we would visit, of course!) And that was because the job of dental hygiene was done by mango leaves! And the process went something like this…

The centre rib of a thoroughly washed leaf would first be carefully removed and saved for later. Then, the two halves of the leaves would be made into a tight little roll and rubbed vigorously over the teeth just like a toothbrush. Next, the roll would be popped into the mouth, chewed for a minute or two and then spat out. Finally, the tongue would be thoroughly scraped with the rib of the leaf. Research has shown that chemicals present in the mango leaves are particularly effective in fighting bacteria in the mouth, especially those that cause plaque and gum disease!

powder, or *aamchur*, is a popular condiment in Indian cooking, especially in North India – both for the delicious tartness that it imparts to the food and for its digestive powers.

But the lesser-known fact about the unripe mango is that, according to Ayurveda, unlike the ripe mango, it is 'cooling' in nature. So much so that when the hot, dry winds of summer blow, it is used to quench thirst and protect the body from heat stroke and dehydration.

Will the Real King Please Stand Up?

Bemissal. Amrapali. Prince. Julie. Laila Majnu. All names of Hindi films? What about Swarnrekha, Sundari, Sindhura, Neeleshwari, Aruna? The names of heavenly *apsaras* who danced in Lord Indra's court? Gopal Bhog, Mohan Bhog, Raj Bhog and Krishna Bhog – *prasadams* at famous temples of Lord Krishna? And Gulab Khas, Mallika, Lab-e-Mashhoq, Hussanara – enchanting courtesans who once graced the *mehefils* of Lucknowi *nawabs* and Mughal emperors?

Perhaps. But they are all also the names of different varieties of mango. In India alone, we grow at least 500 commercial varieties – 82 of them in South India, and according to some estimates, another 150 in Uttar Pradesh alone. India is the world's largest producer of mangoes, growing over 11 million tonnes of the fruit annually – which accounts for over 50 per cent of the global mango crop – over an area of 16,000 square kilometres. The leading mango-growing states are Andhra Pradesh (highest yield per acre) and Uttar Pradesh (highest number of acres under mango cultivation).

To ask an Indian which variety of mango is the best is to ask for trouble. In Karnataka, they will swear by the crunchy Totapuris (also called Bangalora) with their pointy parrot-beak shapes from which they get their names. Others will say that it is the fat, rotund Malgovas, their dark-green skins belying the succulent golden-yellow juicy flesh inside. Many will avow that the true king is none other than the world-famous, smooth-fleshed Alphonso from Maharashtra's Devgad and Ratnagiri districts. Still others will insist that it is the large, pale-gold Banganpalli from Andhra Pradesh that is nonpareil.

The Mango and the Paisley

What would a town in Scotland have to do with the mango?

The mango is an ancient and popular motif in Indian textiles, especially in the exquisite Kashmiri ('cashmere') shawls. They were first introduced to the West when members of the East India Company took them back to England as gifts. But the lady who made these shawls a rage in eighteenth-century Europe was Emperor Napoleon Bonaparte's wife, Josephine, who loved them so much that she owned sixty of them, and some of these had cost as much as twelve thousand francs!

Naturally, only an empress could afford such expensive tastes and soon there was a need to make cheaper, assembly-line, local versions of these shawls that were within the reach of the common man. A need that was met by the ingenuity of a famous silk-weaving Scottish town.

The name of the town? Paisley.

The shawls subsequently went out of fashion but the mango motif – or the 'paisley' – remained an international symbol of elegance.

What's in a Name?

According to the *Puranas,* one of the arrows of love that Kamadeva, the God of Love, shoots from his bow is made of the lacy, spike-like mango blossoms. And so, many of the mango's lesser-known Sanskrit names are inspired by Kamadeva, like *kamanga, kamaphala, kamarasa* and *kamavallabha.*

Language	Name (Ripe Mango)	Name (Raw/unripe mango)
English	Mango	Raw mango
Botanical	Mangifera indica Linn	Mangifera indica Linn
Sanskrit	Amra, amra, aam, kanka, kamaphala, kokilavasa, chuta, phalashreshtha, phalotpati, madhulaka, vasantaduta etc	Apakva amra
Hindi, Punjabi, Bengali	Aam	Kairi, kaccha aam
Gujarati	Ambo	Keri
Marathi	Amba	Kairi
Tamil	Mambazham, mambalam	Mangai
Telugu	Amramu, mamidipandu	Mamidi kai
Kannada	Mavina hannu	Mavina kai
Malayalam	Mambazham, manga	Pacha manga

Mangoes, Great and Small…

Two of the smallest and largest varieties – *moti dana* (meaning 'grain of pearl'), weighing two grams, and *jam-e-jam* (four kilos) were grown by fruit farmer Javed Farukh Faridi in his farm in Rataul near Delhi.

But the man from Uttar Pradesh will swear only by the fabulous Dussehri. It is said to have originated in the village Dussehri – where else?! – near Malihabad where the mother tree is said to be still standing. And it is in Malihabad that Haji Kaleemullah Khan lives. He is a descendant of a family that has been in the mango trade for three hundred years. In his nursery stands an eighty-year-old mango tree on which he has grafted over three hundred different varieties of mango, ranging from Totapari to Alphonso! In 2008, Khan was awarded the Padma Shri for this particular achievement. The tree in Khan's orchard is bettered only by the one in Burail village near Chandigarh – 32 feet in girth with branches up to 80 feet in length, covering an area of almost 22,000 square feet and producing about 17,000 kilos of mangoes every year!

Everyman's Delight

Aam, ambuwa, ambo, amba, mavu, mampalam, mangai. The mango pervades every corner of India, every crevice of the Indian soul. According to one interpretation, the Sanskrit name for mango,

amra, means 'of the people', and so the mango is – a fruit beloved of every Indian. Which is perhaps why, in Hindi, the average person on the street is called *aam aadmi*!

Indeed, the mango is woven into the very fabric of our lives. From the *ambi* (mango) motif in Andhra Pradesh's exquisite Kalamkari prints to thick, delicious *aam ras*, eaten traditionally with hot *puris* or *puranpolis*. From the *mehendi* designs that decorate a bride's hand to *panha*, the traditional sherbet made from unripe mango to beat the summer heat. From the songs of spring and longing to *aam papad* (a kind of layered sweet-and-sour *halwa* made from unripe mango) and *aamchur* (dried unripe mango powder). From the *torans* (strings) of dark-green mango leaves that signal every auspicious or festive occasion to *maanthulir*, the name given to the crimson and green colour combination inspired by the tender mango and used in Kanchipuram saris. From jars of hot, red *avvakai* pickle to the mango-shaped *zari butis* on Banarasi saris.

In our house, the mango season begins around the festival of Ugadi when the first green baby mangoes are fattening on the trees. From then on, it is one long, glorious parade. First, unripe mangoes take over the kitchen, usurping the role of tamarind and lemon in every conceivable manner. Lemon rice takes on a new avatar when the tartness of lemon is substituted with the sourness of fresh grated raw mango. Soon, the kitchen shelves begin to groan with the weight of pickles and chutneys in every conceivable nuance of sweet and sour. Then when the mango ripens, turning different shades of luscious gold inside and outside, and the air stands still and breathless and it's too hot even to think, we scoop and suck and slurp and dive again and again into the delicious, golden flood, surfacing only to make room for more…

Mangoes of all varieties were welcome in our home as we travelled around the country because of my father's job in the Indian Railways. Alphonsos rubbed shoulders with Banganpallis, Malgovas shared the same table as Chausas. Dussehris mingled with Raspuris. Mallikas slummed it with Pairis, and Langdas bedded down with Neelams. Even the mongrel *kantri-kais*, delicious despite the fact that we didn't know their parentage, were never turned away. As long as you could gently cradle them in your hands and they were warm and heavy with the promise of the sweet coming together of earth and sun and air and water, who cared? And if you could tenderly sniff them and feel the mango-ness flood your nostrils and all of your senses, who bothered? And if you could then eagerly, impatiently sink your mouth into their luscious golden flesh, who gave a damn? A mango by any name would do.

So it is befitting that this paean to the mango ends with the name of one more variety of mango. Rumani. Meaning 'romance', 'romantic' or 'soulful'. How apt! For what better thing is there than a mango to breathe a little bit of *rumani* into the most boring meal, the drabbest sari *pallu*, the most uninspired verse, the dullest day, the dreariest life…?

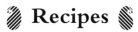 Recipes

Mustardy, Coconutty Mango (Serves 4-5)

A no-cook, tangy, unusual dish from my mother's cornucopia of recipes and a particular favourite in south coastal Karnataka!

INGREDIENTS

½ a coconut, scraped or cut into small pieces for grinding
4-5 dried red chillies
1 tsp mustard
½ tsp turmeric powder (optional)
A ball of tamarind the size of a large pea, soaked in water
1 ½ tsp grated jaggery
(adjust according to the sweetness of the mangoes and how sweet you like the dish to taste)
4 medium-sized mangoes
(the desi, no-pedigree varieties work best, but any mango will do!)
1 tsp salt (adjust to taste)

Tempering
1 tbsp vegetable oil
½ tsp mustard seeds
1 dried red chilli, broken into pieces
7-8 curry leaves
A pinch of asafoetida

METHOD

Roast the dried red chillies on a *tava* over low heat for 2 minutes or till they begin to char and begin to give out a roasted aroma. Grind together with coconut and jaggery till you have a thick, coarse paste. Add the mustard seeds and grind for another minute or so till smooth. (Do not grind for too long as it will alter the taste of the mustard.) Add the turmeric powder, extract of the soaked tamarind and salt and mix well.

Peel and dice the mangoes. Take about a quarter of the diced mango and blend into a paste in the blender. Add to the ground coconut mixture along with the diced mango. Stir well. (Traditionally, the entire mango with the stone is used, but many people may find this messy to eat even though I think this is the best part!)

To temper, heat the oil. Add the pieces of dried red chilli, and when they begin to swell and change colour, add the mustard. Wait till the mustard stops spluttering, add curry leaves and asafoetida. After a few seconds, remove from fire and pour carefully over the mango-coconut mixture. Mix well. Serve with steamed rice or hot *chapattis*.

Raw Mango Panha

In many parts of North India, summer without panha, *a delicious, cooling drink made from raw mangoes (*kairi*), is unthinkable.*

INGREDIENTS

1 cup unripe mango, peeled and diced

1 ½ cups sugar

(Adjust to taste and according to the tartness of the unripe mangoes and how sweet you like the drink. You can substitute the sugar with the same amount of grated jaggery. This is not only healthier – see chapter on Jaggery for details – but the jaggery also lends a lovely flavour to the panha.)

Flavouring

¼ tsp saffron

½ tsp cardamom (elaichi) powder

A pinch of nutmeg (optional)

or ¾ tsp chaat masala

¼ tsp black salt or pepper (adjust to taste)

METHOD

Peel the raw mango, cut into pieces and boil till soft. Cool, then blend in the mixer till smooth. Add the sugar or jaggery and bring to a boil, stirring continuously till the sugar or jaggery dissolves. Now add your chosen flavouring and mix well. Cool again and store in a clean dry bottle. The syrup can be stored for over a month.

To serve: Add a tablespoon or more to a glass of chilled water and mix well. Decorate with a few mint leaves.

Variation: For a wonderful 'smoked' version – instead of boiling, roast the raw mango whole with the skin till the insides are cooked and squishy. Then follow the rest of the recipe.

Sweet and Sour Raw Mango Relish

This simple and delicious relish is also wonderfully versatile – you can serve it as an accompaniment for anything from dosas *and* chapattis *to* samosas *and cutlets, or use it as a sandwich spread, as a pickle, or simply eat it with hot steamed rice and a dash of ghee.*

INGREDIENTS

For the masala powder:

50 gm sesame seeds (preferably black sesame as they have a better flavour)

6-8 dried red chillies

2 medium-sized raw mangoes, washed, dried, peeled and cut into small pieces

1 tbsp vegetable oil

1 dried red chilli, broken into pieces

¾ tsp mustard seeds

METHOD

For the *masala* powder, separately dry-roast the sesame seeds and dried red chillies till they give out a roasted aroma. Grind together to a fine powder. Keep aside.

Heat the oil, then add the red chilli and the mustard seeds. When the seeds stop spluttering, add the curry leaves and asafoetida. Now add the mango pieces and stir for a few minutes till the pieces begin to turn transparent. Then add the salt, jaggery and about half a cup of water and simmer till the jaggery dissolves and the mango is cooked and tender. (Add more water if

A pinch of asafoetida
10-12 curry leaves
1 tbsp salt
¼ kg jaggery, broken into small pieces
(adjust to taste)
Water

necessary.) Taste it and if the mixture is very sour, add more jaggery and/or salt.

Now add the chilli–sesame-seed powder, stir well and cook for a few minutes till the mixture begins to bubble.

Remove from heat, allow it to cool, and store in a dry, airtight glass jar. Use only dry spoons and the relish will keep for at least two weeks.

Jackfruit: Jack of All Trades...and Master of Many

Thiruvananthapuram. Meaning 'City of the Lord Anantha'. My first visit was many years ago and I was soaking in the flavour of the city to use later on to create an advertising campaign for the Kerala tourism authorities. One of my most vivid memories is of the overpowering smell of jackfruit chips frying in hot coconut oil wafting from the handcarts that lined the road leading up to the Padmanabhaswamy temple.

As I rushed around sampling and buying ecstatically, I was consumed by a flood of childhood memories. Of summer holidays and my aunt frying jackfruit chips in a black *kadai* almost large enough to be a small swimming pool. Of the sinful indulgence of having jackfruit chips and coffee for breakfast. (Only I was allowed this, inciting my cousins to have heated arguments with my aunt as to why they weren't similarly favoured!) And of the strange sight of what looked like dried jackfruit seeds inside my cousins' school geometry boxes! Knowing that they could not be of much use in resolving the intricacies of Pythagoras's theorem, I quizzed my cousins about them and was told that the seeds were edible... to be nibbled whenever hunger struck. I remember trying a few, and indeed they were surprisingly delicious. It was a traditional culinary practice (and perhaps it is still prevalent) all over south coastal Karnataka (where my aunt and cousins lived) – to boil jackfruit seeds in salted water and then dry them in the sun. These dried seeds were stored away as emergency rations that were whipped out on a rainy day and turned into delicious curries and *bhajis*. Or then, put into children's geometry boxes as 'nibbling food'!

My love affair with the jackfruit is a lifelong one and you'd think that such a die-hard fan would know everything there is to know about it. But to my astonishment and delight, I found that what I know is just the tip of the... er, jackfruit. For example, I didn't know that the jackfruit originated in the rainforests of the Western Ghats. Or that the word 'jackfruit' comes from the Malayalam word for it, *chakka*. Maybe that was why, when the French Dominican monk Friar Jordanus visited India in 1328 and made acquaintance with the jackfruit, he referred to it as 'chaqui'.

I also didn't know that the first references to the jackfruit are found in Buddhist and Jain literature dating back to 400 BC. That it is mentioned in the *Mahabharata* and the *Ramayana*. That parts of a canoe found by archaeologists in Pattanam in Kerala at the site of what was once the ancient maritime city of Muziris (Muchiri Pattanam) and dating back to between 1300 BC and 100 BC was made from the wood of the jackfruit tree! That Parakramabahu the Great, the famous twelfth-century monarch of Sri Lanka, had a grove of 100,000 varieties of jackfruit trees and it was called *Lakshodyanaya* or 'the grove of 100,000 trees'. And that in ancient India, while the fruit was made into wine, the over-ripe seeds of the jackfruit combined with buttermilk, tamarind and the gruel resulting from boiling aged rice was considered an antidote for hangovers! That the Chinese thought likewise, considering the jackfruit pulp and seeds to be useful in overcoming the influence of alcohol on the system. Or that every part of the jackfruit tree – fruit, wood, leaves, roots, even the dreaded sticky white latex that oozes out of the fruit when it is cut – is of some use…

Jack the Sacred

When the king of Manipur, Bhagyachandra Maharaj (1763-1798), was in exile in the neighbouring kingdom of Assam, his legitimacy as the real king was questioned and he was asked to undergo a test – to single-handedly catch and tame a wild elephant. The distraught king prayed to Lord Krishna for help. And the Lord appeared to him in a dream and instructed him in the art of catching elephants. Lord Krishna also told the king that after his victory, he should have His image carved from the wood of an old jackfruit tree that was growing on the slopes of a nearby hillock called Kaina. The king followed the Lord's instructions and today, the idol stands in the beautiful twin-domed Sri Govindaji temple next to the royal palace in Manipur.

The jackfruit's associations with the divine and the holy are ancient and numerous.

One of the thirty-eight avatars of Lord Ganesha is Bala Ganapati who, in each of his four hands, holds objects that represent the earth's abundance and fertility. They are the banana, mango, sugarcane and, of course, the jackfruit! In Tamil Nadu, during the Tamil New Year, a set of three fruits called *mukkani* – the mango, the banana and the jackfruit – are considered auspicious and offered in ceremonies and rituals.

And in temple complexes in many parts of South India, the jackfruit is the *sthala vriksham* – the sacred tree of the shrine. The ancient Vishnu temple at Thirukkoodalur in Tamil Nadu is one of the 108 temples of Lord Vishnu mentioned in the Tamil hymns composed by the Alwar saints. Many years ago, when an attempt was made to cut a part of the jackfruit tree in the temple complex, a formation in the trunk resembling a conch (Vishnu's symbol) revealed itself. Ever since, devotees flock here to have a *darshan* of this tree.

At the Vishnu temple at Thrikodithanam in Kerala, which is another one of the 108 sacred shrines of Vishnu mentioned by the Alwar saints, the jackfruit tree near the eastern entrance is so old that it is affectionately called *ammachi plavu* or the 'mother jackfruit tree'! And deserving of its grand-old-dame status, during every festival season, the temple priests offer prayers under it before starting the ceremonies. It was in the hollow of another such *ammachi plavu* in the grounds of the Sri Krishna temple at Neyyattinkara near Thiruvanathapuram that the Travancore king Marthanda Varma hid when he was fleeing from his enemies.

The jackfruit tree features in places of worship outside India as well. Near Sri Lanka's ancient city of Kandy stands the famous Gadaladeniya Buddhist temple. The main entrance still has the jackwood doors that were put there over six hundred years ago, on which the original paintings are still visible. In Vietnam, the Tay Phuong Pagoda is famous for the over 70 jackwood statues of the Buddha and the Buddhist deities, Bodhisattvas, Vajrapanis and Arhants.

Jack the Nurturer

'…*rich, gluey and nutritive*…'

Description of the jackfruit by Dr John Fryer, seventeenth-century British physician in his account of his nine-year-long travels in South India.

Not too many people, not even its most passionate aficionados like me, would give the jackfruit very high marks in the nutrition department. But it is indeed of such high nutritional value that in Sri Lanka one of the foods believed to increase breast milk production in nursing mothers is tender jackfruit. And why not? Look at the nutrition that it packs in! Starting with loads of beta-carotene, which is indicated by the sumptuous yellow-gold colour of its insides. Apart from being one of the most powerful disease-fighting antioxidants, beta-carotene is also the raw material which the body converts into Vitamin A. And it is the modern world's greatest irony that the deficiency of a nutrient that is so abundantly and cheaply available causes millions of children in developing countries – including India – to go blind. But better late than never – the jackfruit's cache of beta-carotene is large enough for it to now be recommended in many ongoing campaigns to combat Vitamin A deficiency in Bangladesh. Incidentally, the jackfruit is the national fruit of Bangladesh.

Like so many other tropical fruits, jackfruit is also rich in dietary minerals like calcium, potassium and iron. In fact, it is said to contain more calcium and magnesium than the banana! The jackfruit is also an excellent source of complex carbohydrates and dietary fibre, making it a great energy food. And so, the jackfruit's nutritional profile – a balanced combination of energy-giving carbohydrates, dietary fibre and micronutrients and minerals – makes it the perfect staple food... which it is in many Asian countries, especially among the poor. A single jackfruit can be – as it often is – a meal for an entire family! And that is the reason why in Sri Lanka, it is popularly called 'the rice tree'.

The seeds of the jackfruit are equally nourishing. They are a good source of dietary fibre and certain B vitamins like Vitamin B1 (thiamine) and Vitamin B2 (riboflavin). According to some experts, they also contain vitamins A and C, and minerals like calcium, zinc, sulphur and phosphorus, making them the perfect nutritious snack. Now I know why jackfruit seeds were such regulars in my cousins' geometry boxes!

Jack the Medicine Man

If the jackfruit's nutritional prowess doesn't surprise you, then maybe this will. In December 1982, the Ministry of Environment and Forests of the Government of India set up an information system. One of its objectives was to catalogue India's immense wealth of medicinal plants and among the 7,637 plants listed was *Artocarpus heterophyllus* – or the jackfruit. According to the Ministry's website, it is used in Ayurveda, Unani, Sidha and folk medicine.

In fact, people all over Asia believe that almost every part of the jackfruit has some medicinal property. (Even though the rind has no medicinal use, it makes excellent cattle fodder not only because of its nutritional value but also because the cattle relish the taste!) In both Ayurveda and Chinese medicine, the ripe fruit is regarded as a nutritious and cooling tonic. In Sri Lanka, an infusion made from the leaves of the jackfruit tree is used for treating diabetes, and in Malaysia and the Philippines, the ash of the leaves is used for healing ulcers, boils and wounds. In Kerala, some even say that *kanji* eaten with 'spoons' made of jackfruit leaves is good for respiratory problems! Its root, bark and sap are used for treating an astonishing variety of ailments, including syphilis, intestinal worms, fever, diarrhoea, skin diseases and asthma. Even the more-sticky-than-chewing-gum white latex that oozes from the jackfruit when it is cut and is the bane of every jackfruit lover is used for healing sores and abscesses, even as a treatment for snakebite.

Jack the Artist

'The jaks . . . are such large and interesting fruits and the trees so well behaved that it is difficult to explain the general lack of knowledge concerning them.'
OW Barrett (1928)

What is common to the robes of a Buddhist monk and the boats that glide on the emerald-green backwaters of Kerala? The jackfruit tree of course! The wood of this tree is not only resistant to termites and fungi, it also seasons well and, when polished, becomes a lustrous yellow-gold shade, which deepens to a rich maroon over time. And so, all over Asia, for centuries, the wood of the jackfruit tree (or jackwood as it is sometimes called) has been the favourite of sculptors, wood carvers, inlay workers and furniture and boat makers.

The word *kettuvallam* is the amalgamation of two Malayalam words; *kettu* meaning 'to tie together' and *vallam* meaning 'boat'. And Kerala's famous *kettuvallams* are exactly that – planks of wood tied together with coir rope without the use of a single nail, a testimony to the genius of the state's ancient boat builders. And the wood used to make the hull is none other than jackwood. Once upon a time, these long, graceful boats plied Kerala's water-ways with cargos of rice and spices; today the *kettuvallams* have been converted into houseboats and their 'cargos' are mostly tourists!

Jackwood was also used to build and decorate many of Kerala's exquisite *tharavads* (traditional houses) and palaces. In the fabulous

What's in a Name?

When Captain Cook landed in Tahiti in 1768 on his first expedition on the HMS Endeavour, his botanist, Dr Daniel Carl Solander, chanced upon a local fruit. Impressed by its nutritive qualities, he and his friend, the naturalist Joseph Banks, persuaded King George III to introduce the fruit to his colonies in the West Indies, as food for the slaves who worked in the sugarcane plantations. The fruit was called the breadfruit.

Perhaps this was the reason why the father-and-son team of botanists on Cook's second voyage, Johann and Georg Forster, gave the breadfruit and its relatives the family name of *artocarpus* – derived from the Greek words *artos* meaning 'bread', and *karpos* meaning 'fruit'. And so the botanical name for the jackfruit, close relative of the breadfruit, is *Artocarpus heterophyllus*.

Language	Name
English	Jackfruit, jakfruit, jak
Botanical	Artocarpus heterophyllus, Artocarpus integrifolia
Sanskrit	Panasaphalam
Hindi	Katahal
Gujarati	Phanasa
Marathi	Phanas
Bengali	Kathal (ripe fruit), enchor (unripe fruit)
Tamil	Pala, pilapazham
Telugu	Panasa
Kannada	Halasina hannu (ripe fruit), halasina kai (unripe fruit)
Malayalam	Chakka

Padmanabhapuram palace near Thiruvananthapuram, one of the main tourist attractions is the massive, intricately carved central pillar in the Ekantamandapam ('chamber of solitude'), made from a single piece of jackwood.

And the monk's robes? Well, the jackwood, when boiled, yields a beautiful golden dye that has been traditionally used in many parts of Asia for dyeing the robes of Buddhist monks. In an ancient annual ceremony called *kathina*, started by the Buddha himself, the laity offers new cloth to the *bhikkus* (Buddhist monks). This is then cut, sewn, dyed and dried to become the monks' robes. And one of the dyes used, to this very day, is the dye from the jackfruit tree.

Jack the Musician

It is fairly common knowledge that the wood from the jackfruit tree is used to make *veenas*. The usual reason given for this is the particularly resonant quality of the wood. But one unusual explanation given is that the tradition started in ancient times when the wood was taken from jackfruit trees growing in temple courtyards because it was believed that they had absorbed the resonance of the temple bells! It is also used for making many Indian percussion instruments because the deeply interlocked grain of the wood resists cracking. So the *mridangam, thavil, kanjira, jamidika* and Kerala's famous *chenda* drums are all made from jackwood.

Actually, the jackfruit tree's wood has made music for hundreds of years not just in India, but all over Asia in a fabulous variety of string and percussion instruments. In Indonesia, the famous *gamelan* is a musical ensemble similar to an orchestra, and many of the instruments are made from the wood of the jackfruit tree. Jackwood is often used to make the Cebu guitars in the Mactan Island of the Cebu province of the Philippines, and these guitars are considered to be some of the finest in the world.

Underutilized, Underestimated Jack

In Thailand, the jackfruit is considered an auspicious tree. Its Thai name is *khanoon* and *noon* means 'support'. The tree is often planted at the back of the house and it is believed that its presence in the backyard increases one's good fortune.

So, for thousands of years, the jackfruit has grown all over Asia, providing nourishment, healing, even sustenance. Yet today, the jackfruit is in the United Nations' Food and Agriculture Organization's list of Neglected and Underutilized Species (NUS); plant species that are largely unexploited sources of income, employment and nutrition. Actually, NUS is a term that aptly describes how we Indians often view the enormous wealth of wisdom that is indigenous to our country. We have neglected and underutilized it to the extent that we have even forgotten much of it. Until such time as someone in the West 'discovers' it and we then wake up to its benefits. Like turmeric and *neem* and yoga! And perhaps one day it will be the much-misunderstood jackfruit.

Recipe

Sweet Steamed Jackfruit 'Cakes' (Serves 5-6)

These steamed cakes – or kadubu *as they are called in Kannada – are traditional favourites in south coastal Karnataka, and usually served for breakfast or as a snack.*

INGREDIENTS

¼ kg parboiled rice, washed and soaked overnight
15-20 deseeded and cleaned segments of ripe jackfruit, the riper the better
Grated jaggery to taste
(this is optional depending on how sweet the jackfruit and your tooth are. Add after tasting the batter.)
Banana leaves, washed and dried with the centre rib removed, and cut into 15-20 pieces, roughly 6 x 4 inches each

METHOD

Grind the parboiled rice, jackfruit segments and grated jaggery together (using water only if necessary) to a very thick, slightly coarse consistency. Place about 2 tablespoons of batter on a piece of banana leaf and fold into a 'packet'. Repeat till all the batter is used up. Place all the packets with the folded side down on an idli tray and steam for about 10 minutes in a pressure cooker without using the weight.

Variation: To make a 'cake', spread the entire batter in a cake tray or a shallow pan lined with a greased banana leaf, and steam for about 20 minutes. Cool the cake and cut into wedges.

This can be eaten hot or cold, plain or with hot melted *ghee* or even fresh coconut chutney. (In south coastal Karnataka, the leaves of the teak tree were also traditionally used to wrap these cakes before steaming. These leaves impart a deep reddish-maroon shade to the cakes.)

Jamun: The Real King of Fruits?

Jambudvipa. According to the *Puranas*, it is one of the seven continents of the world and the one in which India is located. *Dvipa* means 'land', 'island' or 'continent', and *jambu* is the name of the wondrous fruit tree that grew on this land, on the southern side of Mount Mahameru. A tree so mighty that its branches reached heaven and cast a shadow on the moon, and its trunk was the axis of the world. The tree bore the *jambu* fruit, which grew so abundantly that when the juice dripped to the ground, it became the Jambu River. And on the banks of this river lived the goddess Jambvadini.

As goddesses go, Jambvadini is easy to please because, according to the *Puranas*, her devotees merely have to think of her to make her happy. She is also a very benevolent and compassionate goddess who cures all diseases and blesses her devotees with health, wealth, happiness and prosperity. So naturally, the waters of the Jambu River were therapeutic and whoever drank it lived in contentment and good health. It is also said that when the juice of the *jambu* fruit was mixed with soil and water and exposed to sunlight, it turned into a kind of gold called *jambunada* that was so superior to all other gold that it was used by the *devas* to make ornaments! Jambudvipa may now be a name familiar only to Puranic scholars, but the *jambu* tree and fruit continue to flourish all over India... only we now know it as the *jamun*.

Sacred Jamun

The *jamun*'s sacred and sublime associations are many. It was the *jamun* fruit that Lord Murugan used to test the faith of his ardent devotee, the Tamil poetess-saint Avvaiyar. As one version of the story goes, Avvaiyar was on her way to Madurai. Tired and thirsty, the old lady saw a young shepherd boy sitting on a *jamun* tree which was loaded with fruit. She asked the boy to pluck some of the fruits for her. The boy asked her whether she wanted 'hot' or 'cold' fruits. Avvaiyar was puzzled by this strange question but to find out what the boy meant, she asked him for 'hot' fruit. The boy then shook the tree and some of the ripe *jamun* fell to the ground. Avvaiyar picked them up and, finding that there were grains of sand stuck to the fruit, she blew on them to get rid of the sand. The boy, who was watching, now teasingly asked Avvaiyar if she was blowing on them because the fruits were too hot to eat. At that moment, it dawned on Avvaiyar that the person she had thought of as an illiterate shepherd boy had fooled her by his play on words. The realization humbled her and when this happened, the boy revealed his true identity as Lord Murugan and stood in front of Avvaiyar in all his glory! It is said that the tree that bore these fruits still stands near the famous Pazhamudircholai temple (near Madurai in Tamil Nadu), said to be one of the six most sacred shrines of Lord Murugan.

It was under the *jamun* tree that the thirteenth Jain Tirthankara, Vimalanath, attained nirvana. And, according to one story, Gautama Buddha too first began to meditate under a *jamun* tree… when he was just seven years old!

But the *jamun*'s most enduring association is with Lord Shiva. According to a story in the *Puranas*, a sage was doing *tapasya* under a *jamun* tree when one of the fruits fell near him. He first offered the fruit to Lord Shiva and then ate it, along with the seed. Soon, the seed took root inside him and grew into a *jamun* tree, bursting forth from his head. The sage was so elated that he danced before Lord Shiva who asked him to return to the spot where he had found the *jamun* fruit. The sage obeyed and this pleased Lord Shiva, who followed him and sat in meditation under that *jamun* tree. From that day onwards, Lord Shiva also became known as Jambunatha or Jambukeswara. And the spot became the site of the magnificent Jambukeswara temple (dating back to the first century BC) in Thiruvanaikoil near Trichy in Tamil Nadu.

Purple, the Colour of Health!

Lord Krishna's skin must have been like the skin of the *jamun* fruit. Satin-soft, gleaming, inky-dark like the heart of a monsoon cloud. This is perhaps why *meghamodini*, *meghavarna* and *shymala* are some of the other names for this fruit in Sanskrit. And, as Mother Nature has a purpose for everything, the *jamun*'s beautiful colour flags the presence of a very remarkable group of antioxidants called anthocyanins – *antho* means 'plant' and *cyan* means 'blue' in Greek. So like all other blue, deep-red or purple vegetables and fruits, the *jamun* is also a rich source of these antioxidants.

Now all antioxidants are powerful disease fighters but anthocyanins have been specially appointed as guardians of the heart because they inhibit LDL, the 'bad' cholesterol that clogs arteries and leads to heart disease. Anthocyanins also help to slow the aging process, protect against heart disease and tumours and fight inflammation and allergies. They improve night vision, help prevent age-related eye diseases, are a great brain food and may even help stroke victims in their recovery.

The presence of anthocyanins in the *jamun* fruit is doubly significant. Dr Albert Szent-Gyorgyi, the Nobel Prize-winning scientist who discovered Vitamin C, found that the therapeutic action of this vitamin is significantly enhanced in the presence of a group of antioxidants called flavonoids. And the *jamun* fruit is not only rich in anthocyanins which are a type of flavonoid, but also contains generous amounts of Vitamin C, signalled by its delicious tartness. A wonderful partnership that makes the *jamun* one of the most nutritious fruits not just in all of Jambudvipa, but in the whole world!

The *jamun* also contains good amounts of Vitamin A, and iron, calcium and phosphorus. And since it is an excellent digestive, stimulates the appetite, and is wonderfully 'cooling' in nature, *jamun* is the perfect summer fruit.

Sweet Succour for Diabetics

As far as the *jamun*'s medicinal properties go, perhaps all that needs to be said is that US companies have sought to patent this fruit (along with *neem*, turmeric and *karela*). Understandably so, because it is renowned as an ancient and powerful 'medicine' for treating diabetes. This has been documented in authoritative treatises both ancient and modern such as the sixteenth-century work, *Bhavaprakash Nighantu*, by Pandit Bhava Mishra, Emperor Akbar's court physician, who is considered one of the great authorities on Indian medicine. And the present-day *Compendium of Indian Medicinal Plants* by RP Rastogi and BN Mehrotra and *Indian Materia Medica* by Dr KM Nadkarni.

The seeds of the *jamun* are particularly effective in the treatment of diabetes because they contain jamboline, a glucoside that not only controls the conversion of starch into sugar but also brings down the levels of sugar in blood and urine.

The best known of the *jamun*'s many therapeutic roles is in the treatment of diabetes. But, as is the case with many other trees that are indigenous to our country, every part of the *jamun* tree has some

What's in a Name?

Related to the clove, the eucalyptus, all-spice and the guava, the *jamun* belongs to a vast botanical clan of over a thousand species that is known by two names – *Eugenia* and *Syzygium*. It is said that name *Eugenia* was to honour Prince Eugene of Savoy (1663-1736), who apart from being one of the most brilliant military generals in European history, was also a patron of botany and horticulture.

Language	Name
English	Java plum, jambolan, black plum, Malabar plum, Portuguese plum, Indian blackberry
Botanical	Eugenia jambolana, Syzygium cumini
Sanskrit	Jambu, nilaphal, phalendra, meghavarna, shymala, meghamodini
Hindi	Jamun, jam
Gujarati	Jambudo
Bengali	Kaalo jam
Marathi	Jambhul
Tamil	Naval
Telugu	Neradu, jambu
Kannada	Nerale hannu, jambu
Malayalam	Naval

medicinal value, especially for treating digestive ailments. The bark, fruit and seeds are used to treat chronic diarrhoea and dysentery, while the fruit is used to treat liver disorders, piles, enlargement of the spleen, and as a diuretic. The fruit, bark and leaves are also used for a host of other ailments from bronchitis and hypertension to mouth ulcers and gingivitis.

Nature's Umbrella and Air Purifier

If the *jamun* fruit is called *phalendra,* or 'king of fruits', the tree is no less impressive. At the start of the twentieth century, when Lutyens' New Delhi was taking shape, the planners – who included William Mustoe, often called Lutyens' 'wizard gardener' – drew up a list of 121 trees that were 'indigenous, shade-giving, stately and long-lived' to line its roads. The *jamun* tree figured in that list and till today, the beautiful avenues of New Delhi, like Rajpath, Moti Lal

Nehru Marg and Shanti Path, are lined with several imposing old *jamun* trees. There is one other reason why the *jamun* tree is perfectly suited to be a 'road tree' – especially in today's context. It is the least affected by the lead content in vehicle exhaust!

What a magnificent tree this is, and truly worthy of bearing the king of fruits. Its mighty umbrella-like crown can spread to a circumference of thirty-six feet and soar up to one hundred feet, making huge, beautiful canopies which provide cool, green shade not just for hot city roads but also for coffee plants to grow under in coffee plantations. Incidentally, there is a fabulous *jamun* tree in the shola forests near Kodaikanal that is more than two hundred feet high and has such a massive trunk that it needs twenty adults with outstretched arms to circle it completely. Local environmentalists say that this tree is about five hundred years old!

Silk, Honey, Boats, Medicine and Music!

Providing shade is only one of the *jamun* tree's multifarious uses. Its delicate, fragrant white flowers are so laden with nectar that most of the honey produced in the Western Ghats – honey that is considered to be among the finest in the country – is from the nectar of *jamun* flowers. The leaves, apart from serving as nutritious fodder for livestock, are also food for the silkworms that produce India's beautiful *tussar* silk!

The termite-resistant wood of the *jamun* tree is so strong that it has been used in the construction of bridges, for making rafters for buildings and for propping up the roofs of mines. In fact, till not so long ago, the wooden 'sleepers' that hold railway tracks together were made of wood from the *jamun* tree. Its water-resistant qualities make it excellent raw material for building boats and making oars and even for lining the inside of wells. And you could say it is also a 'musical tree' because the wood is often used to make musical instruments, especially guitars!

The *jamun* could also play a major role in helping to revive both urban and rural land degraded through soil erosion and loss of green cover. This is because it is a hardy tree that grows easily and requires little care. It can grow in shallow, rocky soils, withstand frost and adapt to both drought and water-logging.

Social forestry is a modern term for an ancient Indian practice of giving trees a special place of honour because they nurture,

nourish, protect and sustain. And the *jamun* is one such tree. For centuries, its delicious fruit has nourished and healed us. Its shade has cooled our summers. In fact, every part of it has sustained us in some way. And under it, gods, sages and saints alike have meditated and attained enlightenment.

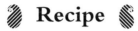 **Recipe**

Two-in-One Diabetic Thirst Quencher

Apart from being a delicious summer drink, in traditional medicine, this combination of mango and jamun *juice is considered particularly effective in relieving the thirst that often plagues diabetics. While the* jamun's *role in treating diabetes is a well-known one, the use of mango juice may come as a surprise because it is a popular and commonly held belief that mangoes are anathema for diabetics. In fact, recent studies indicate the opposite! (See chapter on Mango for details.) The key is to make sure that both juices are freshly made and completely sugar-free. Mix equal parts of* jamun *juice and mango juice. Chill and serve.*

Minerals
The Tom Thumbs of Nutrition

In seventeenth-century Europe, bathing in and drinking mineral waters for their therapeutic properties was a popular practice and it was quite the thing for the wealthy and the famous to flock to 'spa towns' and 'take the waters'. One of the most famous of those 'waters' was discovered in 1618 in the English town of Epsom when a farmer noticed that the water from a particular well seemed to magically heal scratches and rashes. The reason for the water's curative powers was the presence of a mineral salt, magnesium sulphate, christened 'Epsom salt' after the place where it was first discovered.

But the role of minerals in health was known to us for thousands of years before this; recorded evidence is found in all the ancient systems of medicine of the East. For example, in Ayurveda, the very first activity recommended on waking up in the morning is to drink a little water that has been kept overnight in a copper vessel. The tiny amount of copper that leaches into the water during the night is considered generally beneficial for health but specifically good for arthritis and respiratory disorders. And minerals of every denomination ranging all the way from diamond and gold to zinc and manganese are ingredients used in Ayurvedic formulations.

The word 'mineral' usually conjures up mines deep inside the womb of the earth, veined with massive deposits of what are described as 'naturally occurring substances formed through geological processes'. But in the human body, these very same minerals are required in such minuscule quantities that if we were to add up the daily requirements of all the twenty-two minerals which we need for the healthy functioning of our bodies, it would weigh less than a few teaspoonfuls of sugar!

And yet, they make the difference between good health and a host of life-threatening diseases including heart disease, hypertension, diabetes, even cancer. Stored in muscle and bone tissue and in blood, they make sure that your heart beats strong and steady. That your nerves and muscles function in such seamless synchrony that you don't even notice when and how the thought of wanting to pick up that pencil and write got translated into action. That your blood can carry all the oxygen you need, that your bones and teeth are strong and resilient and that your immune system is fully geared up to tackle the most deadly virus. That you can taste and smell and see, that your hair and nails are strong and glossy. And that your libido is tickety-boo!

Of these twenty-two, seven are 'macrominerals'– calcium, chloride, magnesium, phosphorus, potassium, sodium and sulphur. They are thus named because they are needed in larger quantities. But only relatively speaking, because the maximum daily requirement of a macromineral is just 4.7 grams! The other fifteen are needed in even tinier quantities and therefore are called 'trace minerals' or 'microminerals' and the more well known among them are copper, iodine, iron, manganese, molybdenum, selenium and zinc.

Come, let's meet some of these astounding giant-slayers.

Minerals at a Glance

MACROMINERALS

Minerals	Functions	Primary Food Sources
Calcium	Required for bone building, maintenance of the body's skeletal system and clotting of blood Teams up with magnesium to regulate transmission of nerve impulses, heartbeat and muscular contractions Stimulates hormones and regulates enzyme activity Helps protect against colon cancer	Milk, cheese, curd, buttermilk, green leafy vegetables, fenugreek, fennel seeds, sesame seeds, beans, peanuts
Magnesium	Muscle and nerve relaxant Prevents irregular heartbeat, palpitations etc, therefore helps prevent heart attacks Helps lower high blood pressure Required for the activity of over 300 enzymes Helps alleviate symptoms of PMS and menopause Helps prevent osteoporosis Minimizes risk of premature labour and birth defects	Legumes, green leafy vegetables, fruits like dates, raisins and bananas, whole grain, milk and dairy products, nuts like almonds, cashews, peanuts and walnuts, jaggery, sesame, fennel, fenugreek
Sodium	Electrolyte that partners with potassium to regulate heartbeat and transmission of neuromuscular impulses and ensure nourishment of all cells. Needed for producing hydrochloric acid in the stomach and transporting oxygen in the body Helps make other minerals soluble in blood	Table salt is the most obvious source, but because of fast food, junk food, processed foods etc., current-day diets are already overloaded with salt. So cut down on salt in your food and eat lots of fresh fruit and vegetables.
Potassium	Electrolyte that partners with sodium (see above) Lowers blood pressure	Fresh fruits, green leafy vegetables, jaggery, white pumpkin, legumes, whole grains, potatoes, curd and buttermilk
Sulphur (Component of amino acids and so present in every cell in the body)	Necessary for production of collagen and keratin, therefore for healthy skin, hair and nails Maintains healthy liver Detoxifier Component of insulin, so helps regulate blood sugar Needed for proper functioning of nervous system, digestion and synthesis of carbohydrates and fats	Garlic, onion, asafoetida, cabbage, radish, cauliflower and mustard

MICROMINERALS

Copper (Constituent of more than 30 critical enzymes)	Partners with iron in producing haemoglobin and red blood cells Needed for the production of melanin, vital for health of skin, brain and retina Required for normal functioning of thyroid gland Germicide	Whole grain, legumes such as *rajma* (kidney beans) and Bengal gram, fruits such as banana, guava and Indian gooseberry (*amla*), pepper, sweet potato and potato
Iron	Essential for production of haemoglobin Needed for carbohydrate and protein synthesis and for a healthy immune system	Legumes such as *rajma* (kidney beans) and Bengal gram, green leafy vegetables, whole grains, nuts and seeds, jaggery
Iodine	Vital for proper functioning of thyroid gland May help prevent/treat fibrocystic breast disease	Seafood is the richest source but for vegetarians, curd, green leafy vegetables, peanuts and whole wheat are also good sources
Manganese	Needed to regulate blood sugar, for strong bones, healthy functioning of brain, and nervous and immune systems Activates hundreds of enzymes in the body Needed for utilization of thiamine (Vitamin B1), biotin (Vitamin B9), choline and Vitamin C Required for production of mother's milk and sex hormones	Nuts and seeds, whole grains, green leafy vegetables, legumes, banana, fenugreek, fennel, turmeric, jaggery
Selenium (Most effective when combined with Vitamin E – results in 20 to 30 times increase in output of antibodies!)	Antioxidant that helps reduce the risk of cardiovascular diseases and many cancers, including cancers of the prostate, lung, breast, ovaries, bladder, pancreas, colon and rectum.	Whole grains like rice, wheat and *ragi,* nuts, mustard seeds
Zinc	Needed for proper functioning of taste buds and nasal odour receptors Required for protein and carbohydrate synthesis, for production of white blood cells and therefore for healing wounds Helps trigger the body's insulin response A component of semen and required for production of sperm and testosterone	Legumes, nuts and seeds, whole grain, pumpkin and sunflower seeds

Golden Jack – Ripe Jackfruit Pods and Seed

Banana: Happiness in a Peel

'The breeze is wafting the fragrance of flowers of seven-leaved banana plants, and the swarms of honeybees that are singing in accompaniment to the rustle of the breeze are tagging along with that breeze for its fragrance…'

So did Lord Rama describe the Kishkindha forest in Valmiki's *Ramayana*. And according the *Krishnamangal*, a sixteenth-century text, one of the foods that Lord Krishna asked the *gopis* and *gopas* to cook in Brindavan was unripe banana with *paneer*.

The earliest written reference to the banana is in Sanskrit – as *kadali* or *mocha*. Many believe that the banana originated around 4,000 years ago, somewhere in the jungles between Malaysia and India. But ancient remains of plants at the Kuk Swamp in Papua New Guinea suggest that banana cultivation there goes back to at least 5000 BC, maybe even 8000 BC. Alexander the Great may have been one of the first Europeans to taste a banana because he noted that he had seen it growing in India when he invaded the country in 327 BC.

So, you could say that the banana is a fruit with a long and glorious past. The gods favoured it, emperors dined off its leaves, the thighs of beautiful women were compared to its stem, and juice made from the banana was among the foods permitted for Buddhist and Jain monks.

So when did the banana become so… well, ho-hum? Monkey food, inspiration for gags and definitely not something you'd proudly whip out and serve to impress the boss when he comes home for dinner. Well, whenever that happened, it is now about time that we reacquaint ourselves with the magic of this multifariously endowed, multitasking, but what has become perhaps one of the most under-rated of fruits.

Berry or Herb?

Related to the lily and orchid families, cousin to ginger and cardamom, the banana grows on what are actually not trees but giant herbs, and it is classified as a berry albeit a 'false' one!

Stairway to Heaven

The banana is an ancient symbol of fertility and prosperity in many cultures, but especially in India where it occupies pride of place in Hindu rituals. The fruit is offered to the deities along with other auspicious foods like coconut and rice. It is also a commonly used ingredient in *prasadams* as well as in the food cooked and served in temples. For example, the *panchamritam prasadam* at the Murugan temple in Palani, which remains fresh for six weeks, has the banana as one of the main ingredients.

The banana plant is also considered auspicious. Saplings are used to decorate the *puja mandapam* and the gate of the house on festive and religious occasions. In Bengal, it is especially associated with the Goddess Durga. When the idol of Goddess Durga is installed in *puja pandals* at the start of the ten-day Durga Puja festival, the *prana*, or 'the life of the Goddess' is ritually brought from a nearby pond or river in a banana plant and transferred to the idol. The first day of the Durga Puja begins with a pre-dawn *puja* called Nabapatrika or Kolabou. During this *puja*, nine plants, each representing one of the nine avatars of the Goddess, are worshipped. The banana plant represents the Goddess Brahmani.

In Karnataka, we have a lovely saying which goes something like this – because of the jasmine flower, the banana fibre went to heaven. This refers to the practice in many parts of South India of using the fibre from the banana stem to string flowers into garlands. And since jasmine flowers are a popular offering during *pujas*, even the banana fibre gets to be touched by the gods!

Take-It-Easy Banana
Of the banana's various health benefits – and there are many – perhaps the most spectacular is that it is the best natural protection against high blood pressure, high cholesterol, heart disease, stroke and even osteoporosis. And research to support this has come not only from the West, but also from closer home. In 1999, scientists at the Kasturba Medical College in Manipal, Karnataka conducted a study of six popular South Indian varieties of ripe bananas. Their findings showed that the banana inhibits the action of ACE, the enzyme that is responsible for producing Angiotensin-2, which in turn constricts blood vessels and causes high blood pressure. They also found that people who consumed a couple of bananas a day for just a week recorded an amazing 10 per cent fall in blood pressure!

And this is because the banana is one of the best natural sources of potassium, a mineral that plays a very important role in keeping blood pressure at healthy levels. (One medium-sized banana contains about 10 to 13 per cent of your daily requirement of potassium.) So much so that in November 2000, the American Food and Drug Administration classified the banana as a potassium-rich food and allowed bananas sold in the United States to carry a label which says: 'Diets containing foods that are good sources of potassium and low in sodium may reduce the risk of blood pressure and stroke'. Incidentally, unripe bananas also have a similar anti-hypertensive action, though to a lesser extent.

We all know what a nasty thing stress is and all the various equally nasty ailments it can cause, including high blood pressure. But here is an interesting insight. Potassium deficiency – which research now indicates can increase your risk of several health problems including hypertension – can also be caused by stress. The second cause of potassium deficiency is eating processed foods because the processing drains the potassium content from the food. Yet another argument for eating fresh fruits and vegetables and freshly cooked food!

My most enduring association with the banana is the sight of Bjorn Borg at the Wimbledon Tennis Championship wolfing down a big yellow banana between games. And perhaps this is the reason why. Potassium is an athlete's friend – in many ways. Apart from being an excellent source of energy, it is also great 'brain food' that helps boost both concentration and memory and is vital for the muscles to function properly, preventing cramps. What more could a Wimbledon champion – or anyone else for that matter – ask for in a food?

Nature's Mood Booster

Bananas are also one of the best natural sources of Vitamin B6 (pyridoxine) – your average banana is packed with more Vitamin B6 than any other fresh fruit. This vitamin is vital for the synthesis of amino acids and for keeping the blood healthy. Its deficiency can cause anaemia, and skin and nervous disorders.

But Vitamin B6 is of particular importance for a healthy state of mind. Often called 'the happy vitamin', it is critical for the production of serotonin, a chemical neurotransmitter released by the brain that, among its other functions, helps to keep the mood upbeat, regulates appetite and sleep, prevents depression and generally has a calming, positive effect on the body and mind. This is why many antidepressant drugs, the most famous of them being Prozac, work by regulating serotonin levels in the body. It is for this reason that the banana is also particularly beneficial for menopausal

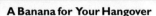

A Banana for Your Hangover

One of the best ways to tackle a hangover is with a banana! Have two glasses of water and a banana just before going to bed, or a banana milkshake sweetened with honey – take your pick.

women as it helps to reduce the depression and insomnia associated with hormonal fluctuations.

One banana can provide as much as one-third of your daily requirement of this vitamin. The presence of Vitamin B6 in the banana is doubly significant because the fruit is also an excellent source of tryptophan, the amino acid that the body converts into serotonin – which it cannot do without the aid of Vitamin B6! So a banana or two a day will not only keep the doctor away but also keep you happy!

Gentle on Your Stomach

Squishy! That's how a banana feels when you mash it with your fingers. And how quickly and smoothly it slips down your throat when you eat it. Easy to eat, easy to digest, and considered a 'cooling food' in Ayurveda, the banana is perfect for treating an upset stomach. It is a natural antacid because its alkaline qualities neutralize over-acidic conditions in the stomach and help produce a thicker protective mucus layer that lines the stomach and protects it against the corrosive action of stomach acids. In traditional medicine, the unripe banana is used to treat dyspepsia that is accompanied by flatulence and acidity. Bananas are now recommended not just for heartburn and hyperacidity but even for those who suffer from chronic ulcers as it also contains chemicals that help fight the bacteria that cause stomach ulcers.

In fact, the banana is one of the few foods recommended for treating constipation *and* diarrhoea. It is used to treat constipation because the high amount of soluble fibre (including pectin) present in both ripe and unripe bananas facilitates easy and regular bowel movements. And it is used in treating diarrhoea because of the presence of that all-important potassium. You see, potassium is an electrolyte, one of a family of minerals that are critical for many vital functions of the body including transmitting neuromuscular impulses, regulating the heartbeat and maintaining the balance of fluids in the body. Electrolytes function in tandem with each other and therefore have to be present in the right quantities. When a person suffers from diarrhoea it causes dehydration which in turn depletes the electrolytes in the body, causing electrolyte imbalance. So, in the treatment of diarrhoea, just drinking water is not enough; you also need to restore the electrolyte balance and the banana helps to do exactly that.

Nature's Pharmacy

But it is not just the banana fruit that has medicinal properties. The flowers are used to treat diabetes, bronchitis, dysentery and menstrual disorders. The sap from the stem is a well-known remedy for urinary disorders, especially kidney stones. Tender banana leaves have been used for hundreds of years in traditional medicine as a dressing for burns and inflammations, even as surgical dressing. In the modern-day treatment of burns, they are proving to be equally valuable. For two reasons. Firstly, unlike conventional dressings, they don't stick to the burns, thus greatly reducing the terrible agony that burn victims suffer during the daily changing of dressings. Secondly, banana leaves are cheaper – just 2 per cent of the cost of expensive conventional dressings! For the lakhs of burn patients hospitalized annually in India, many of them poor, this is a great boon. In 1996, Mumbai's Lokmanya Tilak Municipal General Hospital developed banana-leaf dressings for use in the treatment of burns and has been successfully using it ever since.

And the banana peel is not just a comedian's prop. When the inside of it is rubbed on insect bites, especially mosquito bites, it reduces the swelling and itching. It is also very effective for removing the sting of insects or tiny splinters embedded in the skin – the enzymes in the peel help draw up the splinter or sting to the skin's surface.

A Whole Meal in a Peel!

The banana is a nutritionist's dream. First, it is the perfect energy food – a fully ripe banana is 20-25 per cent carbohydrate. In fact, every 100 grams of banana contains about 100 calories, lots of dietary fibre (about 11 per cent of your daily requirement), but no cholesterol! Second, it is a veritable mine of dietary minerals – not just potassium but also significant amounts of calcium, magnesium, phosphorus, sulphur, iron and copper. It is also a good source of Vitamin C, Vitamin B1 (thiamine) and choline. Some experts say that it also contains some amount of beta-carotene, the phytochemical present in some fruits and vegetables which the body converts into Vitamin A.

And what seals the banana's wonder-food status is the fact that each banana comes in its own untouched-by-human-hands, biodegradable 'travel-pack' that disintegrates in just two weeks to become nutritious plant food, particularly beneficial for rose plants. In fact, a popular eighteenth-century gardening practice was to put

---

'Drunken' Banana

In the East African countries of Uganda, Burundi and Rwanda, the annual consumption of bananas is 250 kilograms per person, the highest in the world. One reason for this could be because a popular drink here is a low-alcohol beer brewed from bananas. Incidentally, this beer is also considered an aphrodisiac.

What's in a Name?

The word 'banana' is derived from the Arabic word for 'finger'.

The banana belongs to the genus called *Musa* in which there are hundreds of species. Most of the bananas that we eat come mainly from two species, *Musa acuminata colla* or the hybrid *Musa paradisiaca L*. There are two versions as to why the word *Musa* was used. According to one version, it refers to Antonius Musa, the physician of the first Roman Emperor, Augustus Caesar, who is said to have first promoted the banana in Europe. According to KT Achaya, author of *Indian Food – A Historical Companion*, it is probably derived from one of the Sanskrit names for banana – *mocha*.

The 'L' in *Musa paradisiaca L* refers to Carolus Linnaeus, the seventeenth-century Swedish botanist, physician and zoologist who laid the foundation for Linnean taxonomy or the system of naming and classifying living things. When it came to finding the banana an appropriate botanical name, he remembered an old belief that the forbidden fruit that Eve offered Adam in the Garden of Eden was not the apple, but the banana. And so he christened the banana *Musa paradisiaca L*. The earlier botanical name for this species was *Musa sapientum*. This name was also coined by Linnaeus. There's a story that when Alexander the Great came across the banana in India, he found that sages meditated under the trees and that their diet consisted almost entirely of bananas. This inspired Linnaeus to name the banana *Musa Sapientum*; *Sapientum* meaning 'wise man'.

One of the banana's Sanskrit names is *rambha*, also the name of the beautiful *apsara* sent by Lord Indra to seduce the great sage Vishwamitra!

Language	Name
English	Banana, plantain
Botanical	Musa paradisiaca L
Sanskrit	Kadali, mocha, rambha
Hindi, Gujarati	Kela
Marathi	Kel
Bengali	Kola
Tamil	Vazhapalam
Telugu	Kadalamu
Kannada	Baley hannu
Malayalam	Vazhapazham

banana peels in the hole in which a rose plant was to be planted. This made the roses healthier. We now know why – it is because banana peels contain many nutrients like calcium, magnesium, sulphur and phosphorus. And since the peels rot quickly, these nutrients are easily available to the plants. So don't throw away those banana peels – just bury them under your rose plants!

Nature's Cooking Pots?

There are hundreds of uses for every part of the banana plant. The fibre from the banana stem is made into paper (which is sometimes used to make tea bags!), rope and thread (which in turn converts into all kinds of fabrics). In the Philippines, till recently, the *barong* (the Filipino national costume) was often made from a beautiful, finely woven fabric called *jusi,* made from banana fibre. In West Africa, it is used to make fishing lines. The stem is also widely used to make everything from padded seats for benches in Ecuador to the soles for inexpensive shoes in Sri Lanka. The flowers and the stem are also edible and are made into a range of delicious curries in India and all over South East Asia. In Thailand, the tender flower is even eaten raw.

But perhaps it is the banana leaf that is used in the most ingenious ways, of which the most popular is as 'crockery'. In India, the practice of eating off banana leaves started in ancient times for reasons of hygiene. A meal eaten off a banana leaf, tricky as it is for the uninitiated, is an experience so satisfying that it is now an international phenomenon – you can get a 'banana-leaf meal' any-where from New York to Singapore! Of course, the bonus is that not only are the banana-leaf 'plates' completely biodegradable, converting into rich plant manure, they are also very good fodder for cattle! The leaves – both fresh and dried – are also used as packaging material, especially for food. In South India, they are used to wrap everything from curd-rice to *biryani,* in Malaysia, they are used to wrap the national rice dish *nasi lemak,* and in Bangkok, the takeaway parcels of the city's famous pavement food!

Banana leaves are equally popular as 'cooking vessels' and as with all other leaves, they are used mainly as 'packets' in which to steam food. Steaming is one of the healthiest ways to cook, but food steamed in leaves is both healthy *and* delicious. That is because, when the food is wrapped in a leaf and steamed, all the moisture

Banana-Leaf Liners

Lining your serving dishes with fresh green banana leaves for a party makes the food look great and reduces the load of washing up later. All you have to do is throw away the leaf liners, then lightly wash the dishes!

and nutrients are sealed in and the food gently stews in its own juices. The leaf wrapper also imparts its own subtle flavour to the food. The result is moist, succulent and incredibly healthy food.

These 'leaf wraps' also make a very dramatic sensory statement. When they are opened, clouds of aromatic steam essay forth, waking up your appetite like no appetizer can!

And so, throughout Asia, Latin America and Central Africa cooking in banana leaves is an ancient art. Needless to say, we Indians have been cooking with banana leaves for centuries, especially in South India where the banana abounds. *Yele appam* (rice batter with jackfruit pulp, jaggery and grated coconut steamed in a banana leaf) dates back to the fifth century AD. No Parsi wedding or celebration is complete without the famous *patra ni machchi* (fish in a leaf). And in Bengali cuisine, *bhapa* (meaning 'steam') is a popular method of steaming spiced vegetables, fish or even yogurt in banana leaves.

Banana leaves are also used to make thatching for roofs. In rain-rich regions, the leaves are used as protection against the elements, becoming impromptu umbrellas and rain hats, even bicycle rain guards in Bali! And in ancient Hawaii, the banana plant was used to signal a truce during war!

Many call the banana 'poor man's food'. And one hopes that will never change because it puts a wealth of nutrition within the easy reach of millions of Indians who would not be able to afford it otherwise. Being a cheap but iron-rich food, the banana is particularly important in India, which has the highest incidence in the world of anaemia among women, and where 60-70 per cent of adolescent girls are anaemic because their diet is deficient in iron. (Incidentally, the banana is the fourth-largest cultivated crop in the world, after rice, wheat and maize, with India growing almost a quarter of the world's annual crop.)

Look at what the banana offers you for just little more than a rupee. Nourishment not just for the body and mind but also for the soul. It's a great way to start the day or perk up one that seems to be flagging. You can eat it because you're hungry or sad, tired, cranky or stressed out, or because your stomach is grumbling; or then, just because you want to stay healthy and happy!

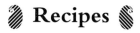 **Recipes**

Sun-Dried Bananas

This is a wonderful way to have a banana on call anywhere, anytime, especially as a snack for hungry kids. It is also a great way to save those over-ripe bananas, which you would otherwise have to throw away.

INGREDIENTS

2-3 kg bananas

METHOD

Start by making a smaller batch using about 2-3 kilograms of bananas, depending on the space you have to dry them. The best variety for this purpose are the small yellow ones available all over South India, but if you cannot get these, the larger green ones will do, but you will need to cut each banana into 2-3 pieces.

Peel the bananas. Spread a large, clean plastic sheet or straw mat in an area that gets a good amount of sunlight. Spread out the banana pieces so that they don't touch or overlap. When the bananas become shrivelled up and totally dry to the touch, store in a dry jar.

Emergency Banana Breakfast   (Serves 1)

This was my dad's favourite breakfast when he was a bachelor working in Mumbai. The emergency could be a bare larder, being late for an important meeting or a kid who won't eat. This simple 'remedy' will not only save the day, but also serve as a bellyful of nourishment!

INGREDIENTS

2 slices of bread
(whole wheat preferably, but any other kind will do… it's an emergency, remember?)
1 medium-sized banana
1 tsp butter
(optional, especially if you are counting calories!)

METHOD

Butter both the slices of bread. Now cut the banana into thin slices and place them in layers on the buttered side of one slice of bread. When you have placed all the banana slices, cover them with the second slice of bread, buttered side down. Enjoy!

Variation: Sprinkle a little *chaat masala* or salt and pepper on the banana slices for a more savoury version. For kids, you might want to try a little sugar or jaggery.

Steamed Rice Pancakes in Banana Leaves

(Serves 4–5)

Called kadubu *in Karnataka and first mentioned in Kannada literature in AD 1430, these pancakes demonstrate what excellent cooking vessels banana leaves make! They are both delicious and healthy and you can eat them in a hundred different ways. As breakfast, 'tiffin' or even supper. You can eat them hot or cold – they keep in the fridge for at least two days. The plain version can be eaten accompanied by anything like chutney and curries or just a little melted ghee. You can also stuff them with all kinds of fillings – sweet, savoury, even leftover* sabzi. *Here's a recipe with a sweet filling.*

INGREDIENTS

For the pancakes

¼ kg rice, washed and soaked overnight (unpolished, red boiled rice is the best, but any other variety is also fine)
15-20 banana leaves, washed, dried and with the centre rib removed, and cut into rectangles, roughly 6x4 inches each
1 tsp salt (adjust to taste)

For the filling

(This will make enough filling for half the batter, with the rest of the batter being used to make plain kadubu*)*
3 tbsp black sesame seeds, roasted
2 tbsp grated jaggery (adjust to taste)
2 tbsp grated fresh coconut
(Variation: You can substitute the sesame with the same amount of coconut.)

METHOD

To make the filling

Grind together all the ingredients.

To make the pancakes

Grind the rice with the salt and a little water to a very thick, coarse paste. Transfer it to a thick-bottomed pan and heat it gently for a few minutes, stirring constantly to prevent it from getting burnt. The batter will thicken to a dough-like consistency. Remove from heat and cool.

For the plain pancakes, grease your fingers with a little oil and spread a portion of the batter evenly on the shiny side of each banana leaf, coating the entire piece – the thinner you spread the dough, the better. Now gently fold the leaf (not very tightly), batter-coated side facing in, into a roll, as you would a bed roll. For the stuffed pancakes, place about 2 tsp of the filling in the centre of the batter-coated leaf and then roll it. Arrange the pancakes on an *idli* stand and steam for about 10 minutes in a pressure cooker without using the weight.

To serve, gently remove the pancakes from the banana leaf and serve with melted *ghee* or any accompaniment of your choice. (An unusual one is marmalade!)

Coconut: Tree of Life

'. . . and from these trees and their fruit are made the following things: sugar, honey, oil, wine, vinegar, charcoal and cordage . . ., and matting . . ., and it serves them for everything they need. And the aforesaid fruit, in addition to what is thus made of it, is their chief food, particularly at sea.'

King Manuel I of Portugal (1469-1521)

August 2, 1943. It was an inky, moonless night, just a few hours before dawn. On a narrow strip of waterway called the Blackett Strait, between two of the Solomon Islands on the Pacific Ocean, an American patrol torpedo boat, the PT 109, running slowly on one engine to avoid detection, was prowling in the dark waters, hunting for Japanese supply ships. Its skipper was a twenty-six-year-old Harvard University student called John F Kennedy.

Before long, the PT 109 found a Japanese vessel – not a supply ship but the Japanese destroyer *Amagiri*. The destroyer rammed into the American boat, which burst into flames, killing two men. The remaining crew members – including Kennedy – abandoned the boat. After swimming for several hours, they reached land – another one of the Solomon Islands.

It was six days before Kennedy and his crew spotted other human beings. They were two islanders, Biuku Gasa and Eroni Kumana, paddling past in a dug-out canoe. Gasa and Kumana were members of the Coastwatchers, a volunteer corps that provided intelligence and ground support to Allied forces, and had come to examine the wreck of a Japanese ship nearby. At first, the two men thought that the Americans were Japanese. But Kennedy managed to convince them that he and his men were members of the Allied forces. He wanted to send a message to the Allied base through them but Gasa and Kumana knew almost no English. It was Gasa's idea that Kennedy carve his message on the husk of a green coconut.

And that is exactly what he did.

'NAURO ISL....COMMANDER....NATIVE KNOWS POS'IT....HE CAN PILOT....11 ALIVE....NEED SMALL BOAT.....KENNEDY.'

Palace Architect

In 1978, Imelda Marcos, then at the height of her power (and acquisitive greed) commissioned the Coconut Palace to be built in Manila, supposedly at a cost of ten million US dollars. The 'palace' was presumably built for Pope John Paul to stay in during his tour of the Philippines in 1981. Apparently the Pope declined, saying that it would be inappropriate to stay in such ostentatious digs in a country where there was so much poverty! Apart from the cost, the other unique thing about the palace is that 70 per cent of the material is from coconut trees.

Gasa and Eroni delivered the message, even though they knew that if they were caught, it meant certain death. The rest is history. When Kennedy became President of the United States of America in 1960, the coconut husk was given a place of honour on his desk. It is now in the John F Kennedy Presidential Library and Museum in Boston.

And what did Kennedy and his men survive on for six days before they were rescued? Coconuts of course!

So, if ever you are marooned on an island, make sure it is one with at least one coconut tree!

'Milk Bottles on the Doorstep of Mankind'

While botanists may differ on the place of origin of the coconut, they concur on two things. One, that the reason why it is virtually impossible to pin down the exact location of its birth is because of the coconut's seafaring abilities – coconuts can float for long periods of time, travelling thousands of miles on the high seas, and still germinate when they beach on dry land. Two, that the coconut is a very ancient denizen of this planet, its ancestors probably originating around two hundred million years ago, when the super-continent called Gondwana was just beginning to break up to form Australia, Africa, South America and India.

And as these new landmasses formed, the 'forefathers' of the present-day coconut travelled the globe, riding the ocean waves, but many of them drifted ashore and took up residence on the coastlines. So by the time our ancestor, the Homo Erectus, began to disperse from his birthplace in Africa into Asia about 1.8 million years ago, he must have stumbled across this wondrous fruit, washed up on the beaches, bobbing in the waves. When he split it open, he would have found that it contained a cool, sweet water that would slake his thirst and a sweet, delicious white flesh that he could eat and be sated. It was – as the coconut expert, Dr Hugh Harries, puts it – as if Nature had left 'milk bottles on the doorstep of mankind'. And thus began one of the longest liaisons between man and fruit!

In India, we have a slightly different version of the story of how the coconut came to be. The mighty sage Vishwamitra had rashly volunteered to help King Trishanku fulfil his ambition of gaining entry into heaven. The sage's powers were legendary and very soon, the king was at heaven's door. But Lord Indra and all the *devas* weren't too taken up with the idea of having a mere mortal hobnobbing in their midst. So, with all their combined divine might, they threw Trishanku back to earth. As he watched the poor king plummeting earthwards, Vishwamitra knew that he had to come up with some kind of an emergency measure. And so, in a flash, he created the coconut tree to break the king's fall – and that is what Trishanku landed on. As one version of the story goes, the king's head became a coconut, which in turn became an offering to the gods. And so, every time a coconut is offered to the gods, Trishanku's wish of going to heaven is granted!

Ego Cracker!

No *puja* or religious ceremony can be conducted, no auspicious occasion celebrated without the coconut. In all Hindu religious ceremonies, the coconut is omnipresent. Sometimes it is broken open at the feet of the deity and offered to it. Sometime it is a part of the *purna kalasha* or the *purna kumbha*. This is a pot (usually made of metal) filled with water, its mouth ringed with a circular arrangement of five, seven or eleven fresh mango leaves, on which a coconut is placed. In Sanskrit, *purna* means 'full' and *kumbha* or *kalasha* means 'pot'. The significance of the *purna kumbha* is very profound, many-layered and ancient, going back to the *Rig Veda*. The pot is said to represent Mother Earth, the womb and the Devi, and therefore, fertility and abundance. Without water there can be no life and so the water represents life itself. The mango leaves are supposed to represent Kama Deva, the God of Love. And the coconut? As fruit and tree that provides nourishment, livelihood and shelter to millions, naturally it symbolizes prosperity.

Perhaps one of the best indications of just how sacred and auspicious the coconut is considered in India comes from the Indian film and television industry where tradition demands that the first shot of a shooting schedule is always inaugurated by the breaking of a coconut!

So why do we break a coconut at the start of something important? The coconut is said to represent the ego and so, the tradition of breaking the coconut in front of a deity symbolizes the surrendering of one's ego!

But whether the coconut originated in India or drifted to its shores floating on the waters of ancient oceans or manifested itself as a pathway to heaven, it soon became revered as the *kalpavriksha*. There are many translations of that word, the most literal being 'wish-granting tree' and the most common being 'tree of life', because the coconut tree provides food, medicine, divine offerings, shelter, fuel, tools, furniture, utensils, even wine – in fact, almost everything you need for a good life! And so, not just in India but all over the tropical world, the coconut is treasured, even worshipped as one of Mother Nature's most precious gifts.

The coconut supposedly made its debut in the West only when Portuguese explorers took it back to Europe from India during the sixteenth century. But there is evidence that the coconut was known to the Europeans much, much earlier. Coconuts were found in an archaeological site that was once a rubbish dumb in Berenike (also known as Berenice), a port in ancient Egypt (now in Sudan), established in 275 BC during the reign of Ptolemy II. The *Periplus of the Erythraean Sea*, a Greek nautical manual that describes navigation and trading opportunities and dates back to about the first century AD, reports that coconut oil was exported from the ancient town of Raphta in present-day Tanzania. The destination must have been Europe.

Even so, for much of the West, the coconut has remained more a symbol of vacations on some faraway, exotic tropical beach than anything else. In the rest of the world however, the coconut flourishes, growing on about 26 million hectares in over 90 countries, and is the primary source of livelihood for at least 10 million families!

Food of Life

'Coco got a lotta iron, four for five
Make you strong like a lion…'

Lyrics from the song 'Coconut Woman' sung by Harry Belafonte

First, a few clarifications about the botanical identity of the coconut. Contrary to what its name suggests, the coconut is not a nut but a fruit, and botanists classify it as a drupe, which means that it is a fruit that has just one large seed (also called 'pit' or 'stone') covered by an outer fleshy part. (Other drupes are coffee, plum, cherry, peach, apricot, almond and mango.)

But even among drupes, the coconut is unique. Firstly because unlike any other drupe, its outer covering is so thick that it comprises almost 50 per cent of the fruit and is made up of two parts – the thick, fibrous outer portion and the hard, inner 'shell'. This makes it difficult to get to the flesh inside, because first the fibrous part has to be peeled off and then the shell has to be broken open. Secondly, the white fleshy interior is hollow and contains a sweet water. When the coconut is left 'unshelled' for a long period of time, this water slowly evaporates and the flesh – which contains 45-50 per cent moisture – dries up, resulting in the hard, oily version of the coconut called copra.

Now as far as nutrition goes, the coconut is a veritable treasure trove! As Harry Belafonte's song says, the coconut flesh is a very good source of iron, but it is also rich in other minerals, especially potassium, magnesium and phosphorus and has good amounts of Vitamin B1 (thiamine), Vitamin B3 (niacin) and folic acid or folate (Vitamin B9).

But its nutritional wealth is just one part of the coconut story. As a food, there are not many that can beat it in terms of versatility. Grind it with spices and herbs and it becomes an array of chutneys or the base for a whole host of delicious curries. Grate it and it is a garnish for everything from salads to curd-rice. Extract the sumptuous creamy 'milk' from it and turn it into mouth-watering stews and *payasams*. And its cool, crunchy delicious flesh can even save your life if you are shipwrecked and marooned on a remote island!

Soft Drink or Intravenous Fluid?

'When the nut begins to grow, water begins to be produced within; and when the nut has arrived at perfection, it is full of water, so that there are some nuts which will contain four and five goblets of water, which water is a most excellent thing to drink ...'
Ludovico de Varthema (1470–1517), Italian traveller and writer

Have you noticed how, almost invariably, when the tender coconut seller begins to make a hole in the top of a tender coconut with the tip of his sickle, a little coconut water spurts out? According to my mother, the popular belief is that the spurt is for the person who planted the coconut tree on which that coconut grew! (Incidentally, the Sanskrit name for the coconut is *narikela* which translates to 'water spring' or 'squirt'!)

The tender coconut, like the banana, demonstrates Nature's mastery at food packaging; the double layers of the thick, fibrous outer husk and the hard inner shell not only serve as protection but also as a thermos flask, keeping the water inside refreshingly cool in the fiercest heat. This combined with the fact that the coconut water inside is packed with nutrients like potassium, phosphorus, magnesium and Vitamin C makes the tender coconut the perfect soft drink – deliciously cool, highly nutritious, totally hygienic, free of preservatives and able to travel for long distances without spoiling. (Given the antiquity of the coconut, it is also the world's very first packaged soft drink!)

How to Extract Milk from a Coconut

Grind coconut pieces in a blender to a very fine paste, adding as little water as possible. Spread a thin, clean cotton cloth over a bowl and carefully pour the paste into the cloth. Gather the cloth to make a pouch and squeeze well. Thick milk will ooze out – this is called the first milk. Squeeze repeatedly till the coconut paste inside the cloth is powdery. Reserve the first milk in a bowl. Now put back the coconut paste into the blender, add a little water and grind once more. Repeat the squeezing process – this milk is thinner and called the second milk and should be squeezed into a separate bowl. If you repeat the process one more time, you will get a 'third milk', even thinner than the second milk. The third milk can be mixed with the second milk and used for cooking. The first milk is usually added at the very end of the cooking process.

Amazingly enough, much of what makes coconut water the perfect soft drink also makes it the perfect intravenous fluid! It is also physiologically compatible with blood and especially useful in the tropics and for emergency situations like war and epidemics because it is plentiful and cheap. Possibly the first recorded instance of coconut water being used successfully as an intravenous fluid was in 1942, when a medical practitioner in the Gilbert Islands used it to treat patients suffering from Weil's disease, a very dangerous bacterial infection transmitted by water contaminated by animal urine, especially that of rats. The Japanese, who had invaded and occupied the islands a year before (on the same day they attacked Pearl Harbour), were so impressed by the results that they also began using coconut water intravenously on their patients! Since then, there have been several instances of coconut water being used both as an intravenous hydration fluid as well as for oral hydration.

Next Only to Mother's Milk?

Now, my favourite coconut-oil story – handed down to me by my mother because it is about her mother. Before 'virgin', 'cold-pressed' oils became the fashion statement of health food stores and organically correct folk, coconut oil (and all other oils) was exactly that – virgin and cold pressed. In other words, ever since we humans discovered the joys of cooking with oils, the method of extracting them from their parent fruit, nut or seed was to simply crush them in a mill that was usually powered by bullocks. And coconut oil that came into my grandmother's house was no different, extracted from the coconuts that grew on her land.

Whenever a consignment of freshly pressed oil arrived, my grandmother had a very unique way of celebrating the 'new arrival'. At lunchtime, after she had served herself a helping of steaming rice, she would dribble a little of the fresh coconut oil on a small portion of the rice and eat this coconut oil and rice mixture accompanied by just a few dabs of mango pickle. According to her, there is very little in the world that can beat the delicious aroma and flavour of a mouthful of hot rice embraced by fresh coconut oil!

Which makes it time to tackle the bull by the horns and try and answer the question – is coconut oil bad for the health?

Let me start by sharing how I went about finding the answer. Like many of you reading this, I too had read and heard time and again about coconut oil increasing the risk of heart disease, increasing

What's in a Name?

At one end of a husked coconut are three small circular indentations, forming a triangle. These are often referred to as the coconut's 'eyes'. In India, according to popular belief, they are said to represent the three eyes of Lord Shiva. (In Bengal, it is said that because the coconut has three eyes instead of the usual two, it will never fall on a person's head!)

But in the West, these eyes did not have the benevolent/sacred associations that they do in India. So, many of the coconut's Western names comes from the Portuguese *coco*, which has been variously translated as 'goblin', 'grinning face' etcetera. In 1534, a Portuguese physician and apothecary named Garcia da Orta arrived in Goa and stayed on for thirty-five years. During this time, he compiled what has been acknowledged as a monumental botanical and pharmacological reference book called *Colloquies on the Simples and Drugs of India*, considered a path-breaking work in introducing sixteenth-century Europe to traditional Indian medicine. In this book, da Orta wrote about the coconut, 'We, the Portuguese, with reference to those three holes, gave it the name of *coco* (Spanish *macoco*, for monkey-faced), because it seems like the face of an ape or other animal.' Hence the botanical name *Cocos nucifera*; *nucifera* meaning 'nut-bearing' in Latin.

Almost all the Indian names come from the Sanskrit *narikela*.

Language	Name
English	Coconut
Botanical	Cocos nucifera
Sanskrit	Narikela
Hindi	Nariyal
Gujarati	Nariyel
Bengali	Narkel
Marathi	Naral
Tamil	Thengai
Telugu	Narikelamu, tenkaya
Kannada	Tengina kai
Malayalam	Thengaa

cholesterol and so on. But what bothered me was this. For hundreds of years – no, make that thousands of years – people all over the tropics, and especially in many parts of South India like Kerala and south coastal Karnataka, have been using coconut oil as a cooking medium. So, if it is indeed so detrimental to health, how is it that the alarming increase in the incidence of heart disease in these areas is only a recent phenomenon?

Fortunately this is a question that many other people were also asking. Some of them were eminent members of the scientific and medical community, even cardiologists! And because of this, some answers are now beginning to struggle through the confusing fog of 'bad-for-the-heart' theories that surround this oil.

Firstly, while it is true that coconut is rich in saturated fatty acids, it is also true that not all saturated fatty acids are equal. What this means is that not all of them are detrimental to health, a fact that has only begun to emerge in recent studies. Coconut oil comprises of mainly medium-chain fatty acids (MCFA) that do not turn into body fat unless consumed in very large quantities. Instead, they are utilized immediately by the body to convert into energy. (Also, these fatty oils do not require pancreatic enzyme for digestion and are digested by the enzymes in the saliva – therefore, they get converted into energy even faster!) Not only that, studies have shown that because these fatty acids are combusted quickly, we actually eat less and therefore they may actually help weight control, even weight loss!

Then, if there are studies that show a connection between coconut oil consumption and elevated levels of cholesterol, there are other more recent ones that have shown that regular consumption of coconut oil does not raise the levels of LDL or 'bad' cholesterol. In fact, one study showed that virgin coconut oil – my grandmother's favourite – actually lowered the bad cholesterol.

But most telling of all is the fact that approximately 50 per cent of the fatty acids in coconut oil is made up of a medium-chain fatty acid called lauric acid. This fatty acid gets converted by the body into monolaurin. And monolaurin happens to be the most important fat contained in mother's milk since it is the building material for a baby's immune system. (Incidentally coconut oil is a popular ingredient in baby foods!) Monolaurin also has powerful antibacterial, antiviral and anti-fungal properties, so potent that it is now being tested for its efficacy in destroying the HIV virus.

So, what are we saying here? That not only is coconut oil good for the health, but that we can go as far as to say that coconut oil is next only to mother's milk? According to Dr BM Hegde, eminent Indian cardiologist, the answer is a resounding yes.

But, even if we were to continue to wear our sceptics' hats and take that to be a rather extreme point of view, it is abundantly clear that it is time for a retrial. There is now enough evidence to indicate that coconut oil may be innocent of all the 'unhealthy' charges levelled against it. Not only that, we may have lost out on something that actually provides a cornucopia of nutrition and healing. In other words, it is time for coconut oil to make a comeback.

The Tree of a Thousand Uses

'Kai motte! Kai motte!'

When I first started living in Mysore, I noticed that every now and then, a little tempo piled high with coconut husks would noisily zip around the area, with a man perched precariously on top or hanging out of one side shouting, *'Kai motte!' Kai* in Kannada is a generic word for any fruit or vegetable but it is also how the coconut is popularly referred to and is a shortened version of *tengina kai*. And *motte* means 'eggs'. But *kai motte* is not some exotic confectionery made with coconut and eggs; rather it is the name given to the dried outer husk of the coconut!

Coconut husk is considered to be one of the most efficient fuels, combusting fiercely and quickly. It is still used in many parts of South India as fuel, especially to heat the large quantities of hot water required for bathing! Other parts of the tree like the dried palm fronds and the shells are equally combustible. Of course, the *kai motte* man has become an endangered species of late, as the coconut husk is making way for the solar-powered heater!

Every part of the coconut tree is of some use, which is why in Malay, the coconut tree is called *pokok seribu guna* or 'the tree of a thousand uses'. And it begins when the coconut is just a tiny golden flower. Growing into what look like sheaves of some pale, golden, exotic grain, these flowers provide nectar for bees when they first begin to bloom. After a while, they begin to drip a sweet sap, which is collected and made into vinegar and sugar, and even fermented into toddy and wine. In Ayurveda and traditional medicine, this sap is used as medicine. In South India, the flowers are considered sacred and used for religious ceremonies; in Kerala, they are used in puberty and wedding rituals. And apparently, if the unfermented juice from the flowers is taken during pregnancy, the baby will be born with a fair complexion!

Coconut oil, that much-misunderstood marvel, is also the key ingredient in soaps, shampoos, cosmetics and toothpaste, not to mention hydraulic fluid, paints, synthetic rubber, plastics, margarine and ice cream! And the residue that is left over from the coconut after extracting the oil converts into highly nutritious cattle fodder.

The outer fibrous husk is more than just fuel. It yields coir, which transforms into a huge range of products from handicrafts and mattresses to ships' cables and rigging (because of its water-resistant quality), from rubberized coir sheets that are used to pack delicate photographic equipment to filters used in the manufacture of olive oil in Italy and Greece! The hard shell of the coconut is equally versatile – it is used as fuel, and made into buttons and spoons and musical instruments.

No wonder then, that in many parts of South India, the coconut tree occupies a status that is almost divine. So much so that it is considered inauspicious to cut down a coconut tree that is bearing fruit. Or to put it in the words of Joseph, a sixteenth-century priest wonder-struck by this multifarious, multitasking marvel, 'In conclusion, it is the most perfect tree that is found, to our knowledge.'

A Fairness Cream in your Coconut?

According to Dr Nadkarni's authoritative treatise on traditional medicine, *The Indian Materia Medica*, 'unfermented juice (extracted from the coconut flowers) taken twice or thrice weekly during pregnancy has a marked effect on the colour of the infant; it will be born of a fair complexion…'!

Now, while many of us may take that remedy with a large pinch of salt, the coconut is a healer of ancient and great repute in Ayurveda, Siddha and Unani medicine and all parts of the tree and fruit have medicinal properties. Here are some of them.

Coconut Product	Ailment/Condition Treated
Tender coconut water	Urinary disorders, exhaustion, excessive thirst, giddiness, vomiting, dehydration, dyspepsia, diarrhoea etc
Flesh of the mature coconut	General debility and weight loss, painful and frequent urination
Coconut shell oil	Skin problems like ringworm, eczema etc
Coconut flower juice	Diuretic, laxative
Coconut oil	Minor burns and scalds, dry skin, baldness
Coconut milk	General debility and weight loss, tuberculosis
Roots of the coconut tree	Dysentery, uterine problems, bronchitis, gingivitis etc

Recipes

Wedding Sherbet

This is a traditional must-have at weddings in south coastal Karnataka. Now, a precise recipe is difficult because it all depends on how tart you like the sherbet and how sweet the tender coconut water is, but here is a broad guideline.

INGREDIENTS

Coconut water from one tender coconut

1 teaspoon lemon juice

Sugar to taste

(you can skip the sugar if you want a
low-calorie drink or if the
coconut water is really sweet)

METHOD

Mix all the ingredients together till the sugar has dissolved completely. This is normally served without chilling because the coconut water is naturally cool, but you can chill in the refrigerator for about 30 minutes before serving.

Variation: Finely chop the firmer part of the flesh of the tender coconut and add to the sherbet before serving.

Kerala–Style Vegetable Stew

(Serves 3-4)

I first tasted this delicious, delicately flavoured stew at the house of my mother's friend in a place as far away from Kerala as possible – Gorakhpur in Uttar Pradesh!

INGREDIENTS

2 tbsp vegetable oil (traditionally, coconut oil is
used but any vegetable oil will do)

2-3 cloves

1-inch stick of cinnamon

2 cardamoms

1 large bay leaf

3-4 peppercorns

2 green chillies, sliced (adjust to taste)

½ inch piece of ginger, cut into thin slivers

5-7 curry leaves

3 cups mixed vegetables (carrots, potatoes, beans,
peas, cauliflower etc), washed, cleaned and
chopped into 1-inch pieces

2 medium-sized onions, finely sliced

1-1½ tsp salt (adjust to taste)

Milk extracted from ½ a coconut

METHOD

Heat the oil in a pan and add the cinnamon, cardamom, cloves, bay leaf and peppercorns. Fry for a few seconds, then add the green chillies, ginger and sliced onions. Fry till the onions turn transparent. Now add all the vegetables and the curry leaves, sauté for about a minute. Meanwhile, add water to the second milk of the coconut so that you have about two cups of liquid. Add this to the vegetables and cook on low heat, adding the salt when the vegetable are half cooked. When the vegetables are completely cooked, gently pour in the first milk, making sure that the heat is low. Cook for about 30 seconds and remove from heat. Serve with *appams, idlis, dosas,* plain steamed rice or even pasta or brown bread!

Important: Do not cook the stew for longer than 30 seconds after adding the first milk or else it will curdle.

Fats
The 'Good', the 'Bad' and the Not-so-Ugly!

'No diet will remove all the fat from your body because the brain is entirely fat.
Without a brain, you might look good, but all you could do is run for public office.'
George Bernard Shaw

Shaw was right – more or less, because approximately 70 per cent of the human brain consists of fat. Without fat both in our food and in our bodies, our vital organs would be vulnerable to trauma, the winter cold would be unbearable, our joints would hurt and slowly stiffen, our hair, skin and nails would become dry and brittle and we would have opened the door to a whole host of diseases like diabetes, heart disease and cancer. And if that sounds like a bunch of wild claims, then it is about time we get to know this most misunderstood of nutrients. Yes indeed, fat is as much a nutrient as carbohydrates, proteins, vitamins and minerals. In fact, it was fat that first led to the discovery of vitamins…

In 1913, two teams of Yale biochemists discovered Vitamin A. But what was curious about this discovery was that the vitamin was found in fat – one team found it in cod liver oil, the other in butter! Even more importantly, both teams discovered that Vitamin A was accessible to the body only when there is sufficient fat present because it is soluble only in fat!

The discovery of Vitamin A was the first in a long list of findings that demonstrated how inextricably fats are connected with good health…

Anatomy of a Fatty Acid – Chain Reaction!
Fatty acids are the basic units that make up all fats and they determine the difference between the various kinds of fats.

You see, all fatty acids are molecular chains and one of the things that differentiates one kind of fatty acid from another is the length of that chain. So, there are short-chain fatty acids (SCFA), medium-chain fatty acids (MCFA) and long-chain fatty acids (LCFA).

The second difference is in the number of hydrogen atoms in the chain. So, when the chain contains as much hydrogen atoms as it can accommodate, then it is a 'saturated' fatty acid and this is the basic unit that 'saturated' fats are made up. However, if there is one or more hydrogen atoms 'missing' in that chain, then it is an 'unsaturated' fatty acid and this is the basic unit that makes up 'unsaturated' fats.

For the ordinary you-and-me, saturated fats are those that tend to solidify at room temperature – like coconut oil and *ghee* – whereas unsaturated fats are those that stay liquid – for example, vegetable oils like peanut and sesame.

The Three-Eyed One – Coconut

Pehelwan's Pet – Mustard Seeds and Flower

The question is – are there 'good' and 'bad' fatty acids and therefore 'good' and 'bad' fats? Well, just like there is place for all kinds of creatures in the jungle, there is a role and place for every kind of fat in our diet. Here's how and why…

The 'Unsaturated' Good Guys

There is complete consensus among the experts that the good guys are the unsaturated fatty acids, which are of two types – 'monounsaturated' fatty acids (MUFA) and 'polyunsaturated' fatty acids (PUFA). Among this galaxy of nutritious 'fatties', the Omega family of unsaturated fatty acids are the nutritional superstars. They consist of three sub-groups, the Omega-3, Omega-6 and Omega-9 fatty acids. Together, their presence ensures the health and proper functioning of almost every body part.

The 'Saturated' Baddies?

The widely held belief is that saturated fatty acids and therefore saturated fats are the 'bad' fats, causing all kinds of health problems from obesity to heart disease and cancer.

But here's the lesser-known picture. First of all, saturated fat is an essential component of all membranes in the body – including the brain (more than half of the fatty acids in the grey matter in our brains are saturated fatty acids), the retina and the lungs.

Secondly, many of the reasons why saturated fats are considered bad for the health are now being re-examined. For example, the popular theory is that saturated fats play a major role in increasing 'bad' cholesterol (LDL) and so cause heart disease. But the current thinking is that while many saturated fats do increase the LDL or the 'bad' cholesterol, some of them – like lauric acid and palmitic acid – also raise HDL or the 'good' cholesterol just as much, if not more, thereby nullifying the 'bad' effect. There are even some saturated fatty acids – like stearic acid – that do not have any effect on the LDL cholesterol!

Also, some saturated fats behave differently depending on the food source. For example, palmitic acid is a saturated fat that is popularly condemned – even by the World Health Organization – as playing a role in increasing the risk of heart disease. Yet, palm oil (extracted from the fruit of the oil palm), which has over 50 per cent saturated fat, most of which is palmitic acid, is considered to be one the richest sources of Vitamin E, an antioxidant that may play a vital role in lowering bad cholesterol. Not only that, some saturated fatty acids actually have very important nutritional and therapeutic benefits. And the two best examples are our very own *desi ghee* (clarified butter) and coconut oil.

Does that mean that you can slather your *chappatis* with *ghee* and pig out on those banana chips fried in coconut oil? Of course not – but our diets should contain every kind of fat – including the right kind of saturated fats. Incidentally, the real villains of the 'fat story' are called trans fats and they are man-made! (For more details, see chapter on Ghee, page 192.)

Finally – Is Your Dietary Fat in Good Company?

If you want the fats in your diet to work in your favour, it is important not only to consider how much and which kind of fat you are eating, but also what other nutrients accompany them.

Fats at a Glance

Type of Fat	Important Fatty Acids	Health Benefits	Sources
Saturated	Lauric acid	Body converts it to monolaurin, a fat with powerful antibacterial, antiviral and antifungal properties.	Coconut oil, palm oil, breast milk
	Palmitic acid	Nullifies the effect of bad cholesterol	Palm oil, butter, cheese
	Stearic acid (a significant percentage of which the body converts to oleic acid)	See oleic acid for benefits	Cocoa butter
	Butyric acid	Antiviral and anti-carcinogenic	Butter, *ghee*
Polyunsaturated Fat Omega-3 group	Alpha-linolenic acid (ALA) – an Omega-3 fatty acid present in plant sources that the body converts into DHA and EPA	See DHA and EPA for benefits	Walnuts, green leafy vegetables, mustard oil, peanut oil, fenugreek seeds
	Docosahexaenoic acid (DHA)	Brain food, therefore vital for ability to think, remember, comprehend and concentrate, needed for healthy retina	Oily fish such as salmon, sardine mackerel, tuna, etc
	Eicosapentaenoic acid (EPA)	Helps regulate blood pressure, increases the clotting time of blood, thereby decreasing the risk of strokes and heart attacks	Oily fish such as salmon, sardine, mackerel, tuna, etc
	Partnership of EPA and DHA	Helps lower LDL cholesterol, boosts body's immune system, helps prevent depression, arthritis, heart disease, breast cancer etc	
Polyunsaturated Fat Omega-6 group	Linolenic acid (LA)	Needed for proper functioning of Omega-3 fatty acids, anti-inflammatory and heart-friendly	Most vegetable cooking oils like peanut, sunflower, safflower
Monounsaturated Fat Omega-9 group	Oleic acid	Helps prevent heart disease	Olive oil, mustard oil, sesame oil, peanut oil
	Erucic acid	Helps prevent heart disease	Mustard oil

For example, antioxidants prevent the oxidation of cholesterol that turns it into bad cholesterol, the culprit that clogs arteries, which ultimately leads to heart disease. Other nutrients also play a key role in this cholesterol-regulating operation. The troika of folate (folic acid/Vitamin B9), Vitamin B6 (pyridoxine) and Vitamin B12 (cobalamin) are vital to keep down the levels of homocystein, an amino acid that is known to increase the risk of hardening of arteries and therefore of heart disease. Niacin is so efficient in increasing levels of HDL cholesterol and decreasing levels of LDL cholesterol that in 2007 it was hailed by *The New York Times* as 'an old cholesterol remedy' that was making a comeback! Finally there is dietary fibre, also doing its precious bit to regulate the levels of the two kinds of cholesterol.

Most experts will grant that our understanding of how fat plays a role in nutrition and health is a work-in-progress. For example, in the 1960s, when the causative role of saturated fats in heart disease had become a popularly accepted hypothesis, especially in America, Dr George Mann, an American scientist, conducted a study among men from the Masai tribe in Kenya and Tanzania who traditionally ate a diet that was more than 60 per cent fat – and half of that saturated. The results were, to say the least, shocking. The men had some of the lowest levels of cholesterol ever monitored and were virtually free of heart disease. But, when British researchers studied men from the same tribe who moved to Nairobi and began consuming a more modern diet, the results were even more surprising – the men's cholesterol had skyrocketed.

Some things however are now clear. There is room for every kind of fat in our bodies and our diet. But the amount of space allocated to each is specified by Nature and when that allocation is violated, the body rebels and the result is ill health. When Nature's laws are respected and when the fat in our diet is in the good company of whole, fresh natural foods, then good health and delicious repasts follow.

Ghee: As Good as Gold

'Promotive of health, memory, intelligence, vital fire, vital essence and nourishment, ghee *is a curative for* vata *and* pitta *disorders.'*

Charaka, author of the *Charaka Samhita*, considered as one of the most influential texts of Ayurveda

I know. Holding forth on the health benefits of eating *ghee* might seem a bit like talking about the plus points of wearing a bikini at the North Pole. Will it help, though, if I tell you that some of those benefits will make many of the gentlemen reading this want to lace their daily plate of breakfast cereal with it?

But more on that later.

First, we need to have the correct perspective on fats, especially with all the current hype about low-fat and fat-free food. A balanced, nutritious diet without a certain amount of dietary fat in it is a contradiction in terms. Let us understand why. Apart from being the most efficient source of energy, generating more than twice the amount that carbohydrates do, fats are vital for the body for many other reasons. For one, they contain fatty acids, which are the building blocks for the membranes of every cell in our bodies. Fatty acids are brain food and make up almost 70 per cent of grey matter. They are vital for good eyesight because they are part of the membranes in the retina. They also occupy the tiny spaces between nerves called synapses through which impulses are transmitted from one nerve to another. Then, vitamins A, E, D and K are fat-soluble vitamins. This means that without the presence of fat, these vitamins will not dissolve and therefore will not be available to the body.

So, as you can see, without a judicious amount of fats in our diet, we will just not be able to function. But the questions remain – wouldn't any kind of fat do? Aren't certain varieties of vegetable oil the healthier option? And what's so special about *ghee*?

Old Gold

'It is the producer of beauty...it is the remover of hysteria, headache, epilepsy, fever, indigestion, excess of bile; it is the increaser of digestion, memory, intellect...semen and life.'

Sushruta, author of the *Sushruta Samhita*, the Ayurvedic treatise considered to be one of the world's oldest texts on surgery.

Grhta. The Sanskrit word for *ghee* is from the root *grh* that means 'flowing luminosity', 'brightness' and 'clarity'. (Sri Aurobindo writes about this is his book, *Hymns to The Mystic Fire*, a commentary on the *Rig Veda*.) And if you look at a cup of freshly made *ghee*, so exquisitely translucent and golden, you will understand why the name is so apt. Since Vedic times, *ghee* has been the symbol of all that is auspicious and sacred, and no Hindu ritual is complete without its presence, fuelling the lamps that burn in front of the deities and poured into sacrificial fires.

The *Atharva Veda* has an entire *sloka* dedicated to *ghee* and ancient Hindu texts have thousands of references to it, too many to enumerate. Interestingly enough, though *ghee* is almost solely an Indian food today, centuries ago, it was exported from Indian ports like Bharuch to Rome and other parts of the Mediterranean and the Middle East, probably along with spices. In fact, according to many food historians, the references to butter in ancient texts originating from the Near Eastern region (Israel, Palestine, Jordan, Syria, Lebanon, Georgia, Armenia, Iraq and the Asian part of modern Turkey) are actually references to *ghee*. One example is the *Periplus of the Erythraean Sea*, a first-century Greek nautical manual that describes navigation and trading opportunities at ports along the coast of the Red Sea, north-east Africa and India. In it, *ghee* is referred to as an article of trade.

As food, the status of *ghee* was no less lofty. Along with milk, the Hindus considered it ritually pure and so, temple food fed to the Brahmins after a *puja* and all other food for religious purposes was always cooked in *ghee*. Also, its presence in food signalled wealth and prosperity – as it still does. In fact, a popular boast in North India till not so long ago was, 'our food is always cooked in *asli* (real) *ghee*'. That was until all the nutritionists came along and pooped that party!

In Ayurveda, *ghee* is considered the ultimate *sattvic* food; *sattvic* being defined as that which is balanced, soothing, peaceful and nourishing. According to Sushruta, *ghee* develops intelligence and Charaka has said that it builds both memory and the body's immunological systems. One of the sixteen *samskaras*, or 'rites of passage', as laid down in Hinduism are a set of ceremonies called *jatakarma*, performed immediately after the birth of the child. In one of these rites, the father, using a gold instrument, feeds the newborn a mixture of honey and *ghee* or just *ghee*. It is said that this act of the father is to build the child's intelligence. In other words, *ghee* is considered to be supreme among nourishing foods.

Ayurveda also deems *ghee* to be one of the most important medicinal substances, infused with many therapeutic qualities. So it is used to treat a whole host of ailments – from minor burns, blisters and wounds to irate digestive tracts, epilepsy, even alcoholism. It is also the primary medium in which many Ayurvedic medicines are administered to the body. For example, the renowned Ayurvedic formulation, *chawanprash*, is made in a base of *ghee* and honey. This is because *ghee* is considered to be an excellent preservative, retaining the freshness and potency of ingredients. *Ghee* is also known to boost the efficacy of certain herbs and has the ability to penetrate deep into body tissues.

Finally, what the gentlemen have been waiting for. I remember many years ago, a taxi driver in Mumbai advising my friend – who after ten years of marriage was still childless – to feed her husband *ghee* every day! At the time, the advice made both of us giggle and scoff at what seemed to be an old wives' tale but it seems that the cabbie knew what he was talking about. According to Charaka, *ghee* promotes virility and sexual prowess and improves the quality of semen. In fact, in the section on *vajikarana* (virilization therapy), *ghee* figures in many of the over thirty formulations listed including one which promises an 'elephantine erection'!

The ladies need not feel left out because *ghee* has something for them too. According to Charaka, *ghee* softens and cools the body and improves the complexion.

And New Gold Too!

But are modern medicine and nutritional experts as ecstatic about *ghee*?

Yes and no.

The 'no', according to me, is perhaps primarily because not enough studies have been done about *ghee* and of the ones that exist, some are contradictory in nature. Since it is a dietary fat that consists predominantly of saturated fats, the predictable finding would be that the consumption of *ghee* raises cholesterol and thus increases the risk of heart disease. And on the face of it, some studies do seem to indicate this.

What's in a Name?

The origin of the word *ghee* is from the Sanskrit *ghrita*, while the origin of the Tamil, Telugu (*ney, neyyi*) and Malayalam names (*neyyu*) is from *ney*, a generic word for any greasy substance – like oil, *ghee* or lard – in Proto-Dravidian, the ancient ancestor of Dravidian languages.

Language	Name
English	Clarified butter
Sanskrit	Ghrta, ghrita
Bengali	Ghee, ghrito
Hindi, Gujarati	Ghee
Marathi	Tup
Tamil, Telugu	Ney, neyyi
Kannada	Tuppa
Malayalam	Neyyu

But a more in-depth examination of the dietary habits of the respondents of such studies has shown that the culprits could be other factors. For example, one study conducted in 1967 about the incidence of heart disease among North Indians and South Indians and published in the *American Journal of Clinical Nutrition* had astonishing results. It showed that though the North Indians were non-vegetarians and consumed nine times more fat (most of it from milk and *ghee*) than the South Indians, the incidence of heart disease among them was seven times lower than it was among their Southern brethren!

More recent studies also show that modern nutritionists may have been too hasty in judging *ghee* as a 'bad' fat. One study conducted in 2004 by the All India Institute of Medical Sciences in Delhi showed that when mustard oil in the diet of young, healthy, physically active respondents was partially substituted with *ghee*, it had no adverse effect on the cholesterol levels. Another study conducted by CFTRI, Mysore on Wistar rats had even more interesting results – it showed that supplementation of diets with *ghee* could actually help lower cholesterol!

There are a few leads emerging as to why this could be so. First of all, while about two-thirds of fat in *ghee* is made up of saturated fatty acids, the remaining one-third consists of monounsaturated fatty acids, the good guys that are in abundance in oils like olive oil and sesame oil.

Secondly, studies now show that saturated fats as a causative factor in heart disease may not be as simple and as direct as it was earlier thought to be. Thirdly, not all saturated fats are created equal. Much of the saturated fat in *ghee* is comprised of short-chain fatty acids (SCFA) like butyric acid. These fatty acids do not turn into body fat unless consumed in very large quantities. Instead, they are quickly assimilated and converted into energy and therefore have no chance to get deposited in the body. Even more importantly, butyric acid has been shown to have both antiviral and anti-carcinogenic properties.

Lastly, according to the latest studies, the real villains of the fatty acids story are trans fats. You see, the food industry has almost always used vegetable oils. But these oils are unstable, which means that they quickly deteriorate and become rancid and therefore, so do the foods that have been cooked in them. So, a process called hydrogenation is used to make these oils more stable. But the price for stability and longer shelf life has been very steep – these 'partially hydrogenated oils' (as they were known till 1999) or trans fats (as they are known today) are now thought to be one of the main causes of heart disease, and are linked with increased risk of cancer, Type 2 diabetes and even infertility. So much so that trans fats are now almost completely banned from use in New York restaurants. Examples of trans fat are many varieties of margarine, and in India, the ubiquitous *vanaspati*, masquerading so cunningly as *ghee*!

Ghee however has no trans fats. Also, there is now some evidence that *ghee* contains nutrients like vitamins A, B2 (riboflavin) and D.

All of which is leading to even the saturated-fat-phobic West to come round to the benefits of eating *ghee*. An article in the *Yoga Journal*, one of America's most reputed magazines on yoga, called it 'liquid gold'!

Now that you know of its many health benefits, there's one other reason to eat *ghee*. (Incidentally, not for a minute am I advocating that you smother your food with *ghee* – approximately two teaspoons a day is the healthful dose.) And that is for the sheer pleasure of it. Shut your eyes and imagine the unmistakable, irresistible fragrance of food cooked in *ghee* wafting out of the kitchen. Or the taste of hot, fluffy rice doused with *dal* or *sambar*, laced with a spoonful of freshly made *ghee*. Or the fabulous sight and smell of this 'liquid gold' lovingly melting and anointing a piping hot *chapatti*. And then remember that it's a spoonful of *ghee* that makes the medicine – and that lunch – go down in the most delightful and healthful way!

Important: *All references to* ghee *in this chapter are to* ghee *made from cow's milk. In India, where both cow's milk and buffalo's milk are widely consumed, it is the popularly held belief that* ghee *made from cow's milk is superior in terms of medicinal as well as nutritional value. While modern data/research explaining the reasons for this is hard to come by, several ancient Indian texts, including the* Vedas, *the* Mahabharata, *the* Charaka Samhita *and the* Sushruta Samhita, *consider cow's milk and cow's milk products (including* ghee*) as sources of nutrition and medicine.*

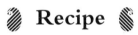

Recipe

Homemade Ghee

Many people think that making butter and ghee *at home is a laborious, time-consuming process, but not if you do it this way.*

INGREDIENTS	METHOD
Cream (about ½ litre)	Carefully skim the cream off milk and collect it in a pot or jar with a capacity of about 1 litre. Do this daily, adding a tablespoonful or two of curd to the cream. (You can also skim the cream that collects on top of the curd and add it to your 'cream collection'.) Store this cream in the refrigerator.
	When the pot is about half full, remove it from the refrigerator and allow the cream to stand at room temperature for at least 4-5 hours. The curd content in the cream will make it curdle. Now, churn this mixture – you can use either an electric whisk or even an old-fashioned wooden buttermilk churn. Because of the fermentation, butter will separate from the mixture in a matter of minutes! Churn till the butter forms thick globs and floats up. Remove the butter,

gently draining out the liquid – this is buttermilk, which you can use for cooking or just drink.

To make *ghee*, place this butter (you can reserve some for use) in a heavy pan and simmer over very low heat till the butter melts slowly and becomes a clear, golden liquid – *ghee*. You will know the *ghee* is ready when a golden froth forms on the surface and a residue separates and turn golden brown. Strain the *ghee*, allow to cool and store in a dry glass jar.

Don't throw away the residue – it is delicious! Mix it with jaggery and slather it on hot *chapattis* – kids will love this. Or simply add it to *dal* or *sambar* or even *pulaos*!

Peanuts: A Handful of Love

'Nothing takes the taste out of peanut butter quite like unrequited love.'
Charlie Brown

I t started off as an occasional cartoon in the newspaper of a small American town and was called 'Li'l Folks'. After a year, when the cartoonist asked to be paid more money, the editor refused. His plea for the cartoon to become a regular on the comic strip page of the newspaper was met with the same response. Disheartened, the cartoonist asked the editor if he should stop drawing the cartoon altogether. Yes, said the editor. One year later, in 1950, after several rejections, the cartoonist finally sold 'Li'l Folks' as a comic strip to United Features Syndicate. But the syndicate decided to change the name because it was too similar to the names of two other popular comic strips of the time – Al Capp's 'Li'l Abner' and 'Little Folks'.

The new name?

'Peanuts'.

It went on to become one of the most widely read and what is considered to be the most influential comic strip of all time.

The cartoonist, Charles Schulz, hated the name. Twenty-five years later, after his readership had swelled to sixty million readers and Charlie Brown, Lucy and Snoopy were featured on the cover of *Time* magazine, Schulz still hated the name. He said, 'I wanted a strip with dignity and significance. "Peanuts" made it sound too insignificant.' Perhaps it was because Schulz was reminded of that often-used, derogatory idiom, 'it's peanuts'.

Ironic, because there is nothing insignificant about the peanut. So, even though it is often sneered at as the poor man's cashew nut and dismissed as a useless, fattening snack, the peanut (and all its derivatives, like peanut oil and butter) is actually one of the most inexpensive yet healthiest of foods.

So, I present to you – the peanut!

This Nut is History!
Till recently, evidence found in ancient Peruvian tombs indicated that the peanut was cultivated at least as early as 2000 BC. But that

date had to be revised when anthropologists from the Vanderbilt University working in the Andes mountains in northern Peru found remains of the peanut that dated back to about 7,600 years ago.

The peanut is said to have originated in Bolivia. And from South America, the peanut sailed out on the ships of European explorers – the Spanish took it to Europe and to several countries in the Far East including the Philippines and Indonesia, while the Portuguese introduced it to Africa. And from Africa, travelling aboard slave ships, the peanut went to North America.

And how and when did it come to India? Well that is a matter of debate. Some experts feel that it arrived in the wake of Vasco da Gama's landing on Malabar's shores. Others think that it may have come from the Philippines or Indonesia or even China. Whatever the route, the peanut was a foreigner, taking up residence in India only about five hundred years ago. Nevertheless we welcomed this nut enthusiastically and today, India is the second-largest producer of the peanut, which is the thirteenth most important food crop of the world and the fourth most important source of edible oil.

Nuts about Your Health

Say 'nutrition' or 'health' and the chances that 'peanut' would be the first thing (or even the twentieth thing) to pop into your head are very, very slim. We all know that peanuts are those delicious but horribly fattening things that we mindlessly munch in front of the telly or at a party or a bar, right? Actually, wrong. Peanuts are fattening only because we fry them and/or eat far too many of them. But if it is cooked the right way and eaten in the right quantities, the peanut can be an astonishing stockpile of nutrition.

For example, did you know that roughly half a billion people in the world rely on peanuts as their primary source of protein and that it is the world's third most important source of vegetable protein? Almost a third of the peanut is protein, which means that weight for weight, peanuts contain more protein than a beefsteak, about twice that of an egg and far, far more than any fruit or veggie.

But that's only a tiny part of the peanut's spectacular nutritional profile because it is also an excellent source of Vitamin B3 (niacin), folate or folic acid (Vitamin B9), choline and Vitamin E, an important antioxidant. It has very good amounts of minerals like phosphorus, magnesium, manganese and copper as well.

The Underground Story

The peanut grows very curiously. The flowers start off above the ground, pollinate themselves and after a few days, stalk-like stems push the soon-to-be peanut pods into the ground where they fatten and mature. Burying the pod in this way is the plant's way of protecting the peanut during dry periods – which is why it is a popular crop in low-rainfall areas.

And the little peanut serves all this up without fattening you up. How so? Well, even an apple baked into a pie loaded with butter, cream and sugar, or spinach that has been deep-fried can be as fattening as fried peanuts. But if you eat just a handful of peanuts every day that are either dry-roasted or boiled, you are *less likely to gain weight than people who never eat nuts.*

As they say in cricket, howzzat?

Nutty Protector

Before I started researching for this book, if someone had said to me that peanuts help reduce the incidence of heart disease and cancer, I would have said, 'You're nuts!' But now I know that this is true. In 1958, an international team of scientists led by Dr Ancel Keys from the University of Minnesota School of Public Health launched a massive study called the Seven Countries Study. It studied the diet, lifestyle and incidence of coronary heart disease among 12,763 middle-aged men from seven countries – USA, Japan, Italy, Greece, the Netherlands, Finland and Yugoslavia. The study lasted over a decade – from 1958 to 1970.

And the results threw up a very curious thing, an eye-opener for the medical fraternity. The men who ate a diet rich in vegetables, grains, fruits, beans and fish (like the Greek and the Japanese) had the lowest rates of heart disease and the highest average life expectancy – in spite of getting up to 40 per cent of their calories from fat! The reason for this was that this fat consisted mainly of monounsaturated fats and came from foods like olive oil and fish.

What does that have to do with the peanut? Well, the peanut is a veritable oil well – 40 to 50 per cent of its content is oil and more than 80 per cent of that oil is made up of polyunsaturated and monounsaturated fats. These are the 'good' fats, containing those all-important Omega-3 and Omega-6 fatty acids essential for – among other things – a healthy ticker. So both peanuts and peanut oil are being increasingly recommended as an excellent way of keeping heart disease at bay. In 2001, scientists at the Pennsylvania State University reviewed and collated the results of sixteen studies conducted on the link between the consumption of nuts and coronary disease. They found that just three to four tablespoons of nuts eaten five or more times a week can result in 25-39 per cent reduction in the risk of heart disease. Even more amazingly, the scientists surmised that at least 50 per cent of the nuts consumed in these studies were peanuts!

That same handful of peanuts will also help prevent diabetes. A 2002 study conducted by the Harvard Public School of Health found that women who ate at least 150 grams of peanuts a week reduced their risk of developing Type 2 diabetes by 21 per cent. And still staying with that handful of peanuts, eating them just two or more times each week could reduce the risk of colon cancer by as much as a whopping 58 per cent in women and 27 per cent in men!

Wait, we aren't done yet…

Wine in a Shell?

What do peanuts have in common with red wine?

Well, let me start by telling you about something called the French Paradox. It's a well-known fact that French cuisine is loaded with cream and cheese and all other kinds of those 'bad' saturated fats. (According to the 2002 Food and Agriculture Organization (FAO) data, the average French person ate 50 per cent more fat per day than the average American, four times as much butter, 60 per cent more cheese and nearly thrice the pork!) The perplexing paradox – first observed by Irish physician Samuel Black – is that despite all this guffing of fat, the incidence of coronary heart disease among the French is significantly lower than among Americans. Even today when the dubious joys of hamburgers and 'French' fries have insinuated themselves among the French, France continues to have lower incidence of coronary heart disease than many developed countries.

The reason?

There are several hypotheses – and one of them is that it is the red wine – which the French consume as copiously as they do all that cream and butter and cheese – that does the trick. Wine – especially red wine – contains an antioxidant called resveratrol which has shown potential anti-carcinogenic, antiviral, even anti-aging properties. It may also help prevent heart disease by increasing levels of 'good' cholesterol and protecting against blocking of arteries.

Now you're thinking: red wine is all very well for those Frenchies but what about us Indians? Well, just reach for those peanuts

What's in a Name?

The peanut's botanical identity and ancestry is in many of its names. Its botanical name is *Arachis hypogaea*; *Arachis* meaning 'legume' in Greek and *hypogaea* meaning 'below the ground'. And that is exactly what the peanut is – not a nut but a legume and a member of the *Fabaceae* family, related to *mung*, beans, green peas, *channa*, etcetera, and also to tamarind and rosewood. (Incidentally, both the almond and the walnut aren't nuts either!)

It is called *mungphali* in Hindi, which mean '*mung*-like bean' and the names in the South Indian languages have the word *kadale* in them which means *channa* (Bengal gram). The peanut is also sometimes called *vilayeti mung* in Hindi, which means 'foreign *mung*', pointing to the peanut's non-Indian origins, as does its Bengali name – *China badam*.

Language	Name
English	Peanut, groundnut, earthnut, goober, goober peas, jack nuts, manila nuts, monkey nuts, etc
Botanical	Arachis hypogaea
Sanskrit	Snehabijaka, bhuchanaka
Bengali	China badam
Gujarati	Shing
Hindi	Mungphali, seng, seng dana, vilayeti mung
Marathi	Sheng
Tamil	Verakadalai, nilakadalai
Telugu	Verushanagalu, nilakadale
Kannada	Kadalekai, kadale bija
Malayalam	Kappalandi

because they are also an excellent source of resveratrol. In fact, ounce for ounce, they have more than half the amount that is contained in red wine. And speaking of antioxidants, a study conducted in 2004 by the University of Florida's Institute of Food and Agricultural Sciences found that peanuts are so rich in antioxidants that they can rival many fruits that are considered antioxidant goldmines – like strawberries and blackberries. In fact, according to the study, peanuts contain more antioxidants than apples, carrots and beets!

A Many-Splendoured Thing

He was born to parents who were slaves on a plantation in Missouri, just as the American Civil War was coming to an end. But the difficult circumstances of his birth and childhood did not dim his love of Nature; in fact, it was this passion that earned him the nickname 'Plant Doctor'. His name was George Washington Carver and he revolutionized agriculture in the southern states of America by using crop rotation to revive the soil that had been depleted of its nutrients by years of growing only tobacco and cotton. One of the crops that he used was the peanut, of which he was an ardent advocate. So ardent that he came up with more than a hundred different products made from peanuts, including buttermilk, mayonnaise, coffee, shaving cream, meat substitutes, paper, laxatives, laundry soap, ink, shaving cream – and nitro-glycerine, the active ingredient that is used in the manufacture of explosives like dynamite!

Many of these uses are valid even today. For example, peanut oil is still used in soaps, face powders, shaving creams, shampoos and paints. The residue left over after the oil is extracted from peanuts makes very good protein supplement for farm animals. As do the peanut plants, though most farmers put them back into the soil so that they decompose to become nitrogen-rich fertilizer. Even peanut shells are useful because they convert into fuel, and high-fibre roughage that is added to livestock feed. They are also used in manufacturing plastics, cork substitutes, abrasives, mulch, particle board and fertilizer.

Yours Lovingly, Peanut...

For me, peanuts are inextricably linked with one of my favourite places in the world – Mumbai. Marine Drive, Juhu Beach, Gateway of India – no waterfront in the city is complete without the peanut sellers selling roasted peanuts and *channa* from wicker baskets slung around their necks, with a small clay pot of live coal embers to keep the peanuts warm and crunchy. These peanut sellers are as much a part of Mumbai as the Arabian Sea and nothing keeps them away, not even the Mumbai monsoons.

And happiness was – and still is – a stroll by the sea, clutching a pointy paper cone full of warm, toasted peanuts and crunching their delicious nuttiness as the moist, warm-yet-cool, salty breath of

the sea mischievously kissed my skin and whipped my hair this way and that...

Snehabijaka or 'seed of love' – the Sanskrit name for the peanut says all that needs to be said about it, because the innumerable gifts of nutrition and health that the peanut offers us can only be gifts of love.

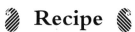

Recipe

Peanut and Fresh Coriander Chutney   (Makes about 1 cup)

This is a superb variation of the traditional coriander and pudina *(mint) chutney. The coriander is anti-microbial, anti-flatulent and a great appetite tickler, besides being rich in disease-fighting phytochemicals. Its union with the equally healthful peanut makes a wonderfully fragrant, nutritious chutney that also doubles as a dip (add to curd and serve with roasted* pappads!*) as well as a low-cal* chapatti/sandwich/anything *spread.*

INGREDIENTS

1 cup fresh coriander leaves, cleaned washed and chopped coarsely
1 cup freshly roasted peanuts
2 green chillies (adjust to taste)
½ tsp lemon juice
¼ tsp cumin seeds (jeera)
½ tsp grated jaggery (optional)
½ tsp salt (adjust to taste)

METHOD

Grind all the ingredients together, adding the cumin last, when the chutney is almost fully ground. Serve with anything – *chapattis, pakoras,* as a sandwich spread or even to perk up your *dal-chawal!*

In fact, you can use the chutney to make this sandwich, borrowed from the famed Mumbai *sandwichwallah.*

Spread two slices of bread with it. Pile one slice with layers of thinly sliced boiled potato, beetroot, raw cucumber, onion (optional) and tomato, sprinkle with *chaat masala* or salt and pepper. Top with second chutneyed slice and press firmly. Sink your teeth into this yummy, wholesome whole meal!

Variation: Delete the coriander and *jeera,* increase the peanuts by half a cup, convert green chillies into red and add 2-3 cloves of garlic and you have a South American peanut relish!

Jaggery: Brown Sweetness

Of late, we have become an anxious, worried bunch. As heart disease and diabetes are becoming more common than the cold, we feverishly count calories and worriedly watch our weight, fretting about blood sugar and blood pressure. And so, 'sweet' is increasingly a bad word, a bugbear. Equally the anathema of the beauty-conscious and the health-conscious, the word has become associated with foods that perpetuate that old myth – anything that tastes good is bad for you!

When, in fact, the sweet taste cues one of the most important food groups in a balanced diet – carbohydrates. There are two kinds of carbohydrates: the complex kind, which includes the starches and takes much longer to digest, and the simple kind, which includes all types of sugars. So even though we associate 'sugar' with just that one substance that we use to sweeten our food and drink, there are several kinds of sugar and they are present in all natural foods. For example, have you ever wondered why onions turn brown when you fry them? It is because the sugar in them gets caramelized with the heat and turns brown. All fruits and many vegetables (like carrots, red pumpkin and tomatoes) contain a type of sugar called fructose. Several of the nuts, seeds, cereals and legumes also have a certain amount of sugar in them. (Hence names like 'sweet corn'!) And milk and its associated products contain a type of sugar called lactose.

Which bring us to the unanswered question – why is 'sweet' considered to be such a bad thing, nutritionally speaking? Well, it is only because we eat sweet foods in all the wrong forms, but even more importantly, because we eat too much of them. So, one of the best ways to satisfy your sweet tooth is – naturally! That means eating not just lots of fruits but also a category of foods that has been all but drowned out by the hype about sugar – natural sweeteners.

And so, this is a tribute to one of the most delicious and healthiest natural sweeteners available to us.

Jaggery.

While it is also made from the sap of different kinds of palm trees like the coconut palm and the date palm, in India, jaggery is most commonly made from sugarcane juice. Not the most prepossessing of foods, it is brownish in colour and usually comes in lumps or in crude cubes or blocks. It tends to crumble messily or disintegrate into a gooey, sticky brown mass if left exposed to the atmosphere. In fact, it is not a patch on pretty, dainty, sparkly-white sugar as far as looks go, but is miles ahead in terms of nutrition.

Honey Without Bees?

'O Devi! The sugarcane juice, when heated, yields a syrup which again heated yields a very delicious and nice thing called gur. *I am presenting this* gur *to Thee…'*

From *The Devi Bhagavatam*

One of my mother's earliest memories is of jaggery-making in her father's house. Come sugarcane season, after the sugarcane had been harvested, a large wood fire would be lit in a patch of open ground near the house. A massive iron *kadai* (frying pan) would be placed on this fire. This would be filled with sugarcane juice, which would be allowed to cook very slowly for hours till it reduced and turned into thick, glossy, golden-brown syrup.

The delicious aroma of sugarcane juice cooking would smoke out the large platoon of children (which included my mother) from the house. Each child would be armed with a little clay pot and a ladleful of the hot, golden liquid would be carefully poured into each little pot, which would be taken away as carefully and allowed to cool.

Then a noisy, happy, glorious feast of jaggery-hogging would follow!

And while the children got blissfully and stickily sated, the rest of the liquid in the *kadai* would be poured into moulds and allowed to cool and harden. And before long, a huge pile of jaggery blocks was ready – enough to last my grandfather's joint family of over fifty members for an entire year!

For thousands of years, jaggery has been made in India exactly as it was in my grandfather's house. In fact, you could say we Indians are old hands at sweeteners. Sugarcane has grown in this country since at least 6000 BC and we have been making both jaggery and sugar at least as far back as the fourth century BC. (The first mention of jaggery is in the works of Panini, the great Sanskrit grammarian.)

Welcome Drink

It's an old and sadly, now almost forgotten, Indian tradition of welcoming guests – with a glass of water and a few pieces of jaggery. Try it when you next have people visiting you!

When the Persian king, Darius I arrived in the Indus Valley in 510 BC, to his astonishment, he observed that the locals had 'a reed that yields honey without the assistance of bees' out of which they made sweeteners! And when Alexander the Great landed in India in 326 BC, one of his most trusted admirals, Nearchus, commented about a reed as large as a tree that 'produced honey without the association of bees'.

Alexander was also amazed to find 'stones the colour of frank-incense and sweeter than figs or honey'. He was referring of course to *khand*, a kind of rock sugar made from sugarcane juice. *The Periplus of the Erythraean Sea* (first century AD) spoke of 'cane honey' that was regularly exported from the Konkan coast and from Barygaza (present-day Bharuch in Gujarat). The incredulity of the Greeks and Persians was natural because the only sweetener known to them at the time was honey.

Interestingly enough, the origin of the word 'sugar' is from the Sanskrit *sharkara* (probably because the two sound so similar), even though *sharkara* is the Sanskrit name for jaggery. The *Mahabhasya* (200 BC), Patanjali's commentary on Panini's work on Sanskrit grammar, mentions *sharkara* repeatedly as does Kautilya's *Arthashastra* along with the other Sanskrit word for jaggery – *guda*. And both Kautilya and Charaka mention the use of jaggery as the fermenting agent as well as the raw material for making alcoholic drinks.

But for some reason, though both sugarcane and sugar were instant hits with the many visitors from the West who came to ancient India to conquer and to trade, jaggery remained popular only in the Indian subcontinent, sweetening our *payasams* and our lives for centuries. South and Central America are the only other regions where a sweetener similar to jaggery is popular. Also made from sugarcane juice, it is called *panela*.

Sweeteners – The Inside Story

Let's first get a few basics out of the way.

There are 'good' sweeteners and 'bad' ones. What separates the two is – naturally – the nutritive content, which, in turn, is almost always determined by the process used to make the sweetener. Sugarcane juice, the raw material commonly used to make both sugar and jaggery, contains nutrients like iron, magnesium, phosphorus and

India's Jaggery Capital

In the heart of the wealthy sugarcane region in Maharashtra is the city of Kolhapur, known as India's jaggery capital. Its over six hundred *gurhals* (small-scale jaggery-making units) have an estimated annual turnover of Rs 760 million. These *gurhals* are something of a tourist attraction – many of them host dinners for visitors which feature local delicacies like the famous, super-spicy Kolhapuri mutton! India's largest jaggery market is in Muzaffarnagar in Uttar Pradesh while the second largest is in Anakapalli in the Visakhapatnam district in Andhra Pradesh.

What's in a Name?

The word 'jaggery' is said to be a combination and corruption of several words: *sharkara* (the Sanskrit name for jaggery), *chakkara*, which means both 'sweet' and 'jaggery' in Malayalam and *jagara* which is a Portuguese term for palm sugar.

Gur, the Hindi word for jaggery, doubles up for two varieties, the more common variety made from sugarcane juice and also the kind that is made from the sap of different varieties of palm trees like coconut and date palms.

Language	Name
English	Jaggery
Sanskrit	Sharkara, guda
Bengali	Gur
Gujarati	Gol
Hindi	Gur
Marathi	Gul
Tamil	Vellam
Telugu	Bellamu
Kannada	Bella
Malayalam	Sharkara, chakkara

calcium and is also a good source of Vitamin B2 (riboflavin). But the processes used to convert sugarcane juice into sugar and jaggery are radically different. Jaggery is made by a simple process of boiling sugarcane juice till it is reduced to a concentrated form that hardens on cooling. Sugar, on the other hand, is made by a much more complicated process which involves the use of chemicals in order to 'refine' the sugarcane juice of its 'impurities' and turn it into those beautiful, sparkling white crystals. But as a result of this 'refinement', all the nutrients are also removed or destroyed.

In the case of jaggery, the simpler process of boiling allows it to retain these nutrients. So, measure for measure, while sugar is nothing but carbohydrates (many in the anti-sugar lobby call them 'naked' carbohydrates!), jaggery retains many of the nutrients that were originally present in the sugarcane juice. So jaggery is an excellent source of potassium, and its iron content makes it an inexpensive dietary solution for anaemia resulting from poor nutrition, a condition very common among poor women and children in India. It is even considered good for babies because it doesn't get them constipated as sugar sometimes tends to do.

Medicinal Sugar!

The *Sushruta Samhita*, the ancient compendium that is one of the cornerstones of Ayurvedic medicine, waxes eloquent about jaggery, saying that it 'purifies the blood, prevents rheumatic afflictions and disorders of bile and possesses nutritive properties of high order'. In Ayurveda, jaggery is used to treat a whole host of ailments including anaemia, piles and other anal diseases, jaundice, bronchitis, tuber-culosis and urinary ailments. It is also used as a blood purifier and as a cardiac tonic. In fact, jaggery is traditionally considered such a trusted food in India that in many communities, jaggery dissolved in water is one of the first things given to the newborn baby. Little wonder then that jaggery is often referred to as 'medicinal sugar'.

Even so, the interest of modern-day nutritionists and researchers in jaggery has been minimal, though there have been a few isolated sparks. For example, a paper presented at the Workshop on Biopersistence of Respirable Synthetic Fibers and Minerals conducted in France in 1992 showed that industrial workers in dusty, smoky or highly toxic surroundings seemed to have little or no bronchial trouble or lung discomfort if they regularly ate jaggery.

All reasons enough to look at this lumpy brown sweetener in a new light. To which, I will add one more reason – a totally personal one and nothing at all to do with health or nutrition. Unlike the bland, 'faceless' sweetness of sugar, jaggery has a distinctive character, a flavour that is both unmistakable and delicious and infuses everything that you add it to.

The Sweet Lesson of Moderation

So does that mean that you can now go to town with this brown sweetness, satisfying that long-deprived sweet tooth, pigging out on all kinds of desserts and sweets because they now contain nutritious jaggery instead of sugar?

The answer is no. For all its nutritive content, jaggery is still a carbohydrate and the inescapable fact is that if you consume more

---

The Better Sugar?

- Try using jaggery to sweeten juices, milkshakes, breakfast cereal, even tea and coffee… and lemonade!

- Substitute sugar with jaggery in Indian sweets like *karanjis* (sweet stuffed *samosas*), *kesari bhath* (sweet *upma*), even rice and vermicelli *payasam* (*kheer*). But since jaggery is slightly less sweeter than sugar, you will need to use approximately 1.25 to 1.5 times the weight of sugar when you are making the substitution.

- A dash of grated jaggery enhances the taste of *dals* and *sambar* and vegetable dishes like *poriyals*.

carbohydrates than your body needs to fuel your energy requirements, it will end up as body fat. But look at it like this. The sweet taste is one of the most wonderful of the four tastes. (Six actually, if you go by Ayurveda.) It is the taste that marks all beginnings. It is the taste with which we celebrate. It is the taste that we offer to the gods, supplicating for their blessings. And it is the taste that comforts and soothes, that symbolizes love, abundance, prosperity and goodness.

So, if sweetness can permeate your life *and* contribute to your health, why banish it completely? In Karnataka, we celebrate the festival of Ugadi with a very meaningful and beautiful tradition. After the morning bath and *puja*, each member of the family eats a small amount of jaggery together with a few flowers of the *neem* tree. The flowers are tiny but bitter and they are eaten along with the jaggery to remind us that life is both bitter and sweet. As it must be, because we know and cherish the value of a thing only because its opposite also exists. So we appreciate white because we know black, a full belly because we have experienced hunger, good because we have seen bad – and sweetness because we have tasted bitterness.

In other words, it's always a balancing act – life and the sweetness on your plate.

CAUTION

If you are suffering from diabetes, please consult your doctor before incorporating jaggery into your diet.

 # Recipe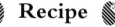

Tamarind and Jaggery Chutney

(Makes about 1–1½ cups)

A yummy substitute for tomato sauce!

INGREDIENTS

Tamarind, size of a large lemon
1 ½ cups jaggery (adjust to taste)
½ tsp ground ginger (optional)
2 tsp cumin, roasted and powdered
1 tsp red chilli powder
½ tsp salt (adjust to taste)
1 tsp chaat masala (optional – reduce the amount of salt if you are adding chaat masala)

METHOD

Soak the tamarind in about half a cup of hot water for about 20 minutes, then extract the juice by squeezing thoroughly. Strain, and add to a pan along with the jaggery and a cup of water. Simmer on low heat till the jaggery has completely melted and the sauce has reduced to a thick, glossy consistency. Add the rest of the ingredients and stir well. Cool and store in the refrigerator – the chutney should keep for a fortnight.

Curd: White Magic

I n the thirty-five-odd years that he worked for the Indian Railways, my father was often posted to places that were to him as alien as a foreign country. Struggling with strange languages (his command over Hindi was at best tenuous!) or coming to terms with even stranger food, homesickness was a frequent problem. But no matter how unfamiliar the place and how far away home seemed to be, succour was always at hand – in a bowl of cool, creamy, soothing curd. Into which would go some plain steamed rice, a pinch of salt and sometimes, a tempering of mustard seeds, curry leaves and red chillies. The whole enchilada would be mixed well, the rice mashed up a little so that it would mingle better with the curd. And hey presto, that South Indian panacea for all ills was ready – curd-rice! Eaten with a dollop of hot mango pickle, there couldn't be a more effective remedy for the severest bout of homesickness!

But 'curd' as we Indians call it in English and 'yogurt' as the rest of the English-speaking world knows it, is much more than just a soothing balm for homesick South Indian hearts…

From Lord Krishna to Gandhi

'*Yasoda, how long can I put up with it?*
How can the daily loss of milk and curds be tolerated?
You come and see the deeds of this son of yours
He eats the curd, feeds it to the boys and flees, breaking the pots…'
From *Sursagar* by Surdas

Hippocrates spoke highly of it. Galen recommended it for stomach problems. Genghis Khan insisted that it be included as part of his soldiers' rations during his long military campaigns. And Mahatma Gandhi recommended it as a staple for all Indians, devoting an entire chapter to it in his book *Diet and Diet Reform*.

The *Vedas*, the *Upanishads*, the *Puranas*, the *Ramayana*, *the Mahabharata* and of course Tamil literature dating back to the first few centuries after the birth of Christ as well as countless other Indian texts of great antiquity are full of references to curd. For example, in the *Devi Bhagavata Purana*, there is a description of the earth being divided into seven continents (*dwipa*) and seven oceans (*sagara*). The sixth ocean is called Dadhi Sagara – or 'ocean of curd'. Both the *Rig*

You Say 'Yogurt', We Say 'Curd'

There is some confusion about the use of the words 'yogurt' and 'curd' and what they mean, and it is primarily because of the word 'curd'. We Indians use it to refer to *dahi* or our version of yogurt. But in the West, it refers to a *paneer*-like product, made by adding rennet (enzymes from the stomach of dairy animals) or lemon juice or vinegar to milk.

And what is yogurt?

According to Dr Keith Steinkraus, an American expert on fermented food, 'yogurt' is a general term used for several fermented milk products, including both what the West calls yogurt and what we Indians call curd. And the difference between yogurt and curd is in the kind of lactic acid bacteria present – in yogurt, they are primarily *Lactobacillus delbrueckii subspecies bulgaricus* and *Streptococcus salivarius subspecies Thermophilus*. But in *dahi*, the lactic acid bacteria come from at least three or four families of lactic acid bacteria.

Veda and the *Mahabharata* have the story of the *rishi* who offered his own ribs to be fashioned into Indra's famous weapon, the *vajrayudha* or 'the thunderbolt'. The name of the *rishi* was Dadhyanca or Dadhica – said to be derived from *dadhi* (curd). (Scholars are stumped, though, as to the reason for this association with curd!) The *Rig Veda* also mentions that curd was made into *shrikhand* (then know as *shirkarini*) and *khadi* (then called *khada*) and that it was eaten in a variety of ways – for example, with barley and with rice. (So curd-rice – so beloved of my father and millions of other South Indians – was eaten even in Vedic times!)

Two references in the *Arthashastra* are particularly interesting and worth mentioning. According to Kautilya, the way to judge the purity of silver is to check whether it is the colour of curd. Kautilya also recommends that the diet for the best horses in the king's army should include curd!

And naturally, curd features prominently in Ayurvedic texts. There are at least sixty-seven references to it in the *Charaka Samhita,* including this very curious one. According to Charaka, other than the skill of the doctor and the right treatment, there are other factors that may also play a role in the cure of a disease. So, if a doctor encounters certain objects or events on his way to a patient's house, they are auspicious signs that augur that the patient's chances of recovery are good. And one of them is… yes, curd!

Also, it seems that in ancient times, curd was no ordinary food, only a few notches below ambrosia and summoned to stamp its benevolent presence upon every auspicious occasion. For example, *madhuparka* – a concoction of *ghee*, honey, milk, curd and sugar – was fed to women in the fifth month of pregnancy. It was touched to the lips of the firstborn son just after birth and fed to the student as he left home for apprenticeship. It even welcomed the bridegroom when he arrived at the bride's home for the wedding! (In fact, according to the *Atharva Veda*, *madhuparka* is also the term given to the ceremony of welcoming the bridegroom with this delicious concoction.) And of course, curd was a favourite of a little butter thief that drove the *gopis* crazy by raiding their pots of curd and milk – Bala Krishna!

So surely there must be something about curd that makes it so deserving of this exalted status.

Monks' Feast!

On the outskirts of Lhasa in Tibet is the magnificent six-hundred-year-old Drepung Monastery. Once one of the largest monasteries in the world, its academic excellence earned it the nickname 'Nalanda of Tibet'. Every August, the monastery celebrates the Shoton or the Yogurt Festival. Several hundred years ago, it was the practice for Tibetan monks to retreat to their temples for the summer to meditate and fast. When summer ended, the monks would come out of their confinement and herders would greet them with pots of curd made from yak's milk. The festival is celebrated in memory of this tradition and cups of curd are distributed to each of the more than forty thousand people who visit the monastery during this time.

The Elixir of Long Life

'When people have learned how to cultivate a suitable flora in the intestines of children as soon as they are weaned from the breast, the normal life may extend to twice my seventy years.'

Ilya Ilyich Mechnikov, Nobel Prize-winning microbiologist

In the Old Testament, when the three angels visit Abraham, the feast that he lays out for his heavenly guests includes curd. Abraham is said to have been 175 years old when he died and according to an old Persian folktale, the secret of Abraham's longevity was... yes, curd! So, in countries where curd has been eaten for thousands of years, it is fairly common knowledge that it is a food that abounds in nutritional and therapeutic properties. But now that it has been rediscovered as a wonder food in the West and enthusiastically researched and minutely studied, we know why...

It all started with a Russian microbiologist called Ilya Ilyich Mechnikov who won the Nobel Prize in 1908 for his work on immunology. He had a pet theory – at the time still unproven – that Bulgarians, Azerbaijanis and other tribes of the Caucasus

Food of Kings

Curd has graced many a royal table and been the favourite of many a kingly palate. It is said that Emperor Akbar started all his meals with curd and rice. But my favourite curd 'n' king story is this one.

Till the recent 'discovery' of its health benefits, curd was not popular in Western Europe – except for this one famous but brief appearance in the court of Francis I of France (1494-1547). As one version of the story goes, the king was ailing and no medicine or doctor seemed to be able to cure him. Till he was told of a Jewish doctor in Constantinople who worked wonders with fermented sheep's milk – or curd, as we know it! Naturally, the king immediately sent for the doctor. Now, Constantinople was then the capital of the Ottoman Empire, ruled by Sultan Suleiman the Magnificent (1494-1566). The sultan also happened to be a good friend of the king, so he made sure that the doctor was dispatched post-haste.

The doctor insisted on walking from Constantinople to Paris, accompanied by his medicine chest – which was his flock of sheep! The treatment worked its magic, the king was cured but the poor sheep, unable to stand the Parisian cold, died. The distraught doctor left immediately, refusing to divulge the secret of making curd, which also left with him. It reappeared only about four hundred years later when, after World War I, Greek and Russian immigrants began to serve curd in their restaurants.

But back to the grateful French king – he dubbed his cure *le lait de vie eternelle* or 'the milk of eternal life'. The royal ailment? Most versions of the story talk about an intestinal disorder, probably diarrhoea. According to this version, it was severe depression. Given the curd's amazing curative powers, both are equally good possibilities!

mountains owed their extraordinary longevity and good health to their habit of regularly eating curd and drinking *kefir*, a fermented milk drink similar to buttermilk. He believed in this theory so completely that he became a passionate advocate, writing about it in a book titled *The Prolongation of Life: Optimistic Studies* and, as the story goes, eating yogurt and drinking 'sour milk' every day!

Did Mechnikov's theory ever get proven to be scientifically true? Well, in a manner of speaking, yes. You see, the theory sparked off interest in the study of these foods, and the findings – which were astounding to say the least – showed that curd is teeming with nutritional and therapeutic benefits.

And that is mainly because it is also teeming with a clan of bacteria called lactic acid bacteria of which the most dominant branches are *Lactobacillus*, *Leuconostoc*, *Lactococcus* and *Streptococcus*. Teeming with bacteria? Isn't that a very bad thing and wouldn't that make curd a perfect breeding ground for disease? In fact, it is a very good thing because these bacteria – whom we shall from now on affectionately refer to as the curd bugs – are the good guys, working all kinds of nutritional and therapeutic magic. (Modern-day nutritionists classify these curd bugs as probiotics – microbes that protect the health of their host and prevent disease – and curd as a probiotic food.)

To start with, these bugs produce an enzyme called lactase, which breaks down milk sugars (lactose) to produce lactic acid, which in turn curdles milk and makes curd taste sour. Then, they protect the body's own colonies of good intestinal bacteria, popularly referred to as 'gut flora'. These 'in-house' microbes aid digestion, produce Vitamin K and biotin (Vitamin B7), and mop up toxins and bad cholesterol. Without their presence, we become susceptible to many intestinal ailments like diarrhoea and dysentery. In fact, research has shown that curd is the perfect palliative food to accompany a course of antibiotics. Why? Very simple. While antibiotics do a great job of destroying the disease-causing bacteria in our body, they also manage to bump off the beneficial ones, including gut flora – leaving us vulnerable to diarrhoea, a common side effect of antibiotics. The curd bugs both protect and help restore these essential bacteria.

The curd bugs are also great digestive aids, crumbling down difficult-to-digest complex carbohydrates and proteins present in

What's in a Name?

The word 'yogurt' or 'yoghurt' comes from the Turkish word *jugurt*. 'Curd' or 'curds' probably comes from the word 'curdle'. The Hindi, Gujarati, Bengali and Marathi names for curd come from a common root – the Sanskrit *dadhi*.

Manth or *matha* are the Sanskrit words for churning and *manthana* is the rod used for churning curd into buttermilk. These are probably the roots from which *matha*, one of the names for buttermilk in Hindi and Gujarati, originated.

Language	Name	
English	Yogurt, yoghurt, curd, curds	Buttermilk
Sanskrit	Dadhi	Takra
Hindi	Dahi	Chaas, lassi, matha
Gujarati	Dahi	Chaas, matha
Bengali	Doi	Ghol
Marathi	Dahi	Taak
Tamil	Thayyir	Moru
Telugu	Perugu	Majjiga
Kannada	Mosuru	Majjige
Malayalam	Thairu	Moru

cereals to the more easily digestible sugars and amino acids. They heighten the nutritional value of the food by boosting the levels of vitamins in it – especially the critical Vitamin B family – and by releasing locked-up nutrients like minerals and converting them into more soluble forms. They also work hard to keep many serious diseases at bay. They lower both bad cholesterol and blood pressure and thus help prevent heart disease. They secrete substances that kill even the nastiest of their bad brethren, including *Helicobater pylori*, the microbes that cause most kinds of ulcers including peptic ulcers. And studies have shown that they may even help prevent colon cancer and prove to be a powerful ally in both curing and preventing arthritis. Last but definitely not the least, these little bugs are powerful immunity builders and their presence makes curd one of the most important immunity-boosting foods.

And as if all this isn't impressive enough, curd is one of the richest sources of calcium (containing 35-40 per cent of your daily requirement), stealing a march on milk not only because its calcium content is higher but also because it is much more easily digestible than milk. This is particularly important for people who are lactose-intolerant – it is estimated that about 70 per cent of adults have this problem. Curd also scores over milk as a better source of protein because it contains a kind of protein that milk does not – whey protein, so christened because it is found in whey, the water that separates from milk when it becomes curd. The current darling of Western nutritionists, health drink manufacturers, even bodybuilders and athletes, whey protein is easily digestible and synthesized by the body. And recent research seems to indicate that it may help to reduce the risk of breast and colon cancer, hypertension and heart disease.

The question is – would all of this contribute to a longer and healthier life as Mechnikov believed? A clue to the answer may lie in the ancient Assyrian word for curd, *lebeny*, which has the same linguistic root as the word that means 'life'. (And 'probiotic' means 'for life'!) So my guess is – yes! Now you know why South Indians never finish a meal without the mandatory serving of curd-rice!

The bonus? Curd can keep your smile beautiful and your breath smelling sweet. Eating just a cup of curd twice a day not only muzzles the hydrogen sulphide and other such smelly compounds that make your breath reek, but it may also help demolish the 'bad' bacteria that coat the tongue. It also reduces plaque formation and the risk of gingivitis and cavities.

If these aren't important enough reasons to make curd a permanent member of your diet, here is the clincher. Curd is the ultimate chameleon food. It can be made to change form and taste to suit every whim and fancy. Hang it up in a piece of cheesecloth overnight and it converts into the most delicious *shrikhand* or cheese, depending on whether you sweeten or salt it. Whip it smooth and add anything from pineapple to *boondi* to a make it into a myriad *raitas* and *pachadis*. Churn it and it transforms into buttermilk – ideal for cooling off during hot summer afternoons. Fold it into batters and flours to make the fluffiest, softest *idlis* and Indian breads. Substitute it for cream in diet recipes. Or then just spoon it into a bowl – unaccompanied, unadorned, serenely white and beautiful – and eat your way to healthfulness!

The Healthiest of the Healthy!
The healthiest kind of curd to eat, especially from a calorie-cholesterol point of view, is curd that is made of skimmed milk, that is milk that has all the cream skimmed off.

Buttermilk Rhapsody

No one who visited my grandmother would ever think of drinking anything other than her famous buttermilk, which flowed like water and was always on tap no matter what time of the day it was. My grandmother's kitchen was one of wood fires and clay cooking pots. No gas stove, no fridge. Every morning, she'd put a pot of milk to slowly simmer through the day on one of those fires. And in the evening, when the milk was reduced and thickened and infused with the most heavenly aroma of wood smoke, she'd cool it and set it to become curd. The next morning, the curd would be churned to give up all its butter in fat, dewy, glistening globs. And the liquid that was left became a never-emptying lake of thick, faintly smoky, cool buttermilk, just tart enough to perk you up and flavoured with nothing but its own deliciousness. Buttermilk that soothed and cooled and refreshed every part of you, like nothing else could. And that remained cool and placid in its clay pot, without refrigeration, no matter how hot it was or how late in the day you quaffed it.

So, my love affair with buttermilk began a very long time ago and we are childhood sweethearts really, inextricably linked with my happiest memories of summer holidays in my grandmother's house. Since buttermilk is also one of the most healthful ways to make your summer a holiday, let me play you my buttermilk rhapsody…

An 'Old-Fashioned' Tale…

First of all, let's clear up a few misconceptions about buttermilk. Basically, it is curd that has been churned or whipped and then diluted with water. The different avatars of buttermilk are a result of either the kind of curd used or the making process. If the curd used is made out of whole milk – as it invariably was during my grandmother's time – and if this curd is churned long enough, the cream will coagulate into butter and float to the top leaving behind… yup, buttermilk. (Some people say that this is the true or 'old-fashioned' buttermilk.) However, if the curd used is made out of skimmed milk – as is often the case nowadays – or if the curd is churned only long enough to make it into a smooth consistency, then the butter will not separate out. There is another way of making buttermilk these days, thanks to the wonders of refrigeration. Cream is collected over a period of time and stored in the fridge. This is later made to ferment by adding curd and churned to yield butter. And when that butter has been completely skimmed off, the leftover liquid is also buttermilk!

We humans have been making buttermilk ever since we have been making curd – for at least seven thousand years! And so, the tradition of fermented milk drinks is an ancient one, especially in Eastern Europe and Asia. For example, *kefir*, a fermented milk drink, has been made in the northern region of the Caucasus Mountains for centuries. It is said that the *kefir* grains used to ferment the milk was a secret given by the Prophet Mohammed and so are also called the 'Grains of the Prophet'. *Kumis* or *koumiss*, made from mare's milk, has been a favourite drink all over Central Asia for at least 2,500 years. The ancient Egyptians sipped on *laban* (in Mesopotamia, it was called *leben*), and the Vikings gifted the Scots *blaand* – or fermented whey that is said to be similar to wine in its alcohol content.

And in India, we had buttermilk! In pre-Aryan South India (third and early second millennium BC), it was both beverage and currency, used to barter for other foods like rice. When the Aryans arrived, they took to buttermilk no less enthusiastically. The *Rigveda* has several mentions of the churning of curd and according to Patanjali's *Mahabhasya*, *mathitika* was the name given to the seller of buttermilk and curd. The *Manasollasa*, written by the Chalukyan king Someswara III (who ruled from AD 1126 to 1138), describes royal feasts where buttermilk was sipped during meals and where the last course was rice and buttermilk, mixed with a little salt – just as it still is in many parts of South India.

'The Coolest One'!

Since buttermilk, like curd, is a fermented milk product, it is a probiotic food and therefore has all the nutritional and healing properties that curd has. So, like curd, it is an excellent digestive aid, crumbling down complex carbohydrates that are otherwise often tough to digest. It is one of the best sources of calcium, potassium and phosphorus, as well as some of the B vitamins. 'Old-fashioned' buttermilk has one other big bonus point. Since it has all the butter skimmed out of it, it is also low on calories!

In Ayurveda, because of its tart, light, cooling and appetizing nature, buttermilk is a star both as healer and as food. Its most well-known therapeutic use is in the treatment of diarrhoea and dysentery. So much so that even current-day paediatricians recommend the use of buttermilk as oral rehydration in the treatment of children's diarrhoea. It is also used in Ayurveda to treat colitis, piles, jaundice, nausea, liver dysfunction and sluggish digestions. And many Ayurvedic medicines, even those not meant for digestive ailments, are administered along with or in buttermilk.

Buttermilk is also the main ingredient in two famous Ayurvedic treatments, both of which are named after it. *Takradhara* is a therapy during which medicated buttermilk (*takra*) is released in a tiny stream (*dhara*) over the patient's forehead. It is used to calm the mind and treat conditions like insomnia, depression and other stress-related problems. *Takrarishta* is a classic Ayurvedic formulation used not only to treat diarrhoea and dysentery but even obesity.

Buttermilk is also used to treat skin disorders like psoriasis and eczema.

Blessed Buttermilk…

It's only natural that the gods should also favour one so delicious and healthful. So, buttermilk gets the nod from many religions as permitted food. The seventh-century Chinese traveller I Ching, who travelled extensively in India, noted that in the meals served in the Buddhist monasteries here, prepared according to the food strictures laid down for Buddhist monks, buttermilk was a favoured beverage. The Koran recommends buttermilk especially during the fasting month of Ramzan, perhaps because of its nurturing and soothing action on the digestive system, stretched to its limit by fasting. Buttermilk is also often served at Sikh *gurudwaras* and every year, to mark the martyrdom of Guru Arjan Dev, the fifth of the eleven gurus of Sikhism, stalls called *chhabil* serving sweetened buttermilk are set up all over Punjab.

Lord Krishna's most endearing and delightful avatar is as the little Makhan Chor or the Divine Butter Thief. So the exquisite idol of the child Krishna in the famous Sri Krishna Temple in Udupi holds the buttermilk churn (*manthan*) in his right hand and the rope used to move the churn in his left. In South India, buttermilk is also an integral part of Ram Navami celebrations, and is served as *prasadam* at not just temples but also at roadside corners.

Pick-me-up, tonic, digestive, infection fighter, nutrition booster, weight watcher. And delicious to boot. So it is only befitting that I end my buttermilk rhapsody with one of Purandaradasa's most famous compositions – 'Bhagyada Lakshmi Baaramma' in which he begs for a visitation by the Goddess Lakshmi. It is a composition as simple, unpretentious, fresh and utterly satisfying as a glass of my grandmother's buttermilk…

> '*Sowbhayda Lakshmi baaramma*
> *Namamma Ni*…
> *Gejjekaalgala dhwaniya torutha, Hejje mele hejjeya nikkuta*
> *Sajjana sadhu poojeya velege, Majjige volagina benne yante*
> *Bhagyalakshmi baramma*'

> 'O Goddess of Good Fortune, come
> To the sound of the anklets on Your feet as You walk,
> As the good people get ready to pray, As butter emerges from buttermilk,
> O Lakshmi of Good Fortune, come…'

Skin Foods

In ancient Persia, curd was a beauty aid, used especially for facials. And the chief beautician in it is the lactic acid. It acts as a mild exfoliant, sloughing off dead skin cells and thus leaving your complexion glowing. And its acidic, astringent nature both lightens and tightens the skin. Curd is also loaded with nutrients. All this coupled with its antibacterial properties make it the perfect skin food. (For skin-care recipes, see box 'Beautiful Bengal Gram', page 48.)

Buttermilk, like curd, is a skin-care specialist. Some say that Cleopatra bathed in it. So did Marie Antoinette – apparently to keep wrinkles at bay! I can't swear to its wrinkle-banishing abilities but rinsing your face regularly with plain buttermilk is an excellent skincare regimen and also a popular traditional remedy for lightening freckles and age spots and for treating sunburn. So, to lighten that suntan, apply slightly sour buttermilk all over your face and body. Wait for about fifteen minutes, then wash thoroughly with warm water.

Recipes

Curd Cheese Sandwich Spread

(Makes 1–1½ cups)

Great on bread, toast, chapattis, *plain crackers, roasted* pappads *or even by itself!*

INGREDIENTS

½ kg curd (made out of skimmed milk)

Seasoning

1-1 ½ tsp salt (adjust to taste) and any combination of seasonings from the ones given below:
8-10 peppercorns crushed coarsely

or

1 tbsp fresh pudina *leaves (mint), finely chopped*

or

1 heaped tsp cumin seeds, roasted and powdered

or

2-3 cloves of garlic, ground to a paste (adjust to taste)

or

½ tbsp spring onions, finely chopped

METHOD

Spread a clean piece of thin cloth over a large bowl so that it covers the bowl completely, but dips slightly in the centre into the bowl. Empty the curd over the cloth and let it remain there till most of the whey has dripped into the bowl. Then tie the cloth around the curd to make a tight 'packet' and hang it up over the kitchen sink or over another bowl for about 5-6 hours till all the whey has dripped out and you are left with a soft paste. Now put the curd paste in a bowl, add salt and the seasoning of your choice and blend well. Store the spread in a dry jar – it will keep for 3-4 days in the refrigerator.

The Secret of Long Life – Curd-Rice

The Pea that ain't a Nut — Raw Peanuts and Peanut Oil

No-Cook Buttermilk Kadhi

(Serves 3-4)

Delicious with plain steamed rice and a salad!

INGREDIENTS

½ litre buttermilk
¼ fresh coconut
2-3 dried red chillies
½-inch piece of ginger
1 tsp salt (adjust to taste)

Tempering

2 tsp oil
½ tsp mustard seeds
½ a dried red chilli, broken into pieces
5-7 curry leaves
A pinch of asafoetida

METHOD

Grind together the coconut, 2-3 dried red chillies and ginger into a smooth, chutney-like paste, adding the ginger last. Add to the buttermilk along with the salt and stir well. Heat the oil; add mustard seeds and red chilli. When the mustard stops spluttering, add the curry leaves and asafoetida. Take off the fire and add to the buttermilk mixture. Stir well again.

Bibliography

RICE

Websites

'The Last Feast of Lady Dai' by Julie Rauer (Asian Art)
http://www.asianart.com/articles/ladydai/index.html

'A New Look at Vedic India' by Paul Kekai Manansala (Asia Pacific Universe)
http://asiapacificuniverse.com/pkm/vedicindia.html

'World's 'Oldest' Rice Found' by Dr David Whitehouse (BBC News Online –
Science)
http://news.bbc.co.uk/2/hi/science/nature/3207552.stm

'India: Germplasm of 20,000 Varieties of Rice Conserved' (International Rice
Research Institute)
http://beta.irri.org/news/index.php/rice-news/india-germplasm-of-20000-varieties-
of-rice-conserved.html

Discussion Of Chinese Domesticated Rice – 10,000-Year-Old Rice At Xianrendong,
Jiangxi Province, Zhang, Pei Qi, Xiantao Middle School, Wuhan, Hubei Province,
(Second Session of International Symposium on Agricultural Archaeology, Oct 1997,
Nanchang, Jiangxi Province)
http://http-server.carleton.ca/~bgordon/Rice/papers/zhang97.htm

Brown Rice (The World's Healthiest Foods)
http://www.whfoods.org/genpage.php?tname=foodspice&dbid=128

Books

Ayurveda – Secrets of Healing by Maya Tiwari

Cereals and Millets by Chittaranjan Kole

Diarrhea by Michael Gracey

Dravidian Theories by R Swaminatha Aiyar

Healing with Whole Foods: Asian Traditions and Modern Nutrition by Paul Pitchford

Indian Food – A Historical Companion by KT Achaya

Pali-English Dictionary by Thomas William Rhys Davids, William Stede

Process and Language – A Study of the Mahabhasya Ad A1.3.1 Bhuvadayo Dhatavah by
Hideyo Ogawa

*Rice Grain Marketing and Quality Issues: Selected Papers from the International Rice Research
Institute Conference* by International Rice Research Institute (IRRI)

Staying Healthy with Nutrition: The Complete Guide to Diet and Nutritional Medicine by
Elson M Haas with Buck Levin

The Cambridge World History of Food edited by Kenneth F Kiple and Kriemhild Conee
Ornelas

The Chinese Way to Healing: Many Paths to Wholeness by Misha Ruth Cohen with Kalia Doner

The Magic Lotus Lantern and Other Tales from the Han Chinese by Haiwang Yuan

Research Papers

'Rice – A Nutraceutical' by Uma Ahuja, SC Ahuja, Rashmi Thakrar and RK Singh, College of Agriculture, and Chaudhary Charan Singh, Haryana Agricultural University (CCSHAU), Rice Research Station, Haryana; published in *Asian Agri-History Vol 12, No. 2,* 2008

'Rice Research in South Asia through Ages' by YL Nene, Asian Agri-History Foundation, Secunderabad, Andhra Pradesh; published in *Asian Agri-History Vol 9, No. 2,* 2005

'Parboiling of Rice, Part II: Effect of Hot Soaking Time on the Degree of Starch Gelatinization' by MA Kaddus Miah, Anwarul Haque, M Paul Douglass and Brian Clarke, Postharvest and Food Technology Group, Institute of BioScience and Technology, Cranfield University, Bedford M, UK; published in *International Journal of Food Science and Technology, 37,* 2002

'Antiquity of the Earliest Cultivated Rice in Central China and its Implications' by Baozhang Chen and Qinhua Jiang, published in *Economic Botany,* Jul 1997

'Energy Consumption Benchmark Studies on Parboiled Rice Cooking in Kerala', a study conducted for Energy Management Centre, Thiruvananthapuram, Kerala by Anoopa PS, Dayana Scaria, Nithya NS and Prajitha M, Kelappaji College of Agricultural Engineering and Technology, Malappuram, Kerala, and by K Madhusoodanan, Energy Management Centre, Thiruvananthapuram, Kerala

Newspapers

'120,000 Varieties', *The Telegraph,* Aug 11, 2005

RAGI

Websites

Official Website of Ministry of Food Processing Industries, Government of India
http://mofpi.nic.in/ContentPage.aspx?CategoryId=1111

'Fiber – Start Roughing It' (The Nutrition Source, Harvard Public School of Health)
http://www.hsph.harvard.edu/nutritionsource/what-should-you-eat/fiber-full-story/index.html#health_effects

Finger Millet (Wikipedia)
http://en.wikipedia.org/wiki/Finger_millet

Books

A History of Kanarese Literature, Second Edition by Edward P Rice

Chad by Martha Kneib

Lost Crops of Africa: Vol I – Grains by National Research Council (US) Board on Science and Technology for International Development

Plant Genetic Resources of Ethiopia by Jan Engels, John Gregory Hawkes and Melaku Worede

Research Papers

'Bioactive Phytochemicals in Indian Foods and their Potential in Health Promotion and Disease Prevention' by BS Narasinga Rao, National Institute of Nutrition, Hyderabad; published in *Asia Pacific Journal of Clinical Nutrition 12 (1)*, 2003

'Nutrient Composition, Amino Acid and Vitamin Contents of Malted Sorghum, Pearl Millet, Finger Millet and their Rootlets' by NG Malleshiand CF Klopfenstein, from the Department of Grain Science and Technology, Central Food Technological Research Institute, Mysore and the Department of Grain Science and Industry, Kansas State University, Manhattan, Kansas, USA; published in *International Journal of Food Sciences and Nutrition, Vol 49, No. 6,* 1998

'Proto-Dravidian Agriculture' by FC Southworth, University of Pennsylvania, USA

Newspapers

'India Epicentre of Diabetes, Over 50 million Affected', *The Indian Express*, Oct 21, 2009

PIGEON PEA

Websites

Tropical Plant Database – Database File for Guandu (Raintree Nutrition)
http://www.rain-tree.com/guandu.html

Complementary Protein and Diet (UC – Clermont College Biology)
http://biology.clc.uc.edu/courses/Bio104/compprot.htm

Books

An English Translation of the Sushruta Samhita, Based on Original Sanskrit Text edited and published by Kaviraj Kunja Lal Bhishagratna

Charaka Samhita Handbook on Ayurveda, Vol II, edited by Gabriel Van Loon

Food Uses of Whole Oil and Protein Seeds edited by Edmund W Lusas, David R Erickson and Wai-Kit Nip

Foods and Nutrition Encyclopedia, Vol 1 by Audrey Ensminger

Genetic Resources, Chromosome Engineering and Crop Improvement: Cereals by Ram J Singh and Prem P Jauhar

Handbook of Nutrition and Diet by BB Desai

Indian Food – A Historical Companion by KT Achaya

New Crops edited by J Janick and JE Simon

Proceedings of the World Congress – Vegetable Protein Utilization in Human Foods and Animal Feedstuffs edited by Thomas H Applewhite

Research Papers

'Antioxidant Activities of Extracts and Main Components of Pigeonpea (*Cajanus cajan (L) Millsp*) Leaves' by Nan Wu, Kuang Fu, Yu-Jie Fu, Yuan-Gang Zu, Fang-Rong Chang, Yung-Husan Chen, Xiao-Lei Liu, Yu Kong, Wei Liu and Cheng-Bo Gu, Key Laboratory of Forest Plant Ecology, Ministry of Education, Northeast Forestry University, Harbin, China, the Second Affiliated Hospital of Harbin Medical University, Harbin, China and the Graduate Institute of Natural Products, Kaohsiung Medical University, Taiwan; published in *Molecules*, 2009

'The Archaeobotany of Indian Pulses: Identification, Processing and Evidence for Cultivation' by Dorian Q Fuller and Emma L Harvey, Institute of Archaeology, University College, London; published in *Environmental Archaeology, Vol 11, No. 2*, 2006

'Indian Pulses Through the Millennia' by YL Nene, Asian Agri-History Foundation, Secunderabad, Andhra Pradesh; published in *Asian Agri-History Vol 10, No. 3*, 2006

'Nutritive Value and Uses of Pigeonpea and Groundnut' compiled by Faujdar Singh and B Diwakar, Human Resource Development Program, International Crops Research Institute for the Semi-Arid Tropics (ICRISAT) Patancheru, Andhra Pradesh, *1993*

Newspapers/Magazines

'US Firm Bags Patent On Arhar Extracts', *Financial Express*, Aug 4, 2003

BENGAL GRAM

Websites

Garbanzo Beans (Chickpeas) (The World's Healthiest Foods)
http://www.whfoods.org/genpage.php?tname=foodspice&dbid=58

Chickpea (Wikipedia)
http://en.wikipedia.org/wiki/Chickpea

Books

Chickpea Breeding and Management edited by Shyam S Yadav, RJ Redden, W Chen and B Sharma

Dr KM Nadkarni's Indian Materia Medica (Vol I), enlarged and revised by AN Nadkarni

History of Agriculture in India, up to circa 1200 AD edited by Lallanji Gopal and VC Srivastava

Indian Food – A Historical Companion by KT Achaya

Nutrition Science by B Srilakshmi

The Vishnu Purana translated by Horace Hayman Wilson

Research Papers

'Bioactive Phytochemicals in Indian Foods and their Potential in Health Promotion and Disease Prevention' by BS Narasinga Rao, National Institute of Nutrition, Hyderabad; published in *Asia Pacific Journal of Clinical Nutrition 12 (1)*, 2003

MUNG	**Books**
	Brahma Purana by Surabhi Sheth
	Food and Drinks in Ancient India: From Earliest Times to c. 1200 AD by Om Prakash
	Food, Medicine and the Quest for Good Health by Nancy N Chen
	Indian Food – A Historical Companion by KT Achaya
	Nitrogen Fixation in Agriculture, Forestry, Ecology and the Environment edited by Dietrich Werner and William Edward Newton
	Pulses, Sugar and Tuber Crops edited by Chittaranjan Kole
	The Laws of Manu translated by George Bühler
	The Mahabharata of Krishna-Dwaipayana Vyasa translated by Kisari Mohan Ganguli
	The Srimad Devi Bhagavatam by Swami Vijnanananda
	The Vishnu Purana translated by Horace Hayman Wilson
	Vishveshvaranand Indological Journal, Vol 13, by Vishveshvaranand Vedic Research Institute, Vishveshvaranand Vishva Bandhu Institute of Sanskrit and Indological Studies

Research Papers

'Indian Pulses Through the Millennia' by Dr YL Nene, Asian Agri-History Foundation, Secunderabad, Andhra Pradesh; published in *Asian Agri-History Vol 10, No. 3*, 2006

URAD	**Books**
	Antidiabetic Plants in India and Herbal-based Antidiabetic Research by T Pullaiah and K Chandrasekhar Naidu
	Dr KM Nadkarni's Indian Materia Medica (Vol I), enlarged and revised by AN Nadkarni
	Food Science by Sumati R Mudambi
	Indian Food – A Historical Companion by KT Achaya
	The Legacy of Caraka by MS Valiathan
	Treatise on Ayurveda by Srikantha Arunachalan
	Varahamihira in the Brhat Samhita translated by M Ramakrishna Bhat

Research Papers

'Plant Remains from an Archaeological Site as Indicators of Vegetation and Agricultural Practice Between (3320 ± 400) and (2080 ± 80) yr BP in Gangetic West Bengal, India' by Ruby Ghosh, Subir Bera, Ashalata D'Rozario, Manju Banerjee and Supriyo Chakraborty, the Department of Botany, University of Calcutta, the Narasinha Dutt College, Calcutta and the Birbal Sahni Institute of Palaeobotany, Lucknow; published in *Journal of Integrative Plant Biology, Vol 48 Issue 6*, Jun 2006

'Indian Pulses Through the Millennia' by Dr YL Nene, Asian Agri-History Foundation, Secunderabad, Andhra Pradesh; published in *Asian Agri-History Vol 10, No. 3,* 2006

POTATO

Websites

'Potatoes Chock Full of Phytochemicals' by Jan Suszkiw (Agriculture Research Service, US Department of Agriculture) http://foodconsumer.org/7777/8888/F_ood_C_hemicals_37/111011032007_Potato es_Chock_Full_of_Phytochemicals.shtml

The World Potato Atlas – Bangladesh (The World Potato Atlas, International Potato Centre)

https://research.cip.cgiar.org/confluence/display/wpa/Bangladesh

Potato (The World's Healthiest Foods) http://www.whfoods.com/genpage.php?tname=foodspice&dbid=48

Books

Dr KM Nadkarni's Indian Materia Medica (Vol I), enlarged and revised by AN Nadkarni

Evolutionary Studies in World Crops: Diversity and Change in the Indian Subcontinent by Joseph Hutchinson

Indian Food – A Historical Companion by KT Achaya

Larousse Gastronomique – The World's Greatest Cookery Encyclopaedia

Natural Stomach Care: Treating and Preventing Digestive Disorders with the Best of

Eastern and Western Healing Therapies by Anil Minocha with David Carroll

The Cambridge World History of Food edited by Kenneth F Kiple and Kriemhild Conee Ornelas

The Lancet – Volume the Second edited by Thomas Wakely

The Oxford Guide to Etymology by Philip Durkin

Newspapers/Magazines

'Peru Celebrates Potato Diversity' by Monte Hayes of The Associated Press in

The Washington Post, Jun 24, 2007

'The Impact of the Potato' by Jeff Chapman, *History Magazine,* Dec-Jan, 2000

COLOCASIA

Websites

Ethnobotany of Ahupua's – Taro (Asia Pacific Digital Library) http://apdl.kcc.hawaii.edu/~ahupuaa/botany/food/taro.htm

The Potato of the Humid Tropics (The Mildred E Mathias Botanical Garden, UCLA) http://www.botgard.ucla.edu/html/botanytextbooks/economicbotany/Colocasia/in dex.html

Books

CRC World Dictionary of Plant Names: Common Names, Scientific Names, Eponyms, Synonyms (Vol I) by Umberto Quattrocchi

Encyclopaedia of Health Nutrition and Family Welfare by Ruchi Mishra and S Wal

Research Papers

'Hawaiian Kalo, Past and Future' by John J Cho, Roy A Yamakawa and James Hollyer, Departments of Plant and Environmental Protection Sciences and Tropical Plant and Soil Sciences and the Agricultural Development in the American Pacific project; published in *Sustainable Agriculture,* Feb 2007

'Key Role of Dietary Fats in Coronary Heart Disease Under Progressive Urbanization and Nutritional Transition' by Gandham Bulliyya, Regional Medical Research Centre, Indian Council of Medical Research, Bhubaneswar, Orissa; published in *Asia Pacific Journal of Clinical Nutrition, Vol 9* , Dec 2000

'Sahul in Review: Pleistocene Archaeology in Australia, New Guinea and Island Melanesia', edited by MA Smith, M Spriggs and B Fankhauser, Department of Prehistory, Research School of Pacific Studies, The Australian National University, Canberra, Australia, 1993

FENUGREEK

Books

75 Exceptional Herbs for Your Garden by Jack E Staub

Advances in Food & Nutrition Research, Vol 56 by Steve Taylor

Antidiabetic Plants in India and Herbal-Based Antidiabetic Research by T Pullaiah and K Chandrasekhar Naidu

CRC Handbook of Medicinal Spices by James A Duke with Mary Jo Bogenschutz-Godwin, Judi duCellier and Peggy-Ann K Duke

Domestication of Plants in the Old World, Third Edition by Daniel Zohary and Maria Hopf

Dr KM Nadkarni's Indian Materia Medica (Vol I), enlarged and revised by AN Nadkarni

Fenugreek: The Genus Trigonella edited by Georgios A Petropoulos

Handbook of Vegetable Science and Technology: Production, Composition, Storage and Processing edited by DK Salunkhe and SS Kadam

Hippocrates, Vol 7 by Hippocrates, edited and translated by Wesley D Smith

Rodale's Illustrated Encyclopedia of Herbs edited by Claire Kowalchik and William H Hylton

Spice Crops by EA Weiss

Research Papers

'Consumption Pattern of Fenugreek Seeds in Rajasthani Families' by P Mathur and M Choudhry, Department of Foods and Nutrition, College of Home Science, Maharana Pratap University of Agriculture and Technology, Udaipur, Rajasthan; published in *The Journal of Human Ecology,* Dec 9, 2009

'Essential Fatty Acids, DHA and Human Brain' by Dr Meharban Singh, Consultant Paediatrician, Child Care and Dental Health Centre, Noida, UP; published in *Indian Journal of Pediatrics, Vol 72,* Mar 2005

'Lipid Classes, Fatty Acids and Tocopherols of Leaves of Six Edible Plant Species' by Rudravarapu Sridhar and Gollamudi Lakshminarayana, Indian Institute of Chemical Technology, Hyderabad; published in *Journal of Agricultural and Food Chemistry,* Jan 1993

Newspapers/Magazines

'Make the Diet Leafy' by Prof KV Peter and Dr PG Sadhan Kumar, *Kerala Calling,* Sep 2007

NFI Bulletin (Bulletin of Nutrition Foundation of India), Vol 26, July 2005

BRINJAL

Websites

Solanaceae (Colonial Williamsburg)
http://www.history.org/history/CWLand/resrch11.cfm

Eggplant, Aubergine or Brinjal: A Basic Overview (Heirloom Vegetable Seeds)
http://www.seedfest.co.uk/tips/eggplant_basicoverview.html

Taxonomy Results – Solanum melongena L (Israel Plant Gene Bank)
http://igb.agri.gov.il/main/resultat11.pl?GENUS=Solanum&SPAUTHOR=L.&SPECIES=melongena

Contents of Ibn Sina's *Canon of Medicine* in English (Saab Memorial Medical Library, American University of Beirut)
http://ddc.aub.edu.lb/projects/saab/avicenna/contents-eng.html

Eggplant (The World's Healthiest Foods)
http://www.whfoods.org/genpage.php?tname=foodspice&dbid=22

Eggplant (Wikipedia)
http://en.wikipedia.org/wiki/Eggplant#History

Books

Annals of the Caliphs' Kitchens: Ibn Sayyar al-Warraq's Tenth-Century Baghdadi Cookbook, translated into English by Nawal Nasrallah

Daily Life in Ancient and Modern Baghdad by Dawn Kotapish

Indian Food – A Historical Companion by KT Achaya

Moveable Feasts: The History, Science and Lore of Food by Gregory McNamee

The Oxford Companion to Food by Alan Davidson

WHITE PUMPKIN **Websites**

'Medicinal Herbs of Chhattisgarh, India Having Less-Known Traditional Uses XXVI – Petha' by Pankai Oudhia (Botanical.com)
http://www.botanical.com/site/column_poudhia/189_petha.html

'New Opportunities in the Cucurbitaceae' by Timothy J Ng (Centre for New Crops and Plant Products, Purdue University)

http://www.hort.purdue.edu/newcrop/proceedings1993/v2-538.html#Old%20World%20Cucurbits

Squash, Winter (The World's Healthiest Foods)
http://whfoods.org/genpage.php?tname=foodspice&dbid=63

Pumpkins and More – Pumpkin History (University Of Illnois Extension)
http://urbanext.illinois.edu/pumpkins/history.cfm

Orto Botanico di Pisa (Wikipedia)
http://en.wikipedia.org/wiki/Orto_botanico_di_Pisa

Books

Dr KM Nadkarni's Indian Materia Medica (Vol I), enlarged and revised by AN Nadkarni

Encyclopaedia of World Medicinal Plants, Vol Three by T Pullaiah

Indian Herbal Remedies: Rational Western Therapy, Ayurvedic and Other Traditional Usage, Botany by CP Khare

Indian Medicinal Plants: A Compendium of 500 Species, Vol 1 by PK Warrier, C Ramankutty, VPK Nambiar and R Vasudevan Nair

Indian Medicinal Plants: An Illustrated Dictionary by CP Khare

Mysore Royal Dasara by Swami Sivapriyananda

Teaching of History by SK Kochhar

The Ancient Sun Kingdoms of the Americas by Victor Wolfgang von Hagen

The Gourd Book by Charles B Heiser, Jr

Research Papers

'Hepatoprotective Effect of Trichosanthes cucumerina (var. Cucumerina L) on Carbon-Tetrachloride-Induced Liver Damage in Rats' by Sathesh Kumar S, Ravi Kumar B and Krishna Mohan G, Department of Pharmacognosy and Centre for Ethnopharmacology, University College of Pharmaceutical Sciences, Kakatiya University, Warangal, Andhra Pradesh; published in *Journal of Ethnopharmacology, 123(2)*, Jun 2009

'Study of Nutritive Value and Medicinal Uses of Cultivated Cucurbits' by AHMM Rahman, M Anisuzzaman, Ferdous Ahmed, AKM Rafiul Islam and ATM Naderuzzaman, Department of Botany, University of Rajshahi, Bangladesh; published in *Journal of Applied Sciences Research, 4(5)*, 2008

'Effect of the Extract of Benincasa hispida on Oxidative Stress in Rats with Indomethacin-Induced Gastric Ulcers' by Beena V Shetty, Albina Arjuman, Aparna Jorapur, Rajashree Samanth, Sudhir Kumar Yadav, Valliammai N, Anna Deepthy Tharian, Sudha K and Gayathri M Rao, Department of Biochemistry, Centre for Basic Sciences, Kasturba Medical College, Mangalore; published in *Indian Journal of Physiology & Pharmacology, 52 (2)*, 2008

'Identification of Benincasa hispida (Wax Gourd) from the Kana Archaeological Site, Western Highlands Province, Papua New Guinea' by Peter J Matthews, published in *Archaeology in Oceania*, Oct 2003

'Extracts of Benincasa hispida Prevent Development of Experimental Ulcers' by JK Grover, G Adiga, V Vats and SS Rathi, Department of Pharmacology, All India Institute of Medical Sciences, New Delhi; published in *Journal of Ethnopharmacology, 78(2-3)*, Dec 2001

'The Wax Gourd – A Year-Round Florida Vegetable with Unusual Keeping Quality' by Julia F Morton, Morton Collectanea, University of Miami, presented at the proceedings of the Florida State Horticultural Society, 1971

Newspapers/Magazines

'Ash Gourd – High Nutritional' by Dr TE George, *Kerala Calling*, Sep 2008

'Vaidya Kumbalam: Medicinal Ash Gourd Variety', by MJ Prabu, *The Hindu*, Aug 24, 2006

CHILLIES

Websites

'Domestication of Chili Pepper (Capsicum spp)' by K Kris Hirst (About.com: Archaeology)
http://archaeology.about.com/od/domestications/g/chili_pepper.htm

Chile: Capsicum frutescens L and Others (Gernot Katzer's Spice Pages)
http://www.uni-graz.at/~katzer/engl/Caps_fru.html

Chili Pepper, Dried (The World's Healthiest Foods)
http://www.whfoods.org/genpage.php?tname=foodspice&dbid=29

Chili Pepper (Wikipedia)
http://en.wikipedia.org/wiki/Chili_pepper

Books

Antidiabetic Plants in India and Herbal-Based Antidiabetic Research by T Pullaiah and K Chandrasekhar Naidu

Peppers: The Domesticated Capsicums (New Edition) by Jean Andrews

Tat Tvam Asi – The Universal Message in The Bhagavadgita (Vol 1) by Pathikonda Viswambara Nath

The Encyclopedia of Herbs: A Comprehensive Reference to Herbs of Flavor and Fragrance by Arthur O Tucker and Thomas DeBaggio

Research Papers

'Capsaicin, a Component of Red Peppers, Inhibits the Growth of Androgen-Independent, p53 Mutant Prostate Cancer Cells' by Akio Mori, Sören Lehmann, James O'Kelly, Takashi Kumagai, Julian C Desmond, Milena Pervan, William H McBride, Masahiro Kizaki and H Phillip Koeffler, from the Division of Hematology/Oncology – Cedars-Sinai Medical Center, University of California at Los Angeles School of Medicine, the Department of Radiation Oncology, David Geffen School of Medicine, University of California at Los Angeles, California, and the Division of Hematology – Department of Internal Medicine, Keio University School of Medicine, Tokyo, Japan; published in *Cancer Research 66*, Mar 15, 2006

CURRY LEAF

Websites

Inclusion of Curry Leaf/Drumstick Leaf Powder in the Nutritious Meal under PT MGR NMP Scheme (Government of Tamil Nadu, Department of Social Welfare and NMP)
http://icds.tn.nic.in/nutri-initiate-curry.htm

Books

Antidiabetic Plants in India and Herbal-Based Antidiabetic Research by T Pullaiah and K Chandrasekhar Naidu

Dr KM Nadkarni's Indian Materia Medica (Vol I), enlarged and revised by AN Nadkarni

Handbook of Herbs and Spices (Vol 1) edited by KV Peter

Indian Food – A Historical Companion by KT Achaya

Magazines/Newspapers

'Curry Leaves May Help Control Diabetes, Scientists Say' by Lee Glendinning, *The Guardian*, Sep 30, 2004

'Turning Over a Curry Leaf' by M Somasekhar, *Business Line*, Aug 16, 2001

MUSTARD

Websites

Nutrition for Breast Cancer Patients and Survivors (Avon Foundation Breast Center, John Hopkins Medicine)
http://www.hopkinsbreastcenter.org/library/diagnosis_treatment/nutrition.shtml

Mustards – Family: N.O. Cruciferae (Botanical.com)
http://www.botanical.com/botanical/mgmh/m/mustar65.html

Glucosinolate (Chemie.de)
http://www.chemie.de/lexikon/e/Glucosinolate/

Singing Mustard's Praises (CEI Community Ventures)
http://www.ceicommunityventures.com/news/documents/TPG_Newsday_081207.pdf

Mustard Seeds (The World's Healthiest Foods)

http://whfoods.org/genpage.php?tname=foodspice&dbid=106

Allyl Isothiocyanate, AITC (Wikipedia)
http://en.wikipedia.org/wiki/Allyl_isothiocyanate

Mustard Oil (Wikipedia)
http://en.wikipedia.org/wiki/Mustard_oil

Books

Ayurvedic Massage: Traditional Indian Techniques for Balancing Body and Mind by Harish Johari

Buddha, the Gospel by Paul Carus

Foodborne Disease Handbook, Vol 3: Plant Toxicants by YH Hui, RA Smith and David G Spoerke

Handbook of Vegetable Preservation and Processing by YH Hui, Sue Ghazala, Dee M Graham, KD Murrell and Wai-Kit Nip

Indian Food – A Historical Companion by KT Achaya

Kautilyan Arthasastra by MB Chande

Larousse Gastronomique – The World's Greatest Cookery Encyclopaedia

Mediterranean Vegetables: A Cook's ABC of Vegetables and Their Preparation in Spain, France, Italy, Greece, Turkey, The Middle East and North Africa by Clifford A Wright

Prescription for Dietary Wellness by Phyllis A Balch

The Laws of Manu translated by Wendy Doniger O'Flaherty and Brian K Smith

The Natural History of Pliny, Vol 4 translated by John Bostock and HT Riley

The Srimad Devi Bhagavatam by Swami Vijnanananda

Research Papers

'Allyl Isothiocyanate as a Cancer Chemopreventive Phytochemical' by Yuesheng Zhang, Department of Cancer Prevention and Control, Roswell Park Cancer Institute, Buffalo, NY, USA; published in *Molecular Nutrition & Food Research, Vol 54 Issue 1*, Dec 2009

'Diet and Risk of Ischemic Heart Disease in India' by Tanuja Rastogi, K Srinath Reddy, Mario Vaz, Donna Spiegelman, D Prabhakaran, Walter C Willett, Meir J Stampfer and Alberto Ascherio, from the Departments of Nutrition (TR, WCW, MJS and AA), Epidemiology (WCW, MJS, DS and AA), and Biostatistics (DS) – Harvard School of Public Health, Boston, the Department of Cardiology – All India Institute of Medical Sciences, New Delhi (KSR and DP) and the Division of Nutrition – St John's Medical College, Bangalore; published in *American Journal of Clinical Nutrition, Vol 79, No. 4*, Apr 2004

GINGER & TURMERIC

Websites

Traded Medicinal Plants Database Search – Shunti (ENVIS Centre on Medicinal Plants, Ministry of Environment and Forests, Government of India)
http://www.frlht.org/newenvis/trade_search.php?txtpart=RHIZOME&lst_part=RHIZOME&txttrade=RAL&lst_trade=SHUNTI

Turmeric, Curcuma longa L (Gernot Katzer's Spice Pages)
http://www.uni-graz.at/~katzer/engl/Curc_lon.html

Contents of Ibn Sina's *Canon of Medicine* in English (Saab Memorial Medical Library, American University of Beirut)
http://ddc.aub.edu.lb/projects/saab/avicenna/contents-eng.html

Turmeric (The World's Healthiest Foods)
http://www.whfoods.org/genpage.php?tname=foodspice&dbid=78

Turmeric (Wikipedia)
http://en.wikipedia.org/wiki/Turmeric

Books

Apicius redivivus or the Cook's Oracle by William Kitchener

Garuda Purana by BK Chaturvedi

Ginger: The Genus Zingiber edited by PN Ravindran and K Nirmal Babu

History of Agriculture in India, up to circa 1200 AD edited by Lallanji Gopal and VC Srivastava

The Healing Trail: Essential Oils of Madagascar by Georges M Halpern with Peter Weverka

The Institutes of Vishnu translated by Julius Jolly

The Koran translated by EH Palmer

The Notebooks of Leonardo da Vinci compiled and edited from the original manuscripts by Jean Paul Richter

The Spice Lilies: Eastern Secrets to Healing with Ginger, Turmeric, Cardamom and Galangal by Susanne Poth and Gina Sauer

The Srimad Devi Bhagavatam (Vol 2) by Swami Vijnanananda

MANGO

Websites

'Mangoes for Diabetes?' by Judy Skatssoon (ABC Science Online)
http://www.abc.net.au/science/news/stories/2006/1798045.html

Abdullah Nursery Home Page (Abdullah Nursery)
http://abdullahnursery.com/

History of Vaishali (Bihar.ws)
http://www.bihar.ws/info/Districts-of-Bihar/History-of-Vaishali.html

Diabetes Forecast – The Healthy Living Magazine (American Diabetes Association)
http://forecast.diabetes.org/magazine/practical-living/ancient-culinary-delight

Diabetes Question – Should I Avoid Sweet Fruits? (MayoClinic.com)
http://www.mayoclinic.com/health/diabetes/AN01691

'Use of Beta-Carotene-Rich Foods for Combating Vitamin A Deficiency' by BS
Narasinga Rao (Nutrition Foundation of India)
http://www.nutritionfoundationofindia.res.in/archives.asp?archiveid=18&back=bydat
e.asp

Mango (Agricultural and Processed Food Products Export Development Authority –
APEDA)
http://www.apeda.com/apedawebsite/SubHead_Products/Mango.htm

Chapter XX – Mango (INPhO – The Information Network on Post-Harvest
Operations) http://www.fao.org/inpho/content/compend/text/Ch20sec1.htm

Press Release – Padma Awards, 2008 (PIB – Press Information Bureau, Government
of India)
http://www.pib.nic.in/release/release.asp?relid=34924

Home Page of Ekambareswarar Temple at Kanchipuram (The Templenet
Encyclopedia –Temples of Tamilnadu)
http://www.templenet.com/Tamilnadu/ekamkanc.html

'The Fruit of Kings & the King of Fruits' by Salman Saeed (the-south-asian.com)
http://www.the-south-asian.com/February2002/mangoes-south%20Asian4.htm

Books

Flowers, Dragons and Pine Trees: Asian Textiles in the Spencer Museum of Art by Mary M
Dusenbury

Fruits of Warm Climates by Julia F Morton

Indian Food – A Historical Companion by KT Achaya

Superfruits by Paul Gross, PhD, 'The Berry Doctor'

Newspapers/Magazines

'Ratan Tata, LN Mittal receive Padma Vibhushan', *The Hindu*, May 11, 2008

'Mango Crop Hopes Turn Sour on Adverse Weather', *Business Line*, Feb 27, 2008

'Ode to the Mango' by Rupa Gopal, *The Hindu*, Mar 25, 2007

JACKFRUIT

Websites

'How Does the Jakfruit Compare to the Banana in Terms of an Energy Source for
People Participating in Sport?' by James Luckman, United Kingdom (The European
Food Information Council - EUFIC)
http://www.eufic.org/web/page.asp?cust=1&lng=en&faqid=191&lowres=1

Bread Fruit and the Bounty (The Mildred E Mathias Botanical Garden, UCLA)
http://www.botgard.ucla.edu/html/botanytextbooks/economicbotany/Artocarpus/index.html

Underutilized Plant Species Research and Development Activities – Review of Issues and Options by Geoffrey Hawtin (FAO)
http://www.fao.org/docs/eims/upload/232403/Hawtin%20REPORT%20GFU-ICUC.pdf

Fruits of the Future, Factsheet No. 6, Mar 2003 (International Centre for Underutilized Crops)
http://www.icuc-iwmi.org/files/News/Resources/Factsheets/jackfruit.pdf

'Tracing the Flavour of Living Heritage in Jak' by Wasantha Wijewardena and Malinda Seneviratne (Koslanda Living Heritage Reserve)
http://koslanda.com/kalpa-vriksha.htm

Mangalam Muthuswamy Home Page (Mangalam Muthuswamy)
http://mangalam-muthuswamy.tripod.com/

Historical Places – Imphal East (Official Website of NIC Imphal District Centre)
http://imphaleast.nic.in/HISTORICAL_PLACES.HTM

Gadaladeniya Temple (Sri Lanka Travel Index)
http://www.info.lk/srilanka/srilankatravelguide/culture/gadaladeniya.htm

Thrikodithanam Temple Complex (Thrikodithanam Mahavishnu Kshetram)
http://www.thrikodithanam.org/complex.htm

Indigenous Knowledge for Disaster Risk Reduction in South Asia, Chapter 4 (SAARC Disaster Management Centre, New Delhi)
http://saarc-sdmc.nic.in/pdf/publications/Indigenous/Chapter_4.pdf

Agroforestry Tree Database – Artocarpus heterophyllus (World Agroforestry Centre)
http://www.worldagroforestry.org/sea/Products/AFDbases/af/asp/SpeciesInfo.asp?SpID=239

The Bhikku's Rules – The Theravadin Buddhist Monk's Rules; Compiled and Explained by Bhikkhu Ariyesako (Dhammaloka Buddhist Centre)

http://74.125.153.132/search?q=cache:_cpQIGs1pZMJ:www.bswa.org/modules/mydownloads/visit.php%3Fcid%3D19%26lid%3D325+kathina+jackfruit+tree+dye&cd=5&hl=en&ct=clnk

Books

Dr KM Nadkarni's Indian Materia Medica (Vol I), enlarged and revised by AN Nadkarni

Field Manual for Extension Workers and Farmers by AKMA Hossain and N Haq

Fruits of Warm Climates by Julia F Morton

Indian Food – A Historical Companion by KT Achaya

Loving Ganesa: Hinduism's Endearing Elephant-Faced God by Satguru Sivaya Subramuniyaswami

The Rough Guide to South India by David Abram

Traditional Trees of Pacific Islands: Their Culture, Environment and Use by Craig R Elevitch, Isabella Aiona Abbott and Roger RB Leakey

Research Papers

'Analysis of Carotenoids in Ripe Jackfruit (Artocarpus heterophyllus) Kernel and Study of their Bioconversion in Rats' by UG Chandrika, ER Jansz, ND Warnasuriya; published in *Journal of the Science of Food and Agriculture, Vol 85, No. 2,* 30 Jan 2005

'Total, Insoluble and Soluble Dietary Fiber Contents of Indian Fruits' by Punna Ramulu and Paruchuri Udayasekhara Rao, Food Chemistry Division, National Institute of Nutrition, Indian Council of Medical Research, Hyderabad; published in *Journal of Food Composition and Analysis 16,* 2003

'Towards Safe Motherhood in Sri Lanka: Knowledge, Attitudes and Practices during the Period of Maternity' by WI De Silva; published in the *Journal of Family Welfare, 41(32),* Sep 1996

'Alleviating Malnutrition through Horticulture' by SM Monowar Hossain; published by International Food Policy Research Institute (IFPRI)

Newspapers/Magazines

'Study Points to 500 BC Kerala Maritime Activity' by C Gouridasan Nair, *The Hindu,* Jan 9, 2008

'Tay Phuong Pagoda – A Museum of Buddha Statues' by Dang Tran, *The Saigon Times Daily,* Oct 11, 2005

JAMUN

Websites

Syzgium Cumini (ENVIS Centre on Medicinal Plants, Ministry of Environment and Forests, Government of India)
http://www.frlht.org/newenvis/plant_details.php?disp_id=2029

Abodes of Shiva – Tiru Aanaikkaa (Templenet)
http://www.indiantemples.com/Tamilnadu/s031.html

Agroforestry Tree Database – Syzygium cuminii (The World Agroforestry Centre)

http://www.worldagroforestry.org/sea/Products/AFDbases/AF/asp/SpeciesInfo.asp?SpID=1576

Jambul (Wikipedia)
http://en.wikipedia.org/wiki/Jambul

Books

Dr KM Nadkarni's Indian Materia Medica (Vol I), enlarged and revised by AN Nadkarni

Fruits of Warm Climates by Julia F Morton

Foods that Heal by HK Bakhru

Prescription for Herbal Healing by Phyllis A Balch

Puranic Encyclopedia by Vettam Mani

Research Papers

'Berry Anthocyanins As Novel Antioxidants In Human Health And Disease Prevention' by Shirley Zafra-Stone, Taharat Yasmin, Manashi Bagchi, Archana Chatterjee, Joe A Vinson and Debasis Bagchi, from the Research and Development Department, InterHealth Research Center, Benicia, California, USA, the Department of Pharmacy Sciences, Creighton University Medical Center, Omaha, Nebraska, USA and the Department of Chemistry, Scranton University, Scranton, Pennsylvania, USA; published in *Molecular Nutrition & Food Research Vol 51 Issue 6*, May 2007

'Protective Effect of *Syzygium cuminii* (*Linn*) Skeels Seed Extract on Lipid Peroxidation in Alloxan-Induced Diabetic Rats' by P Krishnamoorthy, S Vaithinathan and A Bhuvaneswari; published in *Natural Product Radiance*, (Digest of National Institute of Science Communication and Information Resources (NISCAIR)), *Vol 5*, March–April 2006

'Antioxidant Activity of Some Fruits in Indian Diet' by C Kaur and HC Kapoor; published in the International Society for Horticultural Science's *VII International Symposium on Temperate Zone Fruits in the Tropics and Subtropics, Part II*, Nov 2005

BANANA

Websites

'Two Bananas a Day Keep Blood Pressure at Bay' (BBC Online Network)
http://news.bbc.co.uk/1/hi/health/264552.stm

Micronutrient Information Centre – Potassium (Linus Pauling Institute, Oregon State University)
http://lpi.oregonstate.edu/infocenter/minerals/potassium

'Menopause Reviews and Comments Nutrition in Menopause' by Rita Patnaik (Nutrition Foundation of India)
http://nutritionfoundationofindia.res.in/archives.asp?archiveid=152&back=byauthor.asp

Linnaeus Grows Bananas and Comes Up with a 'Modern' Thermometer (Online Linne)
http://www.linnaeus.uu.se/online/life/6_3.html

Book IV, Kishkindha Kanda – The Empire of Holy Monkeys, Chapter [Sarga] 30 (Valmiki Ramayana)
http://www.valmikiramayan.net/kishkindha/sarga30/kishkindha_30_frame.htm

Improving the Reproductive Health of Married and Unmarried Youth in India (International Centre for Research on Women – ICRW)
http://www.icrw.org/docs/publications-2006/R-2_new.pdf

Books

Bananas and Food Security (compilation of papers presented at INIBAP International Symposium, Douala, Cameroon, 10-14 November, 1998) edited by Claudine Picq, Eric Fouré and EA Frison

Dr KM Nadkarni's Indian Materia Medica (Vol I), enlarged and revised by AN Nadkarni

Fruits of Warm Climates by Julia F Morton

Indian Food – A Historical Companion by KT Achaya

Research Papers

'Beneficial Effects of Potassium' by Feng J He and Graham A MacGregor, Blood Pressure Unit, St George's Hospital Medical School, London; published in *British Medical Journal*, Sep 2001

'Role of Gastric Antioxidant and Anti-Helicobactor Pylori Activities in Antiulcerogenic Activity of Plantain Banana (*Musa sapientum var paradisiaca*)' by Goel RK, Sairam K and Rao CV, Department of Pharmacology, Institute of Medical Sciences, Banaras Hindu University, Varanasi; published in *Indian Journal of Experimental Biology*, Jul 2001

Magazines

'The Rose Whisperer: Getting off the Ground' by Lynn Hunt, *The Christian Science Monitor*, May 4, 2009

'More than Skin-Deep' by Sonal Shukla, *Express Healthcare*, Mar 2007

'The Nature of Nutrients', *Newsweek*, Jan 23, 2006

'Was Papua New Guinea an Early Agriculture Pioneer?' by John Roach, *National Geographic News*, Jun 23, 2003

COCONUT

Websites

Pages from Coconut Time Line Website
http://cocos.arecaceae.com/

Coconut Products (Coconut Development Board, Ministry of Agriculture, Government of India)
http://coconutboard.nic.in/tendnutr.htm#tender

Nutritional Facts, Nutrient Data Laboratory (Coconut Research Center)
http://www.coconutresearchcenter.org/nutrition.pdf

Leaflet No. 8 – 1983 – Coconut (FAO Corporate Document Repository)
http://www.fao.org/WAIRdocs/x5425e/x5425e08.htm#coconut%20foods

Heilbrunn Timeline of Art History (The Metropolitan Museum of Art)
http://www.metmuseum.org/toah/hd/kuns/ho_17.190.622ab.htm

Coconut (Wikipedia)
http://en.wikipedia.org/wiki/Coconut#Husks_and_shells

Books

A Doctor's Vietnam Journal by Carl E Bartecchi

Coconut Palm Products: Their Processing in Developing Countries by Brian E Grimwood with contributions from F Ashman, DAV Dendy, CG Jarman, ECS Little and WH Timmins

CRC Handbook of Ayurvedic Medicinal Plants by LD Kapoor

Dr KM Nadkarni's Indian Materia Medica (Vol I) enlarged and revised by AN Nadkarni

Encyclopedia of the Archaeology of Ancient Egypt edited by Kathryn A Bard

Indian Herbal Remedies: Rational Western Therapy, Ayurvedic and Other Traditional Usage, Botany by CP Khare

Introduction to Fruit Crops by Mark Rieger

Nutrients and Foods in AIDS edited by Ronald R Watson

Principles of Orthomolecularism by RAS Hemat

The Cambridge World History of Food edited by Kenneth F Kiple and Kriemhild Conee Ornelas

The Goddess in India: The Five Faces of the Eternal Feminine by Devdutt Pattanaik

World Oilseeds: Chemistry, Technology and Utilization by DK Salunkhe, JK Chavan, RN Adsule and SS Kadam

Research Papers

'Coconut Oil – Ideal Fat Next Only to Mother's Milk (Scanning Coconut's Horoscope)' by Prof BM Hegde; published in *Journal, Indian Academy of Clinical Medicine, Vol 7,* Jan-Mar, 2006

'Beneficial Effects of Virgin Coconut Oil on Lipid Parameters and In-Vitro LDL Oxidation' by KG Nevin and T Rajamohan, Department of Biochemistry, University of Kerala, Thiruvananthapuram; published in *Clinical Biochemistry, Vol 37, Issue 9*, Sep 2004

'Effect of Antimicrobial Factors in Human Milk on Rhinoviruses and Milk-Borne Cytomegalovirus In Vitro' by NM Clarke and JT May, Department of Microbiology, LaTrobe University, Victoria, Australia; published in *Journal of Medical Microbiology: Vol 49*, Aug 2000

'Lauric Acid Inhibits the Maturation of Vesicular Stomatitis Virus' by Beate Hornung, Eberhrad Amtmann E and Gerhard Sauer, German Cancer Research Centre, Department of Molecular Biology of DNA Tumour Viruses, Heidelberg, Germany; published in *Journal of General Virology, 75,* Feb 1994

Magazines

'Kennedy – A Friend in Deed' by Tom Dusevic, *Time* magazine Aug 8, 2005

GHEE

Websites

Nutritional Importance of Traditional Milk Products in the National Diet (FAO Corporate Document Repository)
http://www.fao.org/DOCREP/003/T0251E/T0251E07.htm

What are the Advantages and Disadvantages of Butter and Ghee When it Comes to Cooking? (The World's Healthiest Foods)
http://www.worldshealthiestfoods.net/genpage.php?tname=newtip&dbid=9

Books

Ayurveda for All by Dr Ch Murali Manohar

Essential Ayurveda: What It Is and What It Can Do for You by Shubhra Krishan

Hindu Samskaras: Socio-Religious Study of the Hindu Sacraments by Rajbali Pandey

History of Agriculture in India, up to circa 1200 AD edited by Lallanji Gopal and Vinod Chandra Srivastava

Hymns to the Mystic Fire by Sri Aurobindo

Indian Food – A Historical Companion by KT Achaya

The Dravidian Languages by Bhadriraju Krishnamurti

The Legacy of Caraka by MS Valiathan

Treatise on Ayurveda by Srikantha Arunachalam

Transition to Vegetarianism: An Evolutionary Step by Rudolph Ballentine

Research Papers

'Serum Lipid Response to Introducing Ghee as a Partial Replacement for Mustard Oil in the Diet of Healthy Young Indians' by S Ravi Shankar, RK Yadav, Rooma Basu Ray, RL Bijlani, Tarun Baveja, Nishi Jauhar, Nirankar Agarwal, Suman Vashisht, SC Mahapatra, Nalin Mehta and SC Manchanda, from Departments of Physiology and Cardiology, All India Institute of Medical Sciences, New Delhi and The Mother's Health Centre, Sri Aurobindo Ashram, New Delhi; published in *Indian Journal of Physiology & Pharmacology, 49 (1)*, Jan 2005

'Our Scriptures on Cow Milk – A Paper on Nutritive Value of Cow Milk as Understood by Ancient Indians and as Propounded by Vedas and Other Scriptures' by Ish Kumar Narang, Assistant Commissioner (Dairy Development) Government of India, presented at the seminar, Cow's Milk is Amritam, organized by the Love 4 Cow Trust, at New Delhi on Jul 7, 2002

'Hypocholesterolemic Effect of Anhydrous Milk Fat Ghee is Mediated by Increasing the Secretion of Biliary Lipids' by Matam Vijaya Kumar, Kari Sambaiah and Belur R Lokesh, Department of Biochemistry and Nutrition, Central Food Technological Research Institute, Mysore; published in *The Journal of Nutritional Biochemistry, Vol 11, Issue 2*, Feb 2000

'Conjugated Linoleic Acid and Other Anticarcinogenic Agents of Bovine Milk Fat' by PW Parodi, Human Nutrition Program, Dairy Research and Development Corporation, Melbourne, Australia; published in *Journal of Dairy Science Vol 82, No. 6,* 1999

'Serum Lipids, Dietary Factors and Ischemic Heart Disease' by SL Malhotra, Chief Medical Officer and Head of Medical Department, Western Railway, Bombay, published in *The American Journal of Clinical Nutrition, Vol 20, No. 5,* May 1967

Magazines

'Pass the Ghee, Please', *Yoga Journal*, Nov 2003

PEANUTS

Websites

'Say Nuts to Heart Disease' by Richard N Fogoros, MD (About.com) http://heartdisease.about.com/cs/riskfactors/a/nuts.htm

'Nutritional Features of Groundnut' by msrivani (Agropedia) http://agropedia.iitk.ac.in/?q=content/nutritional-features-groundnut

'Peanuts Rival Fruit as Source of Health-Promoting Antioxidants, UF Researchers Say' (Institute of Food and Agricultural Sciences – University of Florida) http://news.ifas.ufl.edu/2004/12/21/peanuts-rival-fruit-as-source-of-health-promoting-antioxidants-uf-researchers-say/

Chapter XXI – Groundnut (INPhO – The Information Network on Post-Harvest Operations) http://www.fao.org/inpho/content/compend/text/Ch21intro.htm

'Peanuts Provide Possible Answer to Malnourishment' by Jed Levine (Media Global) http://www.mediaglobal.org/article/2007-05-11/peanuts-provide-possible-answer-to-malnourishment

'Nuts for Nutrition...A Handful a Day Keeps the Cholesterol Away' by Deb Arseneau (Purdue Agriculture, Purdue University) http://www.ces.purdue.edu/Tippecanoe/cfs/Nuts%20for%20Nutrition%20Lesson.pdf

Peanuts (The World's Healthiest Foods) http://whfoods.org/genpage.php?tname=foodspice&dbid=101

Complementary Protein and Diet (UC-Clermont College Biology Website) http://biology.clc.uc.edu/courses/Bio104/compprot.htm

Peanuts (Wikipedia) http://en.wikipedia.org/wiki/Peanuts

Books

Back to Eden: The Classical Guide to Herbal Medicine, Natural Foods and Home Remedies since 1939 by Jethro Kloss

Peanuts: The Illustrious History of the Goober Pea by Andrew F Smith

The Book of Edible Nuts by Frederic Rosengarten Jr

Research Papers

'Changes in the Phytochemical Composition and Profile of Raw, Boiled, and Roasted Peanuts' by Yvonne Chukwumah, Lloyd Walker, Bernhard Vogler and Martha Verghese, Department of Food and Animal Sciences, Alabama A&M University and Department of Chemistry, University of Alabama; published in *Journal of Agricultural and Food Chemistry, 55,* Oct 2007

'Wine and Your Heart – A Science Advisory for Healthcare Professionals From the Nutrition Committee, Council on Epidemiology and Prevention, and Council on Cardiovascular Nursing of the American Heart Association' by Ira J Goldberg, Lori Mosca, Mariann R Piano and Edward A Fisher; published in *Circulation, 103:472,* 2001

'Origins of Resistances to Rust and Late Leaf Spot in Peanut (Arachis hypogaea, Fabaceae)' by P Subrahmanyam, V Ramanatha Rao, D McDonald, JP Moss and RW Gibbons, ICRISAT, Patancheru, Andhra Pradesh; published in *Economic Botany, Vol 43, No. 4,* Oct 1989

Newspapers/Magazines

'Earliest-Known Evidence of Peanut, Cotton and Squash Farming Found', *Science Daily,* Jun 29, 2007

'Fat Guy Says Eat Up and Shut Up' by Steven A Shaw, *Salon.com,* Dec 24 1999

JAGGERY

Websites

'Improving Bioavailability of Iron in Indian Diets through Food-Based Approaches for the Control of Iron Deficiency Anaemia' by KK Sharma (FAO Corporate Document Repository)
http://www.fao.org/DOCREP/005/Y8346M/y8346m07.htm

Cane Juice (The World's Healthiest Foods)
http://www.whfoods.org/genpage.php?tname=foodspice&dbid=120

Books

Cupboard Love – A Dictionary of Culinary Curiosities by Mark Morton

Production Technology of Lump Sugar – Gur/Jaggery by Ajit K Ghosh, Ashok K Shrivastava and VP Agnihotri

Healing with Whole Foods: Asian Traditions and Modern Nutrition by Paul Pitchford

Indian Food – A Historical Companion by KT Achaya

Indian Herbal Remedies: Rational Western Therapy, Ayurvedic and Other Traditional Usage, Botany by CP Khare

Plants in Human Health and Nutrition Policy edited by AP Simopoulos and C Gopalan

The Srimad Devi Bhagavatam (Vol 2) by Swami Vijnanananda

Research Papers

'Enhanced Translocation of Particles from Lungs by Jaggery' by Anand P Sahu and Ashok K Saxena, Industrial Toxicology Research Centre, Lucknow; presented at the Workshop on Biopersistence of Respirable Synthetic Fibers and Minerals held in 1992 in Lyon, France; published in *Environmental Health Perspectives Supplements, Vol 102, Number S5*, 1994

Newspaper Articles

'Indian Gur Gets Global Glory' by Suraj Bhan Dahiya, *The Tribune*, Jan 15, 2001

CURD & BUTTERMILK

Websites

'Natural Yoghurt Beats Bad Breath' (BBC News)
http://news.bbc.co.uk/2/hi/health/4367723.stm

Nutritional Importance of Traditional Milk Products in the National Diet (FAO Corporate Document Repository)
http://www.fao.org/DOCREP/003/T0251E/T0251E07.htm

'Murukan in the Indus Script' by Iravatham Mahadevan (Murugan Bhakti)
http://www.murugan.org/research/mahadevan.htm

Yogurt (The World's Healthiest Foods)
http://www.whfoods.org/genpage.php?tname=foodspice&dbid=124

Fermented Milk Products (Wikipedia)
http://en.wikipedia.org/wiki/Fermented_milk_products#Soured_milk

Abraham (Wikipedia)
http://en.wikipedia.org/wiki/Abraham#Later_years

Books

Achar's Textbook of Pediatrics (Third Edition) edited by J Viswanathan and AB Desai

Ayurveda Materia Medica – Todarananda Ayurveda Saukhyam Series I

Essential Procedures in Pediatrics by Baldev Prajapati

Handbook of Dairy Foods and Nutrition by Gregory D Miller, Judith K Jarvis and Lois D McBean

Handbook of Fermented Functional Foods edited by Edward R Farnworth

Handbook of Indigenous Fermented Foods edited by Keith H Steinkraus

Indian Food – A Historical Companion by KT Achaya

Kautilyan Arthasastra by MB Chande

Prescription for Dietary Wellness by Phyllis A Balch

Staying Healthy with Nutrition: The Complete Guide to Diet and Nutritional Medicine by Elson M Haas with Buck Levin

The Bible Knowledge Commentary: Old Testament by John F Walvoord and Roy B Zuck

The Srimad Devi Bhagavatam by Swami Vijnanananda

Research Papers

'On the Kautilya's Characterisation Tests for the Purity of Silver and its Experimental Replication' by RK Dube, Department of Materials and Metallurgical Engineering, Indian Institute of Technology, Kanpur; published in *Materials Characterization, Vol 60, Issue 4,* Apr 2009

NUTRIENTS

Websites

What if a Bad Fat is Actually Good for You (Men's Health)
http://www.menshealth.com/men/nutrition/food-for-fitness/saturated-fat/article/a03ddd2eaab85110vgnvcm10000013281eac

'Low Levels of Vitamin D Tied to Numerous Health Ailments, Studies Find' (PBS Newshour)
http://www.pbs.org/newshour/updates/science/jan-june08/vitamind_06-13.html

Knowledge for Healthy Eating (The Nutrition Source, Harvard School of Public Health)
http://www.hsph.harvard.edu/nutritionsource/index.html

Multiple Pages relating to Nutrients (Wikipedia)
www.wikipedia.com

Books

A History of Food by Maguelonne Toussaint-Samat, translated from French by Anthea Bell

Atherothrombosis and Coronary Artery Disease by Valentin Fuster, Eric J Topol and Elizabeth G Nabel

Handbook of Dietary Fiber by Sungsoo Cho and Mark L Dreher

Nutrition Almanac by John D Kirschmann and Nutrition Search, Inc

Plant Biotechnology and Molecular Markers edited by PS Srivastava, Alka Narula and Sheela Srivastava

Prescription for Nutritional Healing by Phyllis A Balch

Prevention's Healing with Vitamins by the editors of *Prevention Health* book, edited by Alice Feinstein

Reverse Heart Disease Now by Stephen T Sinatra and James C Roberts with Martin Zucker

Staying Healthy with Nutrition: The Complete Guide to Diet and Nutritional Medicine by Elson M Haas with Buck Levin

The Better Brain Book by David Perlmutter and Carol Colman

The China Study by T Colin Campbell with Thomas M Campbell II

The Complete Idiot's Guide to Total Nutrition by Joy Bauer

The Saccharine Disease by TL Cleave

Vitamin C in Health and Disease edited by Lester Packer and Jurgen Fuchs

What's with Fiber? by Gene and Monica Spiller

World Oilseeds: Chemistry, Technology and Utilization by DK Salunkhe, JK Chavan, RN Adsule and SS Kadam

Research Papers

'Bioactive Phytochemicals in Indian Foods and their Potential in Health Promotion and Disease Prevention' by BS Narasinga Rao, published in *Asia Pacific Journal of Clinical Nutrition, Vol 12, Issue 1,* Mar 2003

'Changing Perceptions on the Role of Saturated Fats in Human Nutrition' by Chandrasekharan N and Yusof Basiron, Malaysian Palm Oil Board, Kuala Lumpur, Malaysia; published in *Palm Oil Developments No. 34* (Journal of the Malaysian Palm Oil Board), June 2001

'Toward a New Recommended Dietary Allowance for Vitamin C based on Antioxidant and Health Effects in Humans' by Anitra C Carr and Balz Frei; published in *American Journal of Clinical Nutrition, Vol 69, No. 6,* Jun 1999

'Dietary Carotenoids and Vitamins A, C, and E and Risk of Breast Cancer' by Shumin Zhang, David J Hunter, Michele R Forman, Bernard A Rosner, Frank E Speizer, Graham A Colditz, JoAnn E Manson, Susan E Hankinson and Walter C Willett, the Department of Nutrition, Harvard School of Public Health, Boston; published in the *Journal of the National Cancer Institute, Vol 91, No. 6,* Mar 17, 1999

'Essential Micronutrients in Relation to Carcinogenesis' by Daan Kromhout; published in the *American Journal of Clinical Nutrition,* 1987

'Proteins of Human Semen .I. Two-Dimensional Mapping of Human Seminal Fluid' by JJ Edwards, SL Tollaksen and NG Anderson, published in *Clinical Chemistry, Vol 27,* Aug 1981

Newspapers/Magazines

'Vitamins and your Diet', *Newsweek,* Jan 23, 2006